Modern
Quadrature Amplitude Modulation

Principles and Applications for Fixed and Wireless Communications

Modern
Quadrature Amplitude Modulation

Principles and Applications for Fixed and Wireless Communications

William Webb

B.Eng, Ph.D., C.Eng., MIEE
Multiple Access
* Communications Ltd.,*
Southampton, UK
Currently with
Smith System Engineering Ltd.,
Guildford, UK

Lajos Hanzo

Dipl Ing., MSc., PhD., SMIEEE
Department of Electronics
* and Computer Science,*
University of Southampton, UK, and
Multiple Access Communications Ltd.,
Southampton, UK

WILEY
Publishers Since 1807

IEEE PRESS
The Institute of Electrical and Electronics
Engineers Inc., New York

First published 1994
by Pentech Press Limited
Graham Lodge, Graham Road
London NW4 3DG

This book is a copublication of the
IEEE Press and John Wiley & Sons

Distribution for IEEE is North, South and
Central America
ISBN 0-7803-1098-5   IEEE Order No PC04531

Reprinted 1995
Reprinted May 1998

British Library Cataloguing in Publication Data
Webb, William
    Quadrature Amplitude Modulation
    1. Title   II. Hanzo, Lajos
    621.382

    ISBN 0 471 96421 2

Cover design by J.E.B. Williams
Printed in Great Britain by Antony Rowe Ltd, Chippenham, Wiltshire

Preface

Objectives and Outline

Since its discovery in the early 1960s, quadrature amplitude modulation (QAM) has continued to gain interest and practical application. Particularly in recent years many new ideas and techniques have been proposed, allowing its deployment over fading mobile channels. This book attempts to provide an overview of most major QAM techniques, commencing with simple QAM schemes for the uninitiated, while endeavouring to pave the way towards complex, rapidly evolving areas, such as trellis-coded pilot symbol and transparent tone in band assisted orthogonal multiplex schemes, or arrangements for wide-band mobile channels. The second half of the book is targetted at the more advanced reader, providing a research-oriented outlook using a variety of novel QAM-based arrangements.

The book is structured in four parts. Part I constituted by Chapters 1-4 is a rudimentary introduction for those requiring a background in the field of modulation and radio wave propagation. Part II is comprised of Chapters 5-9 and concentrates mainly on classic QAM transmission issues relevant to Gaussian channels. Readers familiar with the fundamentals of QAM and the characteristics of propagation channels, as well as with basic pulse shaping techniques may decide to skip Chapters 1-5. Commencing with Chapter 6, each chapter describes individual aspects of QAM. Readers wishing to familiarize with a particular subsystem, including clock and carrier recovery, equalisation, trellis coded modulation, standardised modem features, etc. can turn directly to the relevant, whereas those who desire a more complete treatment might like to read all the remaining Chapters as applicable.

Both Part III and IV, including Chapters 10-18, are concerned with QAM for mobile radio channels, although Part IV is entitled 'Advanced QAM Techniques'. These sections provide a research-based perspective and are dedicated to the more advanced reader. Specifically, Chapter 10 concentrates mainly on coherent QAM schemes, including reference-aided transparent tone in band and pilot symbol assisted modulation arrangements. In contrast, Chapter 11 focuses on low-complexity differentially encoded schemes and on their performance with and without forward error correction coding and trellis coded modulation. Chapter 12 details various timing recovery schemes.

Part IV of the book commences with Chapter 13, which is concerned with variable rate QAM using one- to six-bits per symbol signal constellations. Chapter 14 is dedicated to high-rate wide-band transmissions and proposes a novel equaliser arrangement. Various QAM-related orthogonal signaling techniques are proposed in Chapters 15 and 16, while the spectral efficiency of QAM in cellular frequency re-use structures is detailed in Chapter 17. The closing chapter, Chapter 18 concentrates on the deployment of QAM in a source-matched speech communications system, including various speech codecs, error correction codecs, a voice activity detector and packet reservation multiple access, providing performance figures in contrast to one and two bits per symbol bench-mark schemes.

Acknowledgement

The authors would like to express their warmest thanks to Prof. Raymond Steele. Without his shrewd long-term vision the research work on QAM would not have been performed, and without his earnest exhortations a book on the subject would not have been written. Furthermore, Professor Steele has edited some of the chapters and given advice on the contents and style of this book.

Contributions by Dr. P.M. Fortune, Dr. K.H.H. Wong, Dr. R.A. Salami, D. Greenwood, R. Stedman, R. Lucas and Dr. J.C.S. Cheung who were formerly with Southampton University are thankfully acknowledged. We thank Multiple Access Communications Ltd. for supporting the work on QAM, particularly in the framework of the DTI LINK Personal Communications Programme, dealing with high data rate QAM transmission over microcellular mobile channels. Special thanks goes to Peter Gould and Philip Evans for the major part they played in the construction of the star QAM test-bed. We are grateful to John Williams of Multiple Access Communications Ltd. for the many simulation results he provided for Chapter 18, the production of many of the figures involving simulated waveforms, and not least, for the cover design. Much of the QAM work at Multiple Access Communications Ltd. derives from the support of BT Labs. Martlesham Heath, the DTI and the Radio Communications Agency. Specifically, we thank the latter for the support of the research on spectral efficiency which facilitated Chapter 17.

Lastly, we express our gratitude for the creative atmosphere to our colleagues Derek Appleby, Steve Braithwaite, David Stewart at Southampton University and gratefully acknowledge the stimulating embryonic discussions with Prof. G. Gordos (Technical University of Budapest, Hungary), Prof. H.W. Schüssler (University of Erlangen-Nürnberg, Germany) and Dr.Ing. H.J. Kolb as well as the numerous thought-provoking contributions by many established authorities in the field, some of whom appear also in the Index Section of the book. Finally, the authors warmly thank Rita Hanzo for her skilful assistance in typesetting the manuscript in Latex.

William Webb
Lajos Hanzo

Contents

PART I: Background to QAM

PART II: QAM for Gaussian Channels

PART III: QAM for Mobile Radio

PART IV: Advanced QAM Techniques

Chapter 1

Introduction and Background

This book is concerned with the issues of transmitting digital signals via multilevel modulation. We will be concerned with digital signals originating from a range of sources such as from speech or video encoding, or data from computers. A typical digital information transmission system is shown in Figure 1.1. The source encoder may be used to remove some of the redundancy which occurs in many sources such as speech, typically reducing the transmission rate of the source. The forward error correction (FEC) block then paradoxically inserts redundancy, but in a carefully controlled manner. This redundancy is in the form of parity check bits, and allows the FEC decoder to remove transmission errors caused by channel impairments, but at the cost of an increase in transmission rate. The interleaver systematically rearranges the bits to be transmitted, which has the effect of dispersing a short burst of errors at the receiver, allowing the FEC to work more effectively. Lastly, the modulator generates bandlimited waveforms which can be transmitted over the bandwidth-limited channel to the receiver, where the reverse functions are performed. Whilst we will discuss all aspects of Figure 1.1, it is the generation of waveforms in the modulator in a manner which reduces errors and increases the transmission rate within a given bandwidth, and the subsequent decoding in the demodulator, which will be our main concern in this book.

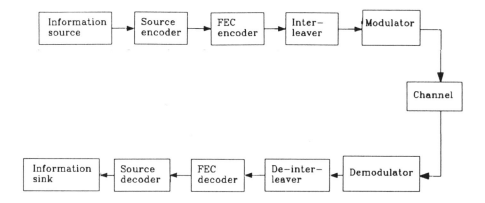

Figure 1.1: Typical digital information transmission system

It is assumed that the majority of readers will be familiar with binary modulation schemes such as binary phase shift keying (BPSK), frequency shift keying (FSK), etc. Those readers who possess this knowledge might like to jump to Section 1.2. For those who are not familiar with modulation schemes we give a short non-mathematical explanation of modulation and constellation diagrams before detailing the history of QAM.

1.1 Modulation methods

Suppose the data we wish to transmit is digitally encoded speech having a bit rate of 16 kbits/s, and after FEC coding the data rate becomes 32 kb/s. If the radio channel to be used is centred around 1 GHz, then in order to transmit the 32 kb/s we must arrange for some feature of a 1 GHz carrier to change at the data rate of 32 kb/s. If the phase of the carrier is switched at the rate of 32 kb/s, being at 0° and 180° for bits having logical 0 or logical 1, respectively, then there are $1 \times 10^9 / 32 \times 10^3 = 31,250$ radio frequency (RF) oscillations per bit transmitted. Figures 1.2 (a) and 1.2 (b) show the waveforms at the output of the modulator when the data is a logical 0 and a logical

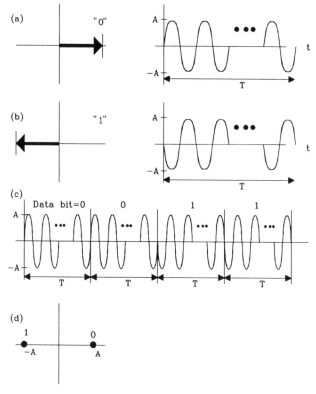

Figure 1.2: Carrier waveform for binary input data

1, respectively. On the left of the sub-figures is the phasor diagram for a logical 0 and a logical 1 where the logical 0 is represented by a phasor along the positive x-axis, and the logical 1 by a phasor along the negative x-axis. This negative phasor represents a phase shift of the carrier by 180°. Figure 1.2 (c) shows the modulator output for a sequence of data bits. Note that no filtering is used in this introductory example. Here the waveform can be seen to change abruptly at the boundary between some of the data symbols. We will see later that such abrupt changes can be problematic since they theoretically require an infinite bandwidth, and ways are sought to avoid them. Figure 1.2 (d) is called a constellation diagram of phasor points, and as we are transmitting binary data there are only two points. As these two points are at equal distance from the origin we would expect them to represent equal magnitude carriers, and that the magnitude is indeed constant can be seen in Figure 1.2 (c).

The bandwidth of the modulated signal in this example will be in excess of the signalling rate of 32 kb/s due to the sudden transition between phase states. Later we will consider the bandwidth of modulated signals in-depth. Suffice to say here that if we decreased the signalling rate to 16 kb/s the bandwidth of the modulated signal will decrease. If the data rate is 32 kb/s, and the signalling rate becomes 16 kb/s, then every symbol transmitted must carry two bits of information. This means that we must have four points on the constellation, and clearly this can be done in many ways. Figure 1.3 shows some four-point constellations. The two bits of information associated with every constellation point are marked on the figure. In Figures 1.3 (a) and Figure 1.3 (b) so-called quadrature modulation has been used as the points can only be uniquely described using two orthogonal coordinate axes, each passing through the origin. The orthogonal coordinate axes have a phase rotation of 90° with respect to each other, and hence they have a so-called quadrature relationship. The pair of coordinate axes can be associated with a pair of quadrature carriers, normally a sine and a cosine waveform, which can be independently modulated and then transmitted within the same frequency band. Due to their orthogonality they can be separated by the receiver. This implies that whatever symbol is chosen on one axis (say the x-axis in the case of Figure 1.3 (a)) it will have no effect on the data demodulated on the y-axis. Data can therefore be independently transmitted via these two quadrature or orthogonal channels without any increase in error rate, although some increase may result in practice and this is considered in later chapters. We have used I and Q to signify the in-phase and quadrature components, respectively, where in-phase normally represents the x-axis and quadrature the y-axis. Figures 1.3 (c) and Figure 1.3 (d) show constellations where the four points are only on one line. These are not quadrature constellations but actually represent multi-level amplitude and phase modulation where both the carrier amplitude and phase can take two discrete values.

For the constellations in Figure 1.3 (a) and Figure 1.3 (b) we have a constant amplitude signal, but the carrier phase values at the beginning of each symbol period in Figure 1.3 (b) would be either 45, 135,

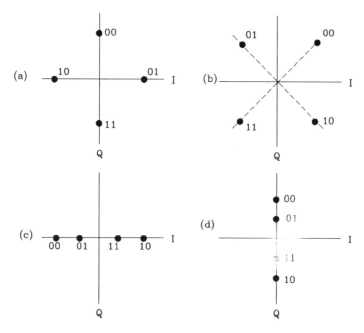

Figure 1.3: Examples of four level constellations

225 or 315 degrees. There are two magnitude values and two phase values for the constellations in Figure 1.3 (c) and Figure 1.3 (d). In order to reduce the bandwidth of the modulated signal whilst maintaining the same information transmission rate we can further decrease the symbol rate by adding more points in the constellation. Such a reduction in the bandwidth requirement will allow us to transmit more information in the spectrum we have been allocated. Such capability is normally considered advantageous. If we combine the constellations of Figure 1.3 (c) and Figure 1.3 (d) we obtain the square QAM constellation having four bits per constellation point as displayed in Figure 1.4. We will spend much time in dealing with this constellation in this book. In general, grouping n bits into one signalling symbol yields 2^n constellation points, which are often referred to as phasors, or complex vectors. The phasors associated with these points may have different amplitude and/or phase values, and this type of modulation is therefore referred to as multilevel modulation, where the number of levels is equal to the number of constellation

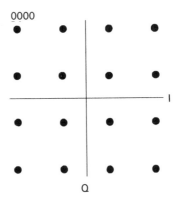

Figure 1.4: Square QAM constellation

points. After transmission through the channel the receiver must identify the phasor transmitted, and in doing so can determine the constellation point and hence the bits associated with this point. In this way the data is recovered. There are many problems with attempting to recover data transmitted over both fixed channels such as telephone lines and radio channels and many of these problems are given a whole chapter in this book. These problems are generally exacerbated by changing from binary to multilevel modulation, and this is why binary modulation is often preferred, despite its lower capacity. In order to introduce these problems, and to provide a historical perspective to quadrature amplitude modulation (QAM), a brief history of the development of QAM is presented.

1.2   History of Quadrature Amplitude Modulation

1.2.1   Determining the optimum constellation

Towards the end of the 1950s there was a considerable amount of interest in digital phase modulation transmission schemes [1] as an alternative to digital amplitude modulation. Digital phase modulation schemes are those whereby the amplitude of the transmitted carrier is held constant but the phase changed in response to the modulating signal. Such schemes have constellation diagrams of the form shown in Figure 1.3 (a). It was a natural extension of this trend to consider the simultaneous use of both amplitude and phase modulation. The first paper to suggest this idea was by C.R. Cahn in 1960, who described a combined phase and amplitude modulation system [2]. He simply extended phase modulation to the multi-level case by allowing there to be more than one transmitted amplitude at any allowed phase. This had the effect of duplicating the original phase modulation or phase shift keying (PSK) constellation which essentially formed a circle. Such duplication lead to a number of concentric circles depending on the number of amplitude levels selected. Each circle had the same number of phase points on each of its rings. Only Gaussian channels characteristic of telephone lines impaired by thermal noise were considered. Using a series of approximations and a wholly theoretical approach, he came to the conclusion that these amplitude and phase modulation (AM-PM) systems allowed an increased throughput compared to phase modulation systems when 16 or more states were used and suggested that such a system was practical to construct.

1.2.1.1 Coherent and non-coherent reception

The fundamental problem with PSK is that of determining the phase of the transmitted signal and hence decoding the transmitted information. This problem is also known as carrier recovery as an attempt is made to recover the phase of the carrier. When a phase point at, say, $90°$ is selected to reflect the information being transmitted, the phase of the transmitted carrier is set to $90°$. However, the phase of the carrier is often changed by the transmission channel with the result that the receiver measures a different phase. This means that unless the receiver knew what the phase change imposed by the channel was it would be unable to determine the encoded information.

This problem can be overcome in one of two ways. The first is to measure the phase change imposed by the channel by a variety of means. The receiver can then determine the transmitted phase. This is known as coherent detection. The second is to transmit differences in phase, rather than absolute phase. The receiver then merely compares the previous phase with the current phase and the phase change of the channel is removed. This assumes that any phase change within the channel is relatively slow. This differential system is known as non-coherent transmission. In his paper, Cahn considered both coherent and non-coherent transmission, although for coherent transmission he assumed a hypothetical and unrealisable perfect carrier recovery device. The process of carrier recovery is considered in Chapter 6, and the details of differential transmission are explained in Chapter 5.

1.2.1.2   Clock recovery

Alongside carrier recovery runs the problem of clock recovery. The recovered clock signal is used to ensure appropriate sampling of the received signal. In Figure 1.2 (c) a carrier signal was shown which had vertical lines indicating each bit or symbol period. It was the phase at the start of this period which was indicative of the encoded information. Unfortunately, the receiver has no knowledge of when these periods occur although it might know their approximate duration. It is determining these *symbol periods* which is the task of clock recovery. So carrier recovery estimates the phase of the transmitted carrier and clock recovery the instances at which the data changes from one symbol to another. Whilst the need for carrier recovery can be removed through differential or non-coherent detection, there is no way to remove the requirement for clock recovery.

Clock recovery schemes tend to seek certain periodicities in the received signal and use these to estimate the start of a symbol (actually they often attempt to select the centre of a symbol for reasons which will be explained in later chapters). Clock recovery is often a complex procedure, and poor clock recovery can substantially increase the bit error rate (BER). The issue of clock recovery is considered in Chapter 6. In his work, Cahn overcame the problem of clock recovery by assuming that he had some device capable of perfect clock recovery. Such devices do not exist, so Cahn acknowledged that the error rate experienced in practice would be worse than that which he had calculated, but as he was unable to compute the errors introduced by a practical clock recovery system, this was the only course open to him.

1.2.1.3 The Type I, II and III constellations

A few months later a paper was published by Hancock and Lucky [3] in which they expanded upon the work of Cahn. In this paper they realised that the performance of the circular type constellation could be improved by having more points on the outer ring than on the inner ring. The rationale for this was that errors were caused when noise introduced into the signal moved the received phasor from the transmitted constellation point to a different one. The further apart constellation points could be placed, the less likely this was to happen. In Cahn's constellation, points on the inner ring were closest together in distance terms and so most vulnerable to errors. They conceded that a system with unequal numbers of points on each amplitude ring would be more complicated to implement, particularly in the case of non-coherent detection. They called the constellation proposed by Cahn a Type I system, and theirs a Type II system. Again using a mathematical approach they derived results similar to Cahn's for Type I systems and a 3dB improvement for the Type II over the Type I system.

The next major publication was some 18 months later, in 1962, by Campopiano and Glazer [4]. They developed on the work of the previous papers but also introduced a new constellation - the square QAM system, which they termed a Type III system. They described this system as "essentially the amplitude modulation and demodulation of two carriers that have the same frequency but are in quadrature with each other" - the first time that combined amplitude and phase modulation had been thought of as amplitude modulation on quadrature carriers, although the acronym QAM was not suggested. They realised that the problem with their Type III system was that it had to be used in a phase coherent mode, that is non-coherent detection was not possible and so carrier recovery was necessary. Again, a theoretical analysis was performed for Gaussian noise channels and the authors came to the conclusion that the Type III system offered a very small improvement in performance over the Type II system, but thought that the implementation of the Type III system would be considerably simpler than that of Types I and II. Examples of the different types of constellation are shown in Figure 1.5.

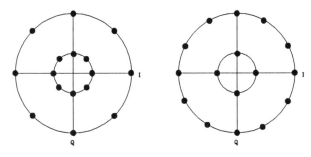

Type I QAM Constellation   Type II QAM Constellation

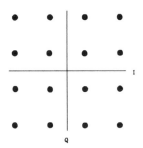

Type III QAM Constellation

Figure 1.5: Examples of types I, II and III QAM constellations

Three months later another paper was published by Hancock and Lucky [5] in which they were probably unaware of the work done by Campopiano and Glazer. They attempted to improve on their previous work on the Type II system by carrying out a theoretical analysis, supposedly leading to the optimal constellation for Gaussian channels. In this paper they decided that the optimum 16 level constellation had two amplitude rings with eight equi-spaced points on each ring but with the rings shifted by 22.5 degrees from each other. This constellation is shown in Figure 1.6.

Again, they concluded that 16 was the minimum number of levels for AM-PM modulation and that a SNR of at least 11dB was required for efficient operation with a low probability of bit error.

After this paper there was a gap of nine years before any further significant advances were published. This was probably due to the difficulties in implementing QAM systems with the technology avail-

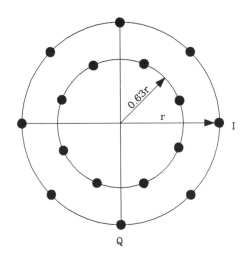

Figure 1.6: "Optimum" 16-level constellation according to
Lucky [5] ©IRE, 1962

able and also because the need for increased data throughput was not
yet pressing. During this nine years period the work discussed in the
above papers was consolidated into a number of books, particularly
that by Lucky, Salz and Weldon [7]. Here they clearly distinguished
between quadrature amplitude modulation (QAM) schemes using
square constellations and combined amplitude and phase modulation schemes using circular constellations. It was around this period
that the acronym QAM started appearing in common usage along
with AM-PM to describe the different constellations.

One of the earliest reports of the actual construction of a QAM
system came from Salz, Sheenhan and Paris [6] of Bell Labs in 1971.
They implemented circular constellations with 4 and 8 phase positions and 2 and 4 amplitude levels using coherent and non-coherent
demodulation. Neither carrier nor clock recovery was attempted.
Their results showed reasonable agreement with the theoretical results derived up to that time. This work was accompanied by that of
Ho and Yeh [8] who improved the theory of circular AM-PM systems
with algorithms that could be solved on digital computers which were
by that time becoming increasingly available.

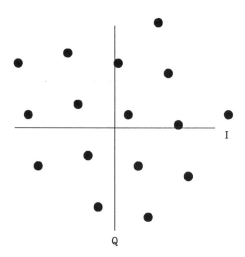

Figure 1.7: "Optimum" 16-level constellation according to Foschini [9] ©IEEE, 1974

Interest in QAM remained relatively low, however, until 1974. In that year there was a number of significant papers published, considerably extending knowledge about quadrature amplitude modulation schemes. At this time, interest into optimum constellations was revived with two papers, one from Foschini, Gitlin and Weinstein [9] and the other from Thomas, Weidner and Durrani [10]. Foschini *et al* attempted a theoretical derivation of the ideal constellation using a gradient calculation approach. They came to the conclusion that the ideal constellation was based around an equilateral triangle construction leading to the unusual 16-level constellation shown in Figure 1.7. This constellation is not in common usage as the complexities involved in its use far outweigh the small gains that were claimed for it. Their conclusions were that this constellation, when limited in terms of power and operated over Gaussian channels, offered a performance improvement of 0.5dB over square QAM constellations. Meanwhile Thomas *et al*, working at COMSAT, empirically generated twenty nine constellations and compared the error probability of each of these constellations.

1.2.2 Satellite links

In the paper by Thomas et al [10] they also mentioned the first application of QAM, for use in satellite links. Satellite links have a particular problem in that satellites only have a limited power available to them. Efficient amplifiers are necessary to use this power carefully, and these had tended to employ a device known as a travelling wave tube (TWT). Such a device introduces significant distortion in the transmitted signal and Thomas et al considered the effects of this distortion on the received waveform. They came to the interesting conclusion that the Type II constellation (in this case 3 points on the inner ring and 5 on the outer) was inferior to the Type I (4 points on inner and outer rings) due to the increased demand in peak to average power ratio of the Type II constellation. Their overall conclusion was that circular Type I constellations are superior in all cases. When they considered TWT distortion they discovered that AM-PM schemes were inferior to PSK schemes because of the need to significantly back off the amplifier to avoid severe amplitude distortion, and concluded that better linear amplifiers would be required before AM-PM techniques could be successfully used for satellite communications. They also considered the difficulties of implementing various carrier recovery techniques, advising that decision directed carrier recovery would be most appropriate, although few details were given as to how this was to be implemented. Decision directed carrier recovery is a process whereby the decoded signal is compared with the closest constellation point and the phase difference between them is used to estimate the error in the recovered carrier. This is discussed in more detail in Chapter 6.

Commensurate with the increasing interest as to possible applications for QAM were the two papers published in 1974 by Simon and Smith which concentrated on carrier recovery and detection techniques. In the first of these [11] they noted the interest in QAM that was then appearing for bandlimited systems, and addressed the problems of carrier recovery. They considered only the 16-level square constellation and noted that the generation of a highly accurate reconstructed carrier was essential for adequate performance. Their solution was to demodulate the signal, quantise it, and then establish the polarity of error from the nearest constellation point, and use it to update the voltage controlled oscillator (VCO) used in the carrier generation section. They provided a theoretical analysis and concluded that their carrier recovery technique worked well in the case of high signal-to-noise (SNR) ratio Gaussian noise, although they noted that gain control was required and would considerably complicate the implementation. They extended their work in Reference [12] where they considered offset QAM or O-QAM. In this modulation scheme the signal to one of the quadrature arms was delayed by half a symbol period in an attempt to prevent dramatic fluctuations of the signal envelope, which was particularly useful in satellite communications. They noted similar results for their decision directed carrier recovery scheme as when non-offset modulation was used.

1.2.2.1 Odd-bit constellations

Despite all the work on optimum constellations, by 1975 interest had centred on the square QAM constellation. The shape of this was evident for even numbers of bits per symbol, but if there was a requirement for an odd number of bits per symbol to be transmitted, the ideal shape of the constellation was not obvious, with rectangular constellations having been tentatively suggested. Early in 1975 J.G.Smith, also working on satellite applications, published a paper addressing this problem [13]. He noted that for even numbers of bits per symbol "the square constellation was the only viable choice." In this paper he showed that what he termed "symmetric" constellations offered about a 1dB improvement over rectangular constellations and he considered both constellations to be of the same implementational complexity. An example of his symmetric constellation for the five bits/symbol case is given in Figure 1.8.

1.2.3 QAM modem implementation

About this time, the Japanese started to show interest in QAM schemes as they considered they might have application in both satellite and microwave radio links. In 1976 Miyauchi, Seki and Ishio published a paper devoted to implementation techniques [14]. They con-

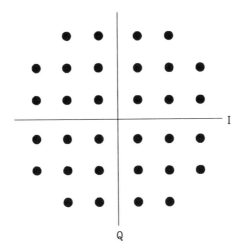

Figure 1.8: "Optimum" 32-level constellation according to Smith [13] ©IEEE, 1975

sidered implementation by superimposing two four level PSK modulation techniques at different amplitudes to achieve a square QAM constellation and using a similar process in reverse at the demodulator, giving them the advantage of being able to use existing PSK modulator and demodulator circuits. This method of implementing QAM is discussed in Chapter 5. They implemented a prototype system without clock or carrier recovery and concluded that its performance was sufficiently good to merit further investigation. Further groundwork was covered in 1978 by W.Weber, again working on satellite applications, who considered differential (i.e. non-coherent) encoding systems for the various constellations still in favour [15]. His paper essentially added a theoretical basis to the differential techniques that had been in use at that point, although suggesting that non-coherent demodulation techniques deserved more attention.

In late 1979 evidence of the construction of QAM prototype systems worldwide started to emerge. A paper from the CNET laboratories in France by Dupuis *et al* [16] considered a 140Mbit/s modem for use in point-to-point links in the 10-11GHz band. This prototype employed the square 16-level constellation and included carrier recovery, although no details were given. Theoretical calculations of impairments were presented followed by measurements made over a 58km hop near Paris. Their conclusions were that QAM had a number of restrictions in its use, relating to its sensitivity to non-linearities, and that in the form they had implemented it, PSK offered improved performance. However, they suggested that with further work these problems might be overcome.

The Japanese simultaneously announced results from a prototype 200Mbits/s 16-QAM system in a paper by Horikawa, Murase and Saito [17]. They used differential coding coupled with a new form of carrier recovery based on a decision feedback method (detailed in Chapter 6). Their modem was primarily designed for satellite applications and their experiment included the use of TWT amplifiers, but was only carried out back-to-back in the laboratory. Their conclusions were that their prototype had satisfactory performance and was an efficient way to increase bandwidth efficiency.

One of the last of the purely theoretical, as opposed to practical papers on QAM appeared in April 1980, marking the progression of QAM from a technical curiosity into a practical system, some twenty years after its introduction. This came from V. Prabhu of Bell Labs [18], further developing the theory to allow calculation of error probabilities in the presence of co-channel interference. Prabhu concluded that 16-QAM had a co-channel interference immunity superior to 16-PSK but inferior to 8-PSK.

1.2.3.1   Non-linear amplification

In 1982 there came a turning point in the use of QAM for satellite applications when Feher turned his attention to this problem. His first major publication in this field [19] introduced a new method of generation of QAM signals using highly non-linear amplifiers which he termed non-linear amplified QAM (NLA-QAM). Two separate amplifiers for the 16-QAM case were used, one operating with half the output power of the other. The higher power amplifier coded the two most significant bits of the four bit symbol only, and the lower power amplifier coded only the two least significant bits. The amplified coded signals were then summed at full output power to produce the QAM signal. Because both amplifiers were therefore able to use constant envelope modulation they could be run at full power with resulting high efficiency, although with increased complexity due to the need for two amplifiers and a hybrid combiner, compared to previous systems which used only a single amplifier. However, in satellite applications, complexity was relatively unimportant compared to power efficiency, and this NLA technique offered a very substantial 5dB power gain, considerably increasing the potential of QAM in severely power limited applications.

1.2.3.2 Frequency selective fading and channel equalisers

This work was soon followed by a performance study of a NLA 64-state system [20] which extended the NLA scheme to 64 levels by using three amplifiers all operating at different power levels. Performance estimates were achieved using computer simulation techniques which included the effects of frequency selective fading.

Frequency selective fading is essentially caused when there are a number of propagation paths between the transmitter and receiver, e.g. by reflection off nearby mountains. When the time delay of the longest path compared to that of the shortest path becomes comparable to a symbol period inter-symbol interference (ISI) is said to result. As every time domain effect has an equivalent frequency domain effect, this can also be termed frequency selective fading. The two are related through the Fourier transform. This fading caused severe problems, leading Feher to conclude that adaptive equalizer techniques would be required for adequate wideband performance. Equalisers are devices which attempt to remove ISI. They do so by calculating the ISI introduced and then subtracting it from the received signals. They are often extremely complex devices and are considered in detail in Chapter 7.

1.2.3.3 Filtering

In a book published around this time [21], Feher also suggested the use of non-linear filtering (NLF) for QAM satellite communications. Since the I and Q components of the time domain QAM signal change their amplitude abruptly at the signalling intervals their transmission would require an infinite bandwidth. These abrupt changes are typically smoothed by a bandlimiting filter. The design an implementation of such filters is critical, particularly when the NLA-QAM signal is filtered at high power level. In order to alleviate these problems Feher developed the NLF technique along with Huang in 1979 which simplified filter design by simply fitting a quarter raised cosine segment between two initially abruptly changing symbols for both of the quadrature carriers. We have already hinted that filtering is required to prevent abrupt changes in the transmitted signal. This issue is considered in more rigour in Chapter 5. This allowed the generation of jitter-free bandlimited signals, which had previously been a problem, improving clock recovery techniques. Feher's work continued to increase the number of levels used, with a paper on 256-QAM in May 1985 [22] noting the problems that linear group delay distortion caused, and a paper in April 1986 on 512-QAM [23] which came to similar conclusions.

1.2.4 Advanced prototypes

Work was still continuing in France, Japan and also in New Zealand. CNET were continuing their attempt to overcome the problems they had found in their initial trials reported in 1979. A paper published in 1985 by M. Borgne [24] compared the performance of 16, 32, 64 and 128 level QAM schemes using computer simulation with particular interest in the impairments likely to occur over point-to-point radio links. Borgne concluded that non-linearity cancellers and adaptive equalizers would be necessary for this application. Soon after this, the first major paper on adaptive equalizers for QAM was published by Shafi and Moore [25]. Much of this paper was concerned with clock and carrier recovery without going into detail as to how these operations were performed. Details were provided of a fractional decision feedback equalizer (DFE) which they considered suitable for point-to-point radio links. They concluded that carrier recovery and clock timing was critical and likely to cause major problems, which were somewhat ameliorated by their fractionally spaced system.

Although lagging somewhat behind Feher, the Japanese made up for this delay by publishing a very detailed paper describing the development of a 256-level QAM modem in August 1986. In this paper from Saito and Nakamura [26], the authors developed on the work announced in 1979 by Saito et al [14] which was discussed earlier. In this new paper they detailed automatic gain control (which he termed automatic threshold control) and carrier recovery methods. The carrier recovery was a slight enhancement to the system announced in 1979 and the AGC system was based on decision directed methods. Details were given as to how false lock problems were avoided (see Chapter 6) and the back-to-back prototype experiments gave results which the authors considered showed the feasibility of the 256-QAM modem. Evidence of the ever increasing interest in QAM was that in the IEEE Special Issue on "Advances in digital communications by radio" there was a substantial section devoted to high level modulation techniques. In a paper by Rustako et al [27] which considered point-to-point applications, the standard times-two carrier recovery method for binary modulation was expanded for QAM. The authors claimed the advantage of not requiring accurate data decisions or interacting with any equalizer. They acknowledged that their system had the disadvantage of slow re-acquisition after fades and suggested that it would only be superior in certain situations. This form of carrier recovery is considered in some detail in Chapter 6.

Clearly, until the late eighties developments were mainly targeted at telephone line and point-to-point radio applications, which led to the definition of the CCITT telephone circuit modem standards V.29-V.33 based on various QAM constellations ranging from uncoded 16-QAM to trellis coded (TC) 128-QAM. Coded modulation is analysed in Chapter 8, while the CCITT standard modem schemes V.29-V.33 for telephone lines will be considered in Chapter 9.

1.2.5 QAM for mobile radio

Another major development occurred in 1987 when Sundberg, Wong and Steele published a pair of papers [28, 29] considering QAM for voice transmission over Rayleigh fading channels, the first major paper considering QAM for mobile radio applications. In these papers, it was recognized that when a Gray code mapping scheme was used, some of the bits constituting a symbol had different error rates from other bits. Gray coding is a method of assigning bits to be transmitted to constellation points in an optimum manner and is discussed in Chapter 5. For the 16-level constellation two classes of bits occurred, for the 64-level three classes and so on. Efficient mapping schemes for pulse code modulated (PCM) speech coding were discussed where the most significant bits (MSBs) were mapped onto the class with the highest integrity. A number of other schemes including variable threshold systems and weighted systems were also discussed. Simulation and theoretical results were compared and found to be in reasonable agreement. They used no carrier recovery, clock recovery or AGC, assuming these to be ideal, and came to the conclusion that channel coding and post-enhancement techniques would be required to achieve acceptable performance.

This work was continued, resulting in a publication in 1990 by Hanzo, Steele and Fortune [30], again considering QAM for mobile radio transmission, where again a theoretical argument was used to show that with a Gray encoded square constellation, the bits encoded onto a single symbol could be split into a number of sub-classes, each subclass having a different average BER. The authors then showed that the difference in BER of these different subclasses could be reduced by constellation distortion at the cost of slightly increased total BER, but was best dealt with by using different error correction powers on the different 16-QAM subclasses. A 16 kbits/s sub-band speech coder was subjected to bit sensitivity analysis and the most sensitive bits identified were mapped onto the higher integrity 16-QAM subclasses, relegating the less sensitive speech bits to the lower integrity classes. Furthermore, different error correction coding powers were considered for each class of bits to optimize performance. Again ideal clock and carrier recovery were used, although this time the problem of automatic gain control (AGC) was addressed. It was suggested that as bandwidth became increasingly congested in mobile radio, microcells would be introduced supplying the required high SNRs with the lack of bandwidth being an incentive to use QAM.

In the meantime, CNET were still continuing their study of QAM for point-to-point applications, and Sari and Moridi published a paper [31] detailing an improved carrier recovery system using a novel combination of phase and frequency detectors which seemed promising. However, interest was now increasing in QAM for mobile radio usage and a paper was published in 1989 by J. Chuang of Bell Labs [32] considering NLF-QAM for mobile radio and concluding that NLF offered slight improvements over raised cosine filtering when there was mild intersymbol interference (ISI).

A technique, known as the transparent tone in band method (TTIB) was proposed by McGeehan and Bateman [33] from Bristol University, UK., which facilitated coherent detection of the square QAM scheme over fading channels and was shown to give good performance but at the cost of an increase in spectral occupancy. This important technique is discussed in depth in Chapter 11. At an IEE colloquium on multi-level modulation techniques in March 1990 a number of papers were presented considering QAM for mobile radio and point-to-point applications. Matthews [34] proposed the use of a pilot tone located in the centre of the frequency band for QAM transmissions over mobile channels.

Huish discussed the use of QAM over fixed links, which was becoming increasingly widespread [35]. Webb et al presented two papers describing the problems of square QAM constellations when used for mobile radio transmissions and introduced the star QAM constellation with its inherent robustness in fading channels [36, 37].

There followed a number of publications by Webb et al describing a number of techniques for enhancing QAM transmissions over mobile radio channels. All of these techniques are described in detail in Chapters 10 to 16 of this book. In December 1991 a paper appeared in the IEE Proceedings [39] which considered the effects of channel coding, trellis coding and block coding when applied to the star QAM constellation. This was followed by another paper in the IEE Proceedings [40] considering equaliser techniques for QAM transmissions over dispersive mobile radio channels. A review paper appearing in July 1992 [41] considered areas where QAM could be put to most beneficial use within the mobile radio environment, and concluded that its advantages would be greatest in microcells. Further work on spectral efficiency, particularly of multi-level modulation schemes [42] concluded that variable level QAM modulation was substantially more efficient than all the other modulation schemes simulated. Variable level QAM was first discussed in a paper by Steele and Webb in 1991 [43].

Further QAM schemes for hostile fading channels characteristic of mobile telephony can be found in the following recent references [44]-[79]. If Feher's previously mentioned NLA concept cannot be applied, then power-inefficient class A or AB linear amplification has to be used, which might become an impediment in light-weight, low-consumption hand sets. However, the power consumption of the low-efficiency class-A amplifier [53], [54] is less critical than that of the digital speech and channel codecs. In many applications 16-QAM, transmitting 4 bits/symbol reduces the signalling rate by a factor of four and hence mitigates channel dispersion, thereby removing the need for an equaliser, while the higher SNR demand can be compensated by diversity reception.

Significant contributions were made by Cavers, Stapleton et al at Simon Fraser University, Burnaby, Canada in the field of pre- and post-distorter design. Out-of-band emissions due to class AB amplifier non-linearities and hence adjacent channel interferences can be reduced by some 15-20 dB using Stapleton's adaptive predistorter [55]-[57] and a class-AB amplifier with 6 dB back-off, by adjusting the predistorter's adaptive coefficients using the complex convolution of the predistorter's input signal and the amplifier's output signal. Further aspects of linearised power amplifier design are considered in references [58] and [59].

A further important research trend is hallmarked by Cavers' work targeted at pilot symbol assisted modulation (PSAM) [60], where known pilot symbols are inserted in the information stream in order to allow the derivation of channel measurement information. The recovered received symbols are then used to linearly predict the channel's attenuation and phase. This arrangement will be considered in Chapter 11. A range of advanced QAM modems have also been proposed by Japanese researchers doing cutting edge research in the field, including Sampei, Sunaga[61, 62], Adachi[63], Sasaoka[52] et al.

A QAM-related orthogonal multiplex scheme originally proposed by Chang in 1966 [64] for dispersive fading channels has also gone through dramatic evolution due to the efforts of Weinstein, Peled, Ruiz, Hirosaki, Kolb, Cimini, Schüssler, Preuss, Rückriem, Kalet et al [64]- [77] and will be standardised as the European digital audio broadcast scheme. The system's operational principle is that the original bandwidth is divided in a high number of narrow sub-bands, in which the mobile channel can be considered non-dispersive. Hence no channel equaliser is required and instead of implementing a bank of sub-channel modems they can be conveniently by the help of a single fast Fourier transformer (FFT). This scheme will be the topic of Chapter 15.

Since QAM research has reached a mature stage, a number of mobile speech, audio and video transmission schemes have been proposed by Steele, Hanzo et al [78]-[88]. Some of these system aspects will be considered in Chapter 18.

1.3 Summary

This concludes our introduction to QAM and the review of publications concerning QAM, spanning a period of over thirty years between the first theoretical study for Gaussian channels through to implementation within microcellular mobile radio environments. We now embark on a detailed investigation of the topics introduced in this chapter.

1.4 Outline of Topics

In Chapter 2 we consider the communications channels over which we wish to send our data. These channels are divided into Gaussian and mobile radio channels, and the characteristics of each are explained.

Chapter 3 forms an introduction to modems, considering the manner in which speech or other source waveforms are converted into a form suitable for transmission over a channel, and introducing some of the fundamentals of modems.

Chapter 4 provides a more detailed description of modems, specifically that of the modulator, considering QAM constellations, pulse-shaping techniques, methods of generating and detecting QAM, as well as amplifier techniques to reduce the problems associated with non-linearities.

Chapter 5 provides details of decision theory and highlights the theoretical aspects of QAM transmission, showing how the BER can be mathematically computed for transmission over Gaussian channels.

Chapter 6 considers clock and carrier recovery schemes whilst Chapter 7 looks at equalisers. Chapter 8 considers trellis coded modulation and provides an introduction to Chapter 9 which deals with modems for Gaussian channels such as telephone lines.

Chapter 10 starts the section on mobile radio by providing a theoretical analysis of QAM transmission over Rayleigh fading mobile radio channels. Chapter 11 then considers some of the practicalities of QAM transmission over these links including constellation distortions and hardware imperfections.

Chapter 12 details clock and carrier recovery schemes for mobile radio, Chapter 13 considers an advanced variable rate QAM scheme, while Chapter 14 proposes various equalisers for wideband transmissions.

In Chapters 15 and 16 we consider a range of orthogonal transmission techniques. Specifically, in Chapter 15 we focus our attention on Fourier transforms in order to implement frequency division multiplexing schemes, whilst in Chapter 16 we treat various orthogonal pulse-shaping techniques.

Chapter 17 considers the spectral efficiency gains that can be achieved when using QAM instead of conventional binary modulation techniques, whilst Chapter 18 provides details of a plethora of practical QAM speech communications systems and compares these with their equivalent binary systems.

Bibliography

[1] **C.R.Cahn**, "Performance of digital phase modulation communication systems", *IRE Trans Comms* Vol.CS-7 May 1959 pp3-6.

[2] **C.R.Cahn**, "Combined digital phase and amplitude modulation communication system", *IRE Trans Comms* Vol.CS-8 Sept 1960 pp150-155.

[3] **J.C.Hancock and R.W.Lucky**, "Performance of combined amplitude and phase modulated communications system", *IRE Trans Comms* Vol.CS-8 Dec 1960 pp232-237.

[4] **C.N.Campopiano and B.G.Glazer**, "A coherent digital amplitude and phase modulation system", *IRE Trans Comms* Vol.CS-10 Mar 1962 pp90-95.

[5] **R.W.Lucky and J.C.Hancock**, "On the optimum performance of N-ary systems having two degrees of freedom", *IRE Trans Comms* Vol.CS-10 June 1962 pp185-192.

[6] **J.Salz, J.R.Sheenhan and D.J.Paris**, "Data transmission by combined AM and PM", *Bell Sys Tech Jnl* Vol.50 No.7 Sept 1971 pp2399-2419.

[7] **R.W.Lucky, J.Salz and E.J.Weldon**, "Principles of data communication" McGraw Hill, New York 1968.

[8] **E.Y.Ho and Y.S.Yeh**, "Error probability of a multilevel digital system with intersymbol interference and Gaussian noise", *Bell Sys Tech Jnl* Vol.50 No.3 March 1971 pp1017-1023.

[9] **G.J.Foschini, R.D.Gitlin and S.B.Weinstein**, "Optimization of two-dimensional signal constellations in the presence of Gaussian noise" *IEEE Trans Comms* Vol.COM-22 No.1 Jan 1974 pp28-38.

[10] **C.M.Thomas,   M.Y.Weidner   and   S.H.Durrani,** "Digital amplitude-phase keying with M-ary alphabets" *IEEE Trans Comms* Vol.COM-22 No.2 Feb 1974 pp168-180.

[11] **M.K.Simon and J.G.Smith,** "Carrier synchronization and detection of QASK signal sets" *ibid* pp98-106.

[12] **M.K.Simon and J.G.Smith,** "Offset quadrature communications with decision feedback carrier synchronization", *IEEE Trans Comms* Vol COM-22 No 10 October 1974 pp1576-1584.

[13] **J.G.Smith,** "Odd-bit quadrature amplitude-shift keying", *IEEE Trans Comms* Vol.COM-23 No.3 pp385-389.

[14] **K.Miyauchi, S.Seki and H.Ishio,** "New techniques for generating and detecting multilevel signal formats", *IEEE Trans Comms* Vol.COM-24 No 2 Feb 1976 pp263-267.

[15] **W.J.Weber,** "Differential encoding for multiple amplitude and phase shift keying systems", *IEEE Trans Comms* Vol.COM-26 No.3 March 1978 pp 385-391.

[16] **P.Dupuis, M.Joindot, A.Leclert and D.Soufflet,** "16 QAM modulation for high capacity digital radio system", *IEEE Trans Comms* Vol.COM-27 No 12 December 1979 pp1771-1781.

[17] **I.Horikawa, T.Murase and Y.Saito,** "Design and performance of a 200Mbit/s 16 QAM digital radio system", *ibid* pp1953-1958.

[18] **V.K.Prabhu,** "The detection efficiency of 16-ary QAM" *Bell Sys Tech Jnl* Vol.59 No.4 April 1980 pp639-656.

[19] **D.H.Morais and K.Feher,** "NLA-QAM: A method for generating high power QAM signals through non-linear amplification", *IEEE Trans Comms* Vol.COM-30 No.3 March 1982 pp517-522.

[20] **T.Hill and K.Feher,** "A performance study of NLA 64-state QAM", *IEEE Trans Comms* Vol.COM-31 No.6 June 1983 pp821-826.

[21] **K.Feher,** "Digital communications satellite/earth station engineering", Prentice-Hall 1983, pp118-120.

[22] **K-T. Wu and K.Feher**, "256-QAM modem performance in distorted channels", *IEEE Trans Comms* Vol.COM-33 No.5 May 1985 pp487-491.

[23] **P.Mathiopoulos and K.Feher**, "Performance evaluation of a 512-QAM system in distorted channels", *IEE Proc Pt F* Vol 133 No 2 April 1986 pp199-204.

[24] **M.Borgne**, "Comparison of high level modulation schemes for high capacity digital radio systems", *IEEE Trans Comms* Vol.COM-33 No 5 May 1985 pp442-449.

[25] **M.Shafi and D.J.Moore**, "Further results on adaptive equalizer improvements for 16 QAM and 64 QAM digital radio", *IEEE Trans Comms* Vol COM-34 Jan 1986 pp59-66.

[26] **Y.Saito and Y.Nakamura**, "256 QAM modem for high capacity digital radio system", *IEEE Trans Comms* Vol.COM-34 No.8 Aug 1986 pp799-805.

[27] **A.J.Rustako, L.J.Greenstein, R.S.Roman and A.A.Saleh**, "Using times four carrier recovery in M-QAM digital radio receivers", *IEEE J-SAC* No 3 April 1987 pp524-533.

[28] **C-E.W.Sundberg, W.C.Wong and R.Steele**, "Logarithmic PCM weighted QAM transmission over Gaussian and Rayleigh fading channels", *IEE Proc Pt. F* Vol.134 Oct 1987 pp557-570.

[29] **R.Steele, C-E.W.Sundberg and W.C.Wong**, "Transmission of log-PCM via QAM over Gaussian and Rayleigh fading channels", *ibid* pp539-556.

[30] **L.Hanzo, R.Steele and P.Fortune**, "A subband coding, BCH coding, and 16-level QAM system for mobile radio communications", *IEEE Proc. Vehicular Tech.* Vol.39 No.4 Nov 1990 pp327-339

[31] **H.Sari and S.Moridi**, "New phase and frequency detectors for carrier recovery in PSK and QAM systems", *IEEE Trans Comms* Vol.COM-36 No 9 September 1988 pp1035-1043.

[32] **J.C.I.Chuang**, "The effects of time-delay spread on QAM with non-linearly switched filters in a portable radio communications channel", *IEEE Trans Comms* Vol.38 No.1, February 1989 pp9-13.

[33] **J.P.McGeehan and A. Bateman**, "Phase-locked transparent tone in band (TTIB): A new spectrum configuration particularly suited to the transmission of data over SSB mobile radio networks", *IEEE Trans Comm, Vol.COM-32*, pp81-87, 1984.

[34] **J.M.Matthews**, "Cochannel performance of 16-level QAM with phase locked TTIB/FFSR processing", *IEE colloquium on multi-level modulation* March 1990, Digest No. 1990/045.

[35] **P.W.Huish and G.D.Richman**, "Increasing the capacity and quality of digital microwave radio", *ibid.*

[36] **W.T.Webb and R.Steele**, "16-level circular QAM transmissions over a Rayleigh fading channel", *ibid.*

[37] **E.Issman and W.T.Webb**, "Carrier recovery for 16-level QAM in mobile radio", *ibid.*

[38] **A.B.Carlson**, "Communication Systems", McGraw Hill 1986

[39] **W.T.Webb, L.Hanzo and R.Steele**, "Bandwidth-efficient QAM schemes for Rayleigh fading channels", *IEE Proc. Part I*, Vol 138 No 3, June 1991, pp169-175.

[40] **W.T.Webb and R.Steele**, "Equaliser techniques for QAM transmissions over dispersive mobile radio channels", *IEE Proc Pt. I*, Vol 138 No 6, Dec 91, pp566-576.

[41] **W.T.Webb**, "QAM, The modulation scheme for future mobile radio communications?", *IEE Electronics & Communications Jnl.*, Vol.4, No.4, Aug 1992, pp1167-176.

[42] **W.T.Webb**, "Modulation methods for PCNs", *IEEE Communications magazine*, Vol.30, No.12, Dec 1992, pp90-95.

[43] **R.Steele and W.T.Webb**, "Variable rate QAM for data transmissions over mobile radio channels", Keynote paper, *Wireless 91, Calgary Alberta* July 91.

[44] **K. Feher**, "Modems for Emerging Digital Cellular Mobile Systems", *IEEE Tr. on VT, Vol 40, No 2*, pp 355-365, May 1991

[45] **M. Iida and K. Sakniwa**, "Frequency Selective Compensation Technology of Digital 16-QAM for Microcellular Mobile Radio Communication Systems", *Proc. of VTC'92*, Denver, Colorado, pp 662-665

[46] **R.J. Castle and J.P. McGeehan**, "A Multilevel Differential Modem for Narrowband Fading Channels", *Proc. of VTC'92*, Denver, Colorado, pp 104-109

[47] **D.J. Purle, A.R. Nix, M.A. Beach and J.P. McGeehan**, "A Preliminary Performance Evaluation of a Linear Frequency Hopped Modem", *Proc. of VTC'92*, Denver, Colorado, pp 120-124

[48] **Y. Kamio and S. Sampei**, "Performance of Reduced Complexity DFE Using Bidirectional Equalizing in Land Mobile Communications", *Proc. of VTC'92*, Denver, Colorado, pp 372-376

[49] **T. Nagayasu, S. Sampei and Y. Kamio**, "Performance of 16-QAM with Decision Feedback Equalizer Using Interpolation for Land Mobile Communications", *Proc. of VTC'92*, Denver, Colorado, pp 384-387

[50] **E. Malkamaki**, "Binary and Multilevel Offset QAM, Spectrum Efficient Modulation Schemes for Personal Communications", *Proc. of VTC'92*, Denver, Colorado, pp 325-378

[51] **Z. Wan and K. Feher**, "Improved Efficiency CDMA by Constant Envelope SQAM", *Proc. of VTC'92*, Denver, Colorado, pp 51-55

[52] **H. Sasaoka**, "Block Coded 16-QAM/TDMA Cellular Radio System Using Cyclical Slow Frequency Hopping", *Proc. of VTC'92*, Denver, Colorado, pp 405-408

[53] **P.B. Kenningto et al.**, "Broadband Linear Amplifier Design for a PCN Base-Station", *Proc. of 41st IEEE VTC*, pp 155-160, May 1991

[54] **R.J. Wilkinson et al.**, "Linear Transmitter Design for MSAT Terminals", *2nd Int. Mobile Satellite Conference*, June 1990.

[55] **S.P. Stapleton and F.C. Costescu**, "An Adaptive Predistorter for a Power Amplifier Based on Adjacent Channel Emissions", *IEEE Tr. on VT*, Vol 41, No 1, pp 49-57, Febr. 1992

[56] **S.P. Stapleton and F.C. Costescu**, "An Adaptive Predistorter for a Power Amplifier Based on Adjacent Channel Emissions", *IEEE Tr. on VT*, Vol 41, No 1, pp 49-57, Febr. 1992

[57] **S.P. Stapleton, G.S. Kandola and J.K. Cavers**, "Simulation and Analysis of an Adaptive Predistorter Utilizing a Complex Spectral Convolution", *IEEE Tr. on VT*, Vol 41, No 4, pp 387-394, Nov. 1992

[58] **A.S. Wright and W.G. Durtler**, "Experimental Performance of an Adaptive Digital Linearized Power Amplifier", *IEEE Tr. on VT*, Vol 41, No 4, pp 395-400, Nov. 1992

[59] **M. Faulkner and T. Mattson**, "Spectral Sensitivity of Power Amplifiers to Quadrature Modulator Misalignment", *IEEE Tr. on VT*, Vol 41, No 4, pp 516-525, Nov. 1992

[60] **J.K. Cavers**, "An Analysis of Pilot Symbol Assisted Modulation for Rayleigh Fading Channels", *IEEE Tr. on VT*, Vol 40, No 4, Nov. 1991, pp 686-693

[61] **S. Sampei, T. Sunaga**: Rayleigh fading compensation for QAM in land mobile radio communications, IEEE Tr. on VT, May 1993, Vol. 42, No. 2, pp 137-147

[62] **T. Sunaga, S Sampei**: Performance of multi-level QAM with post-detection maximal ratio combining space diversity fir digital land-mobile radio communications, IEEE Tr. on VT, Aug. 1993, Vol 42, No. 3, pp 294-301

[63] **F. Adachi, M. Sawahashi**: Performance analysis of various 16 level modulation schemes under Rayleigh fading, Electronics Letters, Vol. 28, Nov. 1992, pp 1579-1581

[64] **R.W. Chang**, "Synthesis of Band-limited Orthogonal Signals for Multichannel Data Transmission", *BSTJ*, Dec 1966

[65] **M.S. Zimmermann and A.L. Kirsch**, "The AN/GSC-10 (KATHRIN) Variable Rate Data Modem for HF Radio", *IEEE Trans. on Comm Technology*, Vol., Com-15, No 2, Apr. 1967

[66] **S.B.Weinstein**, "Data transmission by frequency-division multiplexing using the discrete Fourier transform", *IEEE Trans Comms COM-19* No.5 Oct 1971, pp628-634.

[67] **L.J.Cimini**, "Analysis and simulation of a digital mobile channel using orthogonal frequency division multiplexing", *IEEE Trans. Comms* Com-33 No.7 July 1985, pp665-675.

[68] **M. Alard and R. Lassalle**, "Principles of modulation and channel coding for digital broadcasting for mobile receivers", *EBU Review, Technical* No. 224, Aug. 1987, pp 47-69

[69] Proceedings of the 1st Intern. Symp. on DAB, June, 1992, Montreux, Switzerland

[70] **A. Peled and A. Ruiz**, "Frequency Domain Data Transmission Using Reduced Computational Complexity Algorithms", *Proc. of the ICASSP*, pp. 964–967, 1980

[71] **B. Hirosaki**, "An Orthogonally Multiplexed QAM System Using the Discrete Fourier Transform", *IEEE Trans. Commun.*, vol. COM–29, no. 7, July 1981

[72] **H.J. Kolb**, "Untersuchungen über ein digitales Mehrfrequenzverfahren zur Datenübertragung", *Ausgewählte Arbeiten über Nachrichtensysteme, Universität Erlangen-Nürnberg, no. 50*

[73] **H.W. Schüssler** "Ein digitales Mehrfrequenzverfahren zur Datenübertragung", *Professoren-Konferenz, Stand und Entwicklungsaussichten der Daten und Telekommunikation, Darmstadt, Germany*, pp. 179–196, 1983

[74] **K. Preuss**, "Ein Parallelverfahren zur schnellen Datenübertragung Im Ortsnetz", *Ausgewählte Arbeiten über Nachrichtensysteme, Universität Erlangen-Nürnberg, no. 56*

[75] **R. Rückriem**, "Realisierung und messtechnische Untersuchung an einem digitalen Parallelverfahren zur Datenübertragung im Fernsprechkanal", *Ausgewählte Arbeiten über Nachrichtensysteme, Universität Erlangen-Nürnberg, no. 59*

[76] **I.Kalet**, "The multitone channel", *IEEE Tran. on Comms*, Vol.37, No.2, Feb 1989, pp119-124.

[77] **B. Hirosaki**, "An Analysis of Automatic Equalizers for Orthogonally Multiplexed QAM Systems", *IEEE Trans. Comm.*, vol. COM-28, no. 1, January 1980

[78] **L. Hanzo, R. Salami, R. Steele and P.M. Fortune**, "Transmission of Digitally Encoded Speech at 1.2 KBd for PCN", *Proc. of the IEE-Part I*, Vol 139, No 4, Aug. 1992, pp 437-447

[79] **P.M. Fortune, L. Hanzo and R. Steele**, "On the Computation of 16-QAM and 64-QAM Performance in Rayleigh-Fading Channels", *IEICE Tr. on Comms.*, Vol E75-B, No 6, June 1992, pp 466-475

[80] **R. Stedman, H, Gharavi, L. Hanzo and R. Steele**, "Transmission of Subband Coded Images via Mobile Channels", *IEEE Tr. on Circuits and Systems for Video Technology*, Vol 3, No 1, Febr. 1993, pp 15-27

[81] **X. Lin, L. Hanzo, R. Steele and W.T. Webb**, "A Subband-Multipulse digital audio broadcasting scheme for mobile receivers", *IEEE Tr. on Broadcasting*, Dec. 1993, Vol. 39, No. 4, pp 373-482

[82] **L. Hanzo, J.C.S. Cheung, R. Steele and W.T. Webb**, "A packet reservation multiple access assisted cordless telecommunication scheme", to appear in *IEEE Tr. on Veh. Techn.*, 1994

[83] **L. Hanzo, W. Webb, R. Steele, R.A. Salami**, "On QAM speech transmission schemes for microcellular mobile PCNs", *European Transactions on Telecommunication*, Vol. 4, No. 5, Sept.-Oct. 1993, pp 495-510

[84] **L. Hanzo, et al**, "A low-rate multi-level transceiver for personal communication", submitted to *IEEE Tr. on Veh. Techn.*, 1994

[85] **L. Hanzo, et al**, "A mobile speech, video and data transceiver scheme", *Proc. of VTC'94, Stockholm*, 7-10 June, 1994

[86] **L. Hanzo, et al**, "A mobile HI-FI digital audio broadcasting scheme", *ibid*

[87] **J. Woodard, L. Hanzo**, "A dual-rate algebraic CELP-based speech transceiver", *ibid*

[88] **J. Streit, L. Hanzo**, "A fractal video communicator", *ibid*

Chapter 2

Communications Channels

In this chapter we consider the communication channel which exists between the transmitter and the receiver. Accurate characterisation of this channel is essential if we are to remove the impairments imposed by the channel using signal processing at the receiver. Initially we consider fixed links whereby both terminals are stationary, and then mobile radio communications channels which change significantly with time are investigated.

2.1 Fixed Communication Channels

2.1.1 Introduction

We define fixed communications channels to be those between a fixed transmitter and a fixed receiver. These channels are exemplified by twisted pairs, cables, wave guides, optical fibre and point-to-point microwave radio channels. Whatever the nature of the channel, its output signal differs from the input signal. The difference might be deterministic or random, but it is typically unknown to the receiver. Examples of channel impairments are dispersion, non-linear distortions, delay, and random noise.

Fixed communications channels can often be modelled by a linear transfer function, which describes the channel dispersion. The ubiquitous additive Gaussian noise (AWGN) is a fundamental limiting

34

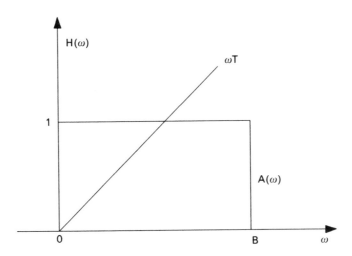

Figure 2.1: Ideal, Distortion-Free Channel Model

factor in communications via linear time-invariant (LTI) channels. Although the channel characteristics might change due to ageing, temperature changes, channel switching, etc., these variations will not be apparent over the course of a typical communication. It is this inherent time-invariance which characterises fixed channels.

An ideal, distortion-free communications channel would have a flat frequency response and linear phase response over the bandwidth (B) of the signals to be transmitted, as seen in Figure 2.1. In this figure $A(\omega)$ represents the magnitude of the channel response at frequency ω, and ωT represents the phase shift at frequency ω. Practical channels always have some linear distortions, i.e., a non-flat frequency response and a non-linear phase response. In addition, the group-delay response of the channel, which is the derivative of the phase response, is often given.

2.1.2 Fixed Channel Types

Conventional telephony uses twisted pairs to connect subscribers to the local exchange. The bandwidth is approximately 3.4 kHz, and the waveform distortions are relatively benign.

For applications requiring a higher bandwidth coaxial cables can be used. Their attenuation increases approximately with the square root of the frequency. Hence for wide-band, long-distance operation they require channel equalisation. Typically, coaxial cables can provide a bandwidth of about 50 MHz, and the transmission rate they can support is limited by the so-called skin effect.

Recent advances in optical communications, such as the invention of the optical amplifiers, render optical fibres more attractive for higher bit rates. Guided optical wave transmission fibres use fine strands of silicon-based, high purity glass. For short haul systems the so-called step-index fibres are used where the higher refractive index internal core is surrounded by a lower refractive index external cladding. Their effective bandwidth is limited by their length and the difference between the refractive index of the core and that of the cladding. For long-distance, high-rate applications the so-called graded-index fibres are more suitable, where the refractive index gradually reduces from the central core towards the cladding. Their relative loss expressed in dB/km versus wavelength characteristic shows a minimum around 1550 nm. This wavelength also allows the design of low-dispersion fibres.

Point-to-point microwave radio channels typically utilise high-gain directional transmit and receive antennae in a line-of-sight scenario, where free-space propagation conditions may be applicable.

2.1.3   Characterisation of Noise

Irrespective of the communications channel used, random noise is always present. Noise can be broadly classified as natural or man-made. Examples of man-made noise are those due to electrical appliances, lighting, etc., and the effects of those sources can usually be mitigated at the source. Natural noise sources affecting radio transmissions include galactic star radiations and atmospheric noise. There exists a low-noise window in the range of 1–10 GHz, where the effects of these sources are minimised.

Natural thermal noise is ubiquitous. This is due to the random motion of electrons and can be reduced by reducing the temperature. Since thermal noise contains practically all frequency components up to some 10^{13} Hz with equal power, it is often referred to as white

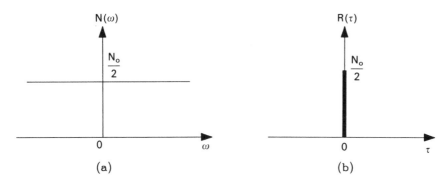

Figure 2.2: Power Spectral Density and Autocorrelation of WN

noise (WN) in an analogy to white light containing all colours with equal intensity. This WN process can be characterised by its uniform power spectral density (PSD) $N(\omega) = N_0/2$ shown together with its autocorrelation function (ACF) in Figure 2.2. The ACF $R(\tau)$ can be computed using the Wiener-Khintchine theorem, which states that $N(\omega)$ and $R(\tau)$ are Fourier transform pairs such that:

$$
\begin{aligned}
R(\tau) &= \frac{1}{2\pi} \int_{-\infty}^{\infty} N(\omega) e^{j\omega\tau} d\omega = \frac{1}{2\pi} \int_{-\infty}^{\infty} \frac{N_0 e^{j\omega\tau}}{2} d\omega \\
&= \frac{N_0}{2} \frac{1}{2\pi} \int_{-\infty}^{\infty} e^{j\omega\tau} d\omega = \frac{N_0}{2} \delta(\tau),
\end{aligned} \tag{2.1}
$$

where $\delta(\tau)$ is the Dirac delta function. Clearly, for any time domain shift $\tau > 0$ the noise is uncorrelated.

Bandlimited communications systems bandlimit not only the signal, but the noise as well, and this filtering limits the rate of change of the time domain noise signal, introducing some correlation over the interval of $\pm 1/2B$. The stylised PSD and ACF of bandlimited white noise are displayed in Figure 2.3. With bandlimiting the auto-

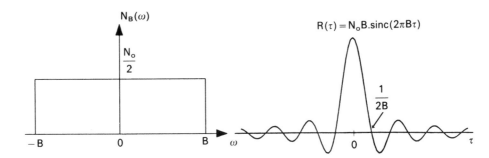

Figure 2.3: Power Spectral Density and Autocorrelation of Bandlimited WN

correlation function becomes

$$
\begin{aligned}
R(\tau) &= \frac{1}{2\pi} \int_{-B}^{B} \frac{N_0}{2} e^{j\omega\tau} d\omega = \frac{N_0}{2} \int_{-B}^{B} e^{j2\pi f\tau} df \\
&= \frac{N_0}{2} \left[\frac{e^{j2\pi f\tau}}{j2\pi\tau} \right]_{-B}^{B} = N_0 B \frac{\sin(2\pi B\tau)}{2\pi B\tau}.
\end{aligned} \tag{2.2}
$$

In the time domain the amplitude distribution of the white thermal noise has a so-called normal or Gaussian distribution and since it is inevitably added to the received signal, it is usually referred to as additive white Gaussian noise (AWGN). Note that AWGN is therefore the noise generated in the receiver. The probability density function (PDF) is the well-known bell-shaped curve of the Gaussian distribution, given by:

$$
p(x) = \frac{1}{\sigma\sqrt{2\pi}} e^{-(x-m)^2/2\sigma^2}, \tag{2.3}
$$

where m is the mean and σ^2 is the variance. The effects of AWGN can be mitigated by increasing the transmitted signal power and thereby reducing the relative effects of noise. The signal-to-noise ratio (SNR) at the receiver's input provides a good measure of the

| SNR | | C/B |
Ratio	dB	bit/sec/Hz
1	0	1
3	4.8	2
7	8.5	3
15	11.8	4
31	14.9	5
63	18.0	6
127	21.0	7

Table 2.1: Relative Channel Capacity versus SNR

received signal quality. This SNR is often referred to as the channel SNR.

If an analogue channel's bandwidth is B and the prevailing SNR is known, then according to the Shannon-Hartley theorem the maximum transmission rate at which information can be sent without errors via this channel is given by:

$$C = B \log_2(1 + SNR) \text{ [bit/sec]}, \tag{2.4}$$

where C is referred to as the channel capacity. The Shannon-Hartley law has a number of fundamental consequences, of which we emphasize here only one. Namely, expressing the ratio C/B in terms of SNR we have:

$$\frac{C}{B} = \log_2(1 + SNR) \left[\frac{\text{bit/sec}}{\text{Hz}} \right], \tag{2.5}$$

and selecting the SNR values seen in Table 2.1 we arrive at the near-linear curve seen in Figure 2.4. It can be seen that the channel capacity for a given bandwidth B is nearly linearly proportional to the SNR. Consequently, using a binary signalling scheme with low C/B ratio when high SNR values are available results in an inefficient use of the channel. This fact provides the main motivation for using the multilevel modulation schemes discussed in this book.

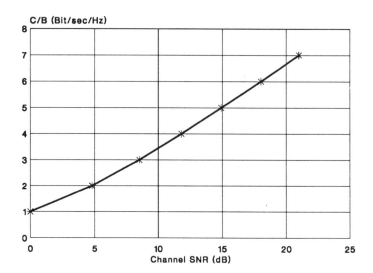

Figure 2.4: Relative Channel Capacity versus SNR

2.2 Telephone Channels

The ubiquitous telephone lines play an important role as data transmission circuits. Although their attenuation and group delay characteristics vary widely, the international leased telephone lines commonly used for multilevel data transmission must comply with the CCITT recommendations, particularly M1020 and M1025. In general, the overall loss is unknown, but should be less than -13dB relative (dBr) for 4-wire circuits, with a variation of less than $\pm 4dB$. The attenuation and group delay characteristics as specified by the M1020 and M1025 recommendations are given in Figures 2.5, 2.6, 2.7 and 2.8.

When multilevel modems are used for data transmissions over these lines as described in Chapter 9, the number of sudden amplitude hits greater than $\pm 2dB$ should not exceed 10 in any 15 minutes. The pshophometrically weighted noise power for longer than 10,000km lines must be below -38dBm, where dBm is related to 1 mWatt measured across a load resistance of 600 Ohms. However, for shorter lines the pshophometrically weighted noise power must be proportionally lower, e.g. about -50dBm at 1,000km. The number of impulse noise peaks exceeding -21dBm should not be more than 18 in 15 minutes.

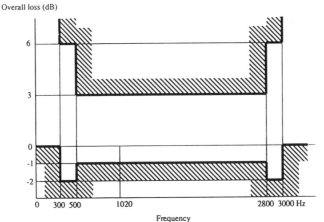

Figure 2.5: Circuit loss as recommended by M1020

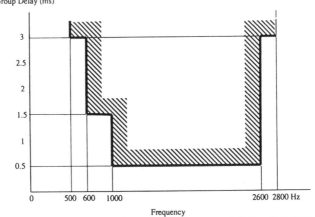

Figure 2.6: Group delay as recommended by M1020

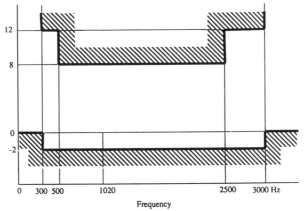

Figure 2.7: Circuit loss as recommended by M1025

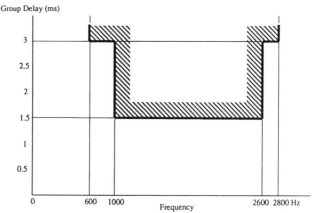

Figure 2.8: Group delay as recommended by M1025

The maximum allowed phase jitter is limited to 15° peak-to-peak. The signal-to-total-distortion power ratio should be better than 28dB when measured with a 1020Hz -10dBm sine wave. The level of single tone interference must be at least 3dB below the random noise level while the maximum frequency error is specified as $\pm$5Hz.

Further standards, such as M1030, impose less stringent requirements and are applicable to lower transmission rates or to private switched networks.

Having briefly considered fixed communications channels, we now consider the more complex mobile radio channels.

2.3   Mobile Radio Channels

2.3.1   Introduction

The mobile radio channel has been characterised in a number of excellent treatises by Jakes[1], Lee[2], Steele[3], Parsons[4] et al. In this Section we follow a similar approach to Steele [3], Greenwood, Hanzo [5] and Cheung[6], while maintaining the treatment of mobile channels as simple and practical, as possible.

Mobile radio links are established between a fixed base station (BS) and a number of roaming mobile stations (MSs) [1, 2, 3]. In order to cover a large area it is necessary to have a number of transmitters. The coverage area of each transmitter is defined as the area in which satisfactory communications between the mobile and the transmitter can be achieved, and this is known as a cell. First and second generation mobile systems are using cells with radii up to some 35km, which implies that the existence of a line-of-sight (LOS) path between transmitter and receiver will be rare. Nearby cells are assigned different frequencies, but as the distance between cells increases, the interference between them reduces, and it becomes possible to reuse frequencies, thus increasing system capacity.

In areas, where the generated traffic density is high or when only low power handhelds are available, such as the British Cordless Telecommunications system CT-2 or the Digital European Cordless Telecommunications (DECT) system, the cell size is necessarily reduced. If the BS antenna is mounted below the roof-top level of surrounding buildings, i.e. fixed to the side of a building, the resulting radio cell is termed a microcell, and typically has a radius of some 200-400m [7, 8]. In such cells, due to the proximity to the BS, there is an increased likelihood of a LOS path with the resulting effect that multipath fading is often less severe.

Propagation mechanisms can be divided into three types, distance effects, slow and fast fading. In this section we will neglect the slow fading caused by large obstructions. The distance effect is simply that as the separation between a BS and a MS increases, the received mean signal level tends to decrease. Over distances of a few metres the mean signal level is essentially constant, but the instantaneous signal level can vary rapidly by amounts typically up to 40 dB. These rapid variations are known as fast fading. This is because the MS receives a number of versions of the signal transmitted by the BS, which have been reflected and diffracted by buildings, mountains and other obstructions and have a range of delays, attenuations and frequency shifts. These various signals are all summed at the MS antenna. When this summation is constructive because all paths are received with the same phase change the received signal level is enhanced. However, when the multipath signals sum destructively because of phase changes which cause cancellation the received signal level is much reduced and the receiver is said to be in a fade. Because differences of 180° in the carrier phase could change the interference from constructive to destructive, and at a carrier frequency of 2GHz this corresponds to some 7cm, the change in instantaneous signal level can be rapid and so is termed fast-fading. As previously suggested, these fades typically occur every half-wavelength.

In mobile communications digital information is transmitted at a certain bit rate. The propagation phenomena are highly dependent on the ratio of the symbol duration to the delay spread of the time variant radio channel. The delay spread may be defined as the length of the channel's impulse response. We can see that if we transmit data at a slow rate the individual symbols can be resolved at the receiver. This is because the numerous reflected paths all arrive at the receiver before the next symbol is transmitted. However, if we increase the transmitted data rate a point will be reached where this no longer occurs and each data symbol significantly spreads into adjacent symbols, a phenomenon known as intersymbol interference (ISI). Without the use of channel equalisers to remove the ISI the bit error rate (BER) may become unacceptably high.

Measurements show that cellular radio networks using large cells, where the excess delay spread may exceed 10 μs, need equalisers when the bit rate is relatively low, say 64kb/s, while cordless communications in buildings where the excess delay spread is often significantly below a microsecond may exhibit flat fading when the bit rate exceeds a megabit/sec. Very small cells, sometimes referred to as picocells may support many megabits/sec without equalisation because the delay spread is only tens of nanoseconds.

2.3.2   Equivalent Baseband and Passband Systems

When modelling mobile radio systems it is advantageous to model them at baseband rather than radio frequencies as this dramatically simplifies the analysis. In this section we show how baseband equivalent models can be developed, following the approach of Proakis [9].

In general the modulated signal $s(t)$ occupies a relatively narrow bandwidth B, when compared to the carrier frequency f_c, where $f_c \gg B$, and can be represented by:

$$s(t) = a(t) \cos[2\pi f_c t + \Theta(t)] = \Re\{a(t)e^{j[\omega_c t + \Theta(t)]}\}, \qquad (2.6)$$

where $\Re$ represents the real part of a complex expression. The modulated signal's amplitude is represented by $a(t)$ and its phase by $\Theta(t)$. The carrier f_c is amplitude modulated by the signal $a(t)$ and phase modulated by the signal $\Theta(t)$. It is common practice to refer to the modulated radio signal $s(t)$ as a narrowband bandpass signal. In computer simulations, however, it is impractical to directly model the above equation. This can be appreciated by the following example:-

If we have a signal bandwidth of 16 kHz transmitted at 2 GHz, then for every cycle of our baseband signal, the RF signal goes through $(2 \times 10^9)/(16 \times 10^3) = 1.25 \times 10^5$ cycles. To simulate each cycle of the RF carrier, we must oversample by a minimum of a factor of two. This means that an order of a quarter of a million operations are required for every baseband symbol transmitted, in addition to the simulation of RF mixers, filters, etc.

Fortunately, we can translate the bandpass signal to an equivalent baseband signal with no loss of accuracy. Expanding Equation 2.6 leads to

$$
\begin{aligned}
s(t) &= a(t)\cos\Theta(t)\cos(2\pi f_c t) - a(t)\sin\Theta(t)\sin(2\pi f_c t) \\
&= u_I \cos(2\pi f_c t) - u_Q \sin(2\pi f_c t) \qquad (2.7)
\end{aligned}
$$

where u_I and u_Q are termed the quadrature components of $s(t)$ and modulate quadrature carriers, and therefore are defined as

$$
\begin{aligned}
u_I &= a(t)\cos\Theta(t) \\
u_Q &= a(t)\sin\Theta(t). \qquad (2.8)
\end{aligned}
$$

This is a cartesian or rectangular representation of the baseband signal $u(t)$ with u_I and u_Q corresponding to in-phase (I) and quadrature (Q) signals. There is an equivalent polar representation which is often convenient, given by

$$
u(t) = a(t)e^{j\Theta(t)}, \qquad (2.9)
$$

where $u(t) = u_I(t) + ju_Q(t)$ is the complex baseband envelope or complex lowpass equivalent of $s(t)$. When combining Equations 2.6 and 2.9, this leads to

$$
s(t) = \Re\left[u(t)e^{j2\pi f_c t}\right] \qquad (2.10)
$$

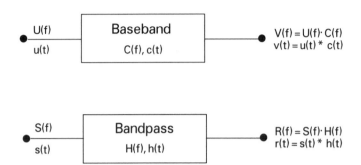

Figure 2.9: Equivalent baseband and passband channels

where $\Re[]$ represents the real part of $[]$. This equation implies that the knowledge of $u(t)$ and f_c uniquely describes the modulated signal $s(t)$, where all the useful information is conveyed by $u(t)$.

In order to establish the validity of the complex baseband model for studying bandpass systems, we will show that the response of a bandpass system to a bandpass signal is identical to the response of the equivalent baseband system to the equivalent baseband signal. This confirms that any operations such as filtering, which are carried out at RF in hardware, can be represented as baseband operations in software, and thus simulations can be carried out at baseband. In order to show this, we take a bandpass modulated signal $s(t)$ with its equivalent lowpass signal $u(t)$ as defined in Equation 2.9. We then allow $s(t)$ to excite a narrowband bandpass system having impulse response $h(t)$ and equivalent baseband impulse response $c(t)$. The baseband equivalent response $c(t)$ is derived from $h(t)$ in the same way as $u(t)$ was derived from $s(t)$. The notations used are summarised in Figure 2.9.

The time domain response $r(t)$ of the bandpass system is given by:

$$r(t) = \int_{-\infty}^{\infty} s(\tau)h(t - \tau)d\tau. \tag{2.11}$$

This is the well-known convolution integral and is often simply written as

$$r(t) = s(t) * h(t), \tag{2.12}$$

where * indicates convolution. When translating Equation 2.12 to the frequency domain we have:

$$R(f) = S(f)H(f), \tag{2.13}$$

where $S(f)$ is the Fourier transform of $s(t)$, given by:

$$S(f) = \int_{-\infty}^{\infty} s(t)e^{-j2\pi ft}dt. \tag{2.14}$$

Upon substituting $s(t)$ from Equation 2.10 into Equation 2.14 we can write:

$$S(f) = \int_{-\infty}^{\infty} \left\{\Re\left[u(t)e^{j2\pi f_c t}\right]\right\} e^{-j2\pi ft}dt. \tag{2.15}$$

Noting the identity

$$\Re(z) = \frac{1}{2}(z + z^*), \tag{2.16}$$

where the asterisk represents the complex conjugate and taking into account that $\mathcal{F}\{u^*(t)\} = U^*(-f)$, where $\mathcal{F}$ represents the Fourier transform, we can rewrite Equation 2.15 as:

$$\begin{aligned} S(f) &= \frac{1}{2}\int_{-\infty}^{\infty} \left[u(t)e^{j2\pi f_c t} + u^*(t)e^{-j2\pi f_c t}\right] e^{-j2\pi ft}dt \\ &= \frac{1}{2}[U(f - f_c) + U^*(-f - f_c)], \end{aligned} \tag{2.17}$$

where $U(f)$ is the Fourier transform of $u(t)$. The spectra $U(f)$ of $u(t)$ and $S(f)$ of $s(t)$ are shown in Figures 2.10a and b, respectively. Observe that the multiplication of $u(t)$ by $e^{j2\pi f_c t}$ in Equation 2.15 shifts the baseband spectrum $U(f)$ to $\pm f_c$ and its conjugate complex symmetry implies that the modulated signal $s(t)$ is real. It is worth noting that since $f_c \gg B$, the energy is concentrated in a tight band around the carrier frequency.

In a similar fashion, the conjugate complex symmetric frequency response $H(f)$ of the bandpass system can be described by the help of shifted versions of the equivalent baseband system's frequency response. Since the bandpass system's impulse response $h(t)$ is real, $H(f)$ is conjugate complex symmetric, i.e., $H(f) = H^*(-f)$. Defining

$$C(f - f_c) = \begin{cases} H(f) & \text{if } f > 0 \\ 0 & \text{if } f \leq 0 \end{cases} \tag{2.18}$$

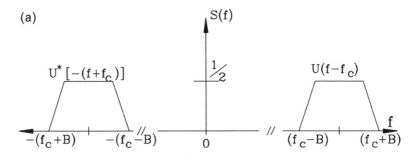

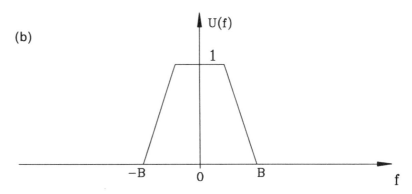

Figure 2.10: Relationship Between the Baseband Spectrum $U(f)$ and the Bandpass Spectrum $S(f)$

and

$$C^*[-(f + f_c)] = \begin{cases} 0 & \text{if } f \geq 0 \\ H^*(-f) & \text{if } f < 0 \end{cases}, \qquad (2.19)$$

as seen in Figure 2.11 allows us to express $H(f)$ as

$$H(f) = C(f - f_c) + C^*(-f - f_c). \qquad (2.20)$$

When returning to the time domain the relationship of the baseband and passband impulse responses is given by:

$$\begin{aligned} h(t) &= c(t)e^{j\omega_c t} + c^*(t)e^{-j\omega_c t} \\ &= 2\Re\{c(t)e^{j\omega_c t}\}, \end{aligned} \qquad (2.21)$$

indicating that the complex baseband equivalent impulse response $c(t)$ forms the time domain envelope of $h(t)$, where $c(t)$ can be de-

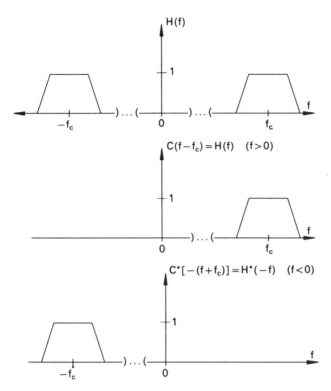

Figure 2.11: Spectral Relationship of Bandpass and Lowpass Equivalent Systems

scribed by its in-phase and quadrature phase components as follows:

$$c(t) = c_I(t) + jc_Q(t). \qquad (2.22)$$

The received passband signal $r(t)$ or $R(f)$ can now be expressed also by the help of the baseband equivalents $U(f)$ and $C(f)$ or $u(t)$ and $c(t)$. Substituting Equations 2.17 and 2.20 into Equation 2.13 yields:

$$R(f) = \frac{1}{2}[U(f - f_c) + U^*(-f - f_c)][C(f - f_c) + C^*(-f - f_c)]. \qquad (2.23)$$

Figures 2.10 and 2.11 reveal that $U(f - f_c) \cdot C^*(f - f_c) = 0$ if $f \le 0$ and $U^*(-f - f_c) \cdot C(-f - f_c) = 0$ if $f \ge 0$, hence Equation 2.23 simplifies to:

$$R(f) = \frac{1}{2}[U(f - f_c)C(f - f_c) + U^*(-f - f_c)C^*(-f - f_c)]$$

$$= \frac{1}{2}[V(f - f_c) + V^*(-f - f_c)], \tag{2.24}$$

where

$$V(f) = U(f)C(f) \tag{2.25}$$

is the response of the baseband system $C(f)$ to excitation $U(f)$. But for a real impulse response $v(t)$ we have

$$V(f) = V^*(-f) \tag{2.26}$$

giving that the passband system's response is constituted by the shifted baseband responses, i.e.:

$$R(f) = \frac{1}{2}[V(f - f_c) + V(f + f_c)]. \tag{2.27}$$

The baseband systems' response $v(t)$ to the baseband information signal $u(t)$ can be expressed by the following convolution:

$$v(t) = u(t) * c(t). \tag{2.28}$$

Substituting the quadrature decomposition of $u(t)$ and $c(t)$ from Equations 2.22 and 2.8 into Equation 2.28 gives

$$
\begin{aligned}
v(t) &= [u_I(t) + ju_Q(t)] * [c_I(t) + jc_Q(t)] \tag{2.29}\\
&= [u_I(t) * c_I(t) - u_Q(t) * c_Q(t)] + \\
&\quad j[u_I(t) * c_Q(t) + u_Q(t) * c_I(t)] \\
&= v_I(t) + jv_Q(t),
\end{aligned}
$$

where the quadrature components of the equivalent baseband system's response are:

$$
\begin{aligned}
v_I(t) &= u_I(t) * c_I(t) - u_Q(t) * c_Q(t) \\
v_Q(t) &= u_I(t) * c_Q(t) + u_Q(t) * c_I(t). \tag{2.30}
\end{aligned}
$$

These operations are portrayed in Figure 2.12.

In summary, in this section we revealed the equivalence of bandpass and lowpass systems. The relationships portrayed allow us to study bandpass systems in the baseband both by computer simulation and analytical methods. The relevant equivalences are summarised in Table 2.2.

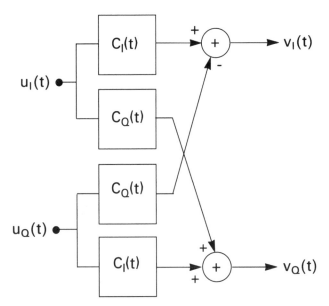

Figure 2.12: Complex convolution in the baseband

2.3.3 Gaussian Mobile Radio Channel

The simplest type of channel is the Gaussian channel as described in Section 2.1.3. Basically it is a linear time-invariant transmission system impaired by the thermal noise generated in the receiver. The noise is assumed to have a constant power spectral density (PSD) over the channel bandwidth, and a Gaussian amplitude probability density function (PDF). This type of channel is occasionally realised in digital mobile radio communications mainly in microcells where it is possible to have a line-of-sight (LOS) with essentially no multipath propagation. Even when there is multipath propagation, but the mobile is stationary and there are no other moving objects, such as vehicles, in its vicinity, the mobile channel may be thought of as Gaussian. This is because due to the zero mobile speed the fading is represented by a local path loss.

The Gaussian channel is also important for providing an upper bound on system performance. For a given modulation scheme we may calculate or measure the BER performance in the presence of a Gaussian channel. When multipath fading occurs the BER will in-

Type	Equations
Inputs	$s(t) = \Re\left\{u(t)e^{j2\pi f_c t}\right\}$ $S(f) = \frac{1}{2}[U(f - f_c) + U^*(-f - f_c)]$
System Description	$r(t) = s(t) * h(t)$ $R(f) = S(f)H(f)$ $v(t) = u(t) * c(t)$ $V(f) = U(f)C(f)$ $h(t) = 2\Re\{c(t)e^{j2\pi f_c t}\}$ $H(f) = C(f - f_c) + C^*(-f - f_c)$ $c(t) = c_I(t) + jc_Q(t)$
Outputs	$r(t) = \Re\left\{v(t)e^{j2\pi f_c t}\right\}$ $R(f) = \frac{1}{2}[V(f - f_c) + V^*(-f - f_c)]$ $u(t) = u_I(t) + ju_Q(t)$ $v(t) = v_I(t) + jv_Q(t)$

Table 2.2: Summary of Baseband and Bandpass System Equations

crease for a given channel SNR. By using techniques to combat multipath fading, such as diversity, equalisation, channel coding, data interleaving, and so forth, that are to be described throughout the book, we can observe how close the BER approaches that for the Gaussian channel.

2.3.4 Narrow-band fading Channels

Propagation in narrowband mobile radio channels can be divided into three phenomena. These are:

1. Propagation pathloss law.

2. Slow fading statistics.

3. Fast fading statistics.

These all vary with the propagation frequency, surrounding natural and man-made objects, vehicular speed, etc. Consequently a deterministic treatment is not possible and so statistical methods are used instead. The calculation of a power-budget for a mobile radio link considering the propagation pathloss law, the slow fading and fast fading margins is shown in Figure 2.13.

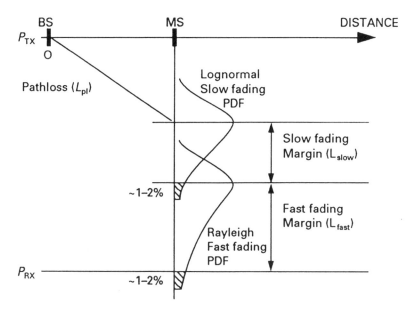

Figure 2.13: Pathloss, slow-fading and fast-fading [3]©1992, Steele

Since most existing public mobile radio systems use the 0.45-1.8 GHz band, we concentrate on channels in this range. These frequencies fall in the so-called Ultra High Frequency (UHF) band. At these frequencies the signal level drops quickly once over the radio horizon, limiting cochannel interference when the frequencies are re-used in neighbouring cell clusters. At these frequencies, even if there is no line-of-sight path between transmitter and receiver, sufficient signal power may be received by means of wave scattering, reflection and diffraction to allow communications.

The prediction of the expected mean or median received signal power plays a crucial role in planning the coverage area of a specific base station and in determining the closest acceptable reuse of the propagation frequency deployed. For high antenna elevations and large rural cells a more slowly decaying power exponent is expected than for low elevations and densely built-up urban areas. As suggested by Figure 2.13, the received signal is also subjected to slow or shadow fading which is mainly governed by terrain and topographical features in the vicinity of the mobile receiver such as small hills and tall buildings. When designing the system's power budget and coverage area pattern, the slow fading phenomenon is taken into account by including a shadow fading margin as demonstrated by Figure 2.13.

Slow fading is compensated by increasing the transmitted power P_{tx} by the slow fading margin L_{slow}, which is usually chosen to be the $1 - 2\%$ quartile of the slow fading probability density function (PDF) to minimise the probability of unsatisfactorily low received signal power P_{rx}. Additionally, the short term fast signal fading due to multipath propagation is taken into account by deploying the so-called fast fading margin L_{fast}, which is typically chosen to be also a few percent quartile of the fast fading distribution. There remains a certain probability that both of these fading margins are simultaneously exceeded by the superimposed slow and fast envelope fading. This situation is often referred to as "fading margin overload", and results in a very low received signal level which may cause call dropping in mobile telephony. The worst-case probability of these events can be taken to be the sum of the individual fading margin overload probabilities.

Mathematical models can be derived, or measurements made, to determine appropriate margins, which can then be used to analyse likely system performance. For practicality, any models used must consider signals to have been transmitted at baseband through a channel which is equivalent to the mobile radio channel as previously derived.

2.3.4.1   Propagation Pathloss Law

When considering the propagation path loss, the parameter of prime concern is normally the distance from the BS. Path loss increases with distance due to the increasing area of the circular wavefront expanding from the BS. More details about path loss calculations can be found in [1, 2, 10]. Path loss calculations become significantly more complex when there is any form of obstruction between the transmitter and receiver. In large cells these obstructions will often be hills or undulating terrain. In modelling tools these obstacles are often considered to be knife edges at the point of the summit of the obstruction, and knife edge diffraction techniques can then be used [10, 11] to predict the path loss. The analysis becomes increasingly complex if there are a number of hills between the transmitter and receiver. An alternative approach is to determine which Fresnel zone the hill obstructs and perform the prediction accordingly [12].

In urban areas modelling becomes more complex, and in the case of large cells it is rarely possible to model each individual building, although this can be achieved in microcells [13]. Typically this situation is resolved by adding a clutter loss dependent on the density of the buildings in the urban area, and also allowing for a shadowing loss behind buildings when computing the link budget. This approximation leads to sub-optimal network design, with overlapping cells and inefficient frequency reuse. Nevertheless, it seems unlikely that more accurate tools will become available in the near future.

In our probabilistic approach it is difficult to give a worst-case pathloss exponent for any mobile channel. However, it is possible to specify the most optimistic scenario. This is given by propagation in free space. The free-space pathloss, L_{pl} is given by [10]:

$$L_{pl} = 10 \log_{10} G_T + 10 \log_{10} G_R - 20 \log_{10} f - 20 \log_{10} d + 147.6 dB,$$
$$(2.31)$$

where G_T and G_R are the transmitter and receiver antenna gains, f is the propagation frequency in MHz and d is the distance from the BS antenna in km. Observe that the free-space pathloss is increased by 6 dB every time, the propagation frequency is doubled or the distance from the mobile is doubled. This corresponds to a 20 dB/decade decay and at d=1 km, f=1 MHz and $G_T = G_R = 1$ a pathloss of $L_F = 147.6\ dB$ is encountered. Clearly, not only technological difficulties, but also propagation losses discourage the deployment of higher frequencies. Nevertheless, spectrum is usually only available in these higher frequency bands.

In practice, for UHF mobile radio propagation channels of interest, the free-space conditions do not apply. There are however a number of useful pathloss prediction models that can be adopted to derive other prediction bounds. One such case is the "plane earth" model. This is a two-path model constituted by a direct line of sight path and a ground-reflected one which ignores the curvature of the earth's surface. Assuming transmitter base station (BS) and receiver mobile station (MS) antenna heights of $h_{BS}, h_{MS} \ll d$, respectively, the plane earth pathloss formula [10] can be derived:

$$L_{pl} = 10 \log_{10} G_T + 10 \log_{10} G_R + 20 \log_{10} h_{BS} + \qquad (2.32)$$
$$20 \log_{10} h_{MS} - 40 \log_{10} d,$$

where the dependence on propagation frequency is removed. Observe that a 6 dB pathloss reduction is resulted, when doubling the transmitter or receiver antenna elevations, and there is an inverse fourth power law decay with increasing the BS-MS distance d. In the close vicinity of the transmitter antenna, where the condition h_{BS} or $h_{MS} \ll d$ does not hold, Equation 2.33 is no longer valid.

Hata [14] developed three pathloss models for large cells which are widely used, forming the basis for many modelling tools. These were developed from an extensive data base derived by Okumura [15] from measurements in and around Tokyo. *The typical urban Hata model* is defined as:

$$L_{Hu} = 69.55 + 26.16 \log_{10} f - 13.82 \log_{10} h_{BS} - a(h_{MS}) +$$
$$(44.9 - 6.55 \log_{10} h_{BS}) \log_{10} d \; [dB], \qquad (2.33)$$

where f is the propagation frequency in MHz, h_{BS} and h_{MS} are the BS and MS antenna elevations in terms of metres, respectively, $a(h_{MS})$ is a terrain dependent correction factor, while d is the BS-MS distance in km. The correction factor $a(h_{MS})$ for small and medium sized cities was found to be

$$a(h_{MS}) = (1.1 \log_{10} f - 0.7) h_{MS} - (1.56 \log_{10} f - 0.8), \qquad (2.34)$$

while for large cities is frequency-parametrized:

$$a(h_{MS}) = \begin{cases} 8.29 [\log_{10}(1.54 h_{MS})]^2 - 1.1 & \text{if } f \le 200MHz \\ 3.2 [\log_{10}(11.75 h_{MS})]^2 - 4.97 & \text{if } f \ge 400MHz \end{cases} .$$
$$(2.35)$$

The typical suburban Hata model applies a correction factor to the urban model yielding:

$$L_{Hsuburban} = L_{Hu} - 2[\log_{10}(f/28)]^2 - 5.4 \; [dB]. \qquad (2.36)$$

The rural Hata model modifies the urban formula differently, as seen below:

$$L_{Hrural} = L_{Hu} - 4.78(\log_{10} f)^2 + 18.33 \log_{10} f - 40.94 \, [dB]. \quad (2.37)$$

The limitations of its parameters as listed by Hata are:-

$$f : \quad 150 - 1500 MHz$$
$$h_{BS} : \quad 30 - 200m$$
$$h_{MS} : \quad 1 - 10m$$
$$d : \quad 1 - 20km.$$

For a 900 MHz Public Land Mobile Radio (PLMR) system these conditions can be usually satisfied but for a 1.8 GHz typical Personal Communications Network (PCN) urban microcell all these limits have to be slightly stretched.

Microcellular channels can be described by a four-path model including two more reflected waves from building walls along the streets [16, 17]. In this scenario it is assumed that the transmitter antenna is below the characteristic urban skyline. The four-path model used by Green [16] assumed smooth reflecting surfaces yielding specular reflections with no scattering, finite permittivity and conductivity, vertically polarised waves and half-wave dipole antennas. The resultant pathloss profile vs. distance becomes rather erratic with received signal level variations in excess of 20 dB, which renders pathloss modelling by a simple power exponent rather inaccurate, however attractive it would appear due to its simplicity. Figure 2.14 also allows a comparison of the two-path model, the inverse second law and the inverse fourth law characteristics.

2.3.4.2 Slow Fading Statistics

Having studied a few propagation pathloss prediction models we briefly focus our attention on the characterisation of the slow fading phenomena, which constitutes the second component of the overall power budget design of mobile radio links, as portrayed in Figure 2.13. In slow fading analysis the effects of fast fading and pathloss have to be removed. The fast fading fluctuations are removed by averaging the signal level over a distance of typically some 20

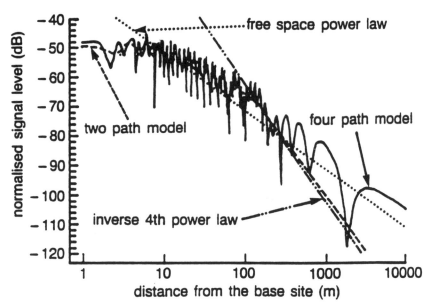

Figure 2.14: Signal level profiles for the two- and four-path models. Also shown are the free space and inverse 4th power laws [16] ©1990, Green.

wavelengths. The slow fading fluctuations are separated by subtracting the best-fit pathloss regression estimate from each individual 20 wavelength spaced averaged received signal value. A slow fading histogram derived this way is depicted in Figure 2.15. The figure suggests a lognormal distribution in terms of dBs caused by normally distributed random shadowing effects. Indeed, when subjected to rigorous distribution fitting using the lognormal hypothesis, the hypothesis is confirmed at a high confidence level. The associated standard deviation in this particular case is 6.5 dB.

2.3.4.3 Fast Fading Statistics

Irrespective of the distribution of the numerous individual constituent propagation paths of both quadrature components (a_i, a_q) of the received signal, their distribution will be normal due to the central limit theorem. Then the complex baseband equivalent signal's amplitude and phase characteristics are given by:

$$a(k) \quad = \quad \sqrt{a_i^2(k) + a_q^2(k)} \qquad (2.38)$$

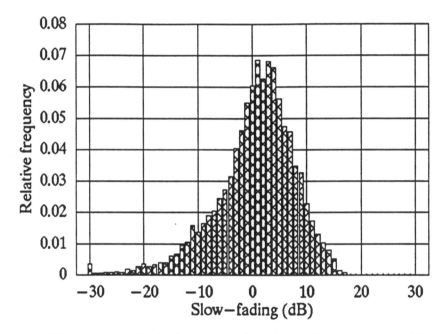

Figure 2.15: Typical microcellular slow fading histogram [3]
©1992, Steele

$$\phi(k) = \arctan[a_q(k)/a_i(k)]. \qquad (2.39)$$

Our aim is now to determine the distribution of the amplitude $a(k)$, if $a_i(k)$ and $a_q(k)$ are known to have a normal distribution.

In general, for n normally distributed random constituent processes with means $\overline{a_i}$ and identical variances σ^2, the resultant process $y = \sum_{i=1}^{n} a_i^2$ has a so-called χ^2 distribution with a PDF given below [9]:

$$p(y) = \frac{1}{2\sigma^2} \left(\frac{y}{s^2}\right)^{(n-2)/4} \cdot e^{-(s^2+y)/2\sigma^2} \cdot I_{(n/2)-1}\left(\sqrt{y}\frac{s}{\sigma^2}\right) \qquad (2.40)$$

where

$$y \geq 0 \qquad (2.41)$$

and

$$s^2 = \sum_{i=1}^{n} (\overline{a_i})^2 \qquad (2.42)$$

is the so-called non-centrality parameter computed from the first moments of the component processes $a_1 \cdots a_n$. If the constituent processes have zero means, the χ^2 distribution is central, otherwise non-central. Each of these processes have a variance of σ^2 and $I_k(x)$ is the modified k-th order Bessel-function of the first kind, given by

$$I_k(x) = \sum_{j=0}^{\infty} \frac{(x/2)^{k+2j}}{j!\Gamma(k+j+1)} , \quad x \geq 0. \qquad (2.43)$$

The Γ function is defined as

$$\begin{aligned}
\Gamma(p) &= \int_0^{\infty} t^{p-1} e^{-t} dt && \text{if } p > 0 \\
\Gamma(p) &= (p-1)! && \text{if } p > 0 \text{ integer} \\
\Gamma(\tfrac{1}{2}) &= \sqrt{\pi} , \quad \Gamma(\tfrac{3}{2}) = \frac{\sqrt{\pi}}{2}.
\end{aligned} \qquad (2.44)$$

In our case we have two quadrature components, i.e. $n = 2$, $s^2 = (\overline{a_i})^2 + (\overline{a_q})^2$, the envelope is computed as $a = \sqrt{y} = \sqrt{a_i^2 + a_q^2}$, $a^2 = y$, $p(a)da = p(y)dy$, and hence $p(a) = p(y)dy/da = 2ap(y)$ yielding the Rician PDF

$$p_{\text{Rice}}(a) = \frac{a}{\sigma^2} e^{-(a^2+s^2)/2\sigma^2} I_o\left(\frac{as}{\sigma^2}\right) \qquad a \geq 0. \qquad (2.45)$$

Formally introducing the Rician K-factor as

$$K = s^2/2\sigma^2 \qquad (2.46)$$

renders the Rician distribution's PDF to depend on one parameter only:

$$p_{\text{Rice}}(a) = \frac{a}{\sigma^2} \cdot e^{-\frac{a^2}{2\sigma^2}} \cdot e^{-K} \cdot I_o\left(\frac{a}{\sigma} \cdot \sqrt{2K}\right), \qquad (2.47)$$

where K physically represents the ratio of the power received in the direct line-of-sight path, to the total power received via indirect scattered paths. Therefore, if there is no dominant propagation path, $K = 0$, $e^{-K} = 1$ and $I_0(0) = 1$ yielding the worst-case Rayleigh PDF:

$$p_{\text{Rayleigh}}(a) = \frac{a}{\sigma^2} e^{-\frac{a^2}{2\sigma^2}}. \qquad (2.48)$$

Conversely, in the clear direct line-of-sight situation with no scattered power, $K = \infty$, yielding a "Dirac-delta shaped" PDF, representing a step-function-like cumulative distribution function (CDF). The signal at the receiver then has a constant amplitude with a probability of one. Such a channel is referred to as a Gaussian channel. This is because although there is no fading present, the receiver will still see the additive white Gaussian noise (AWGN) referenced to its input. If the K-factor is known, the fast fading envelope's distribution is completely described. The set of Rician PDFs for K=0, 1, 2, 4, 10, and 15 is plotted in Figure 2.16.

Note that the relationship between the variances and means of the Rayleigh and the component Gaussian distributions is given by [9]:

$$\sigma_R^2 = (2 - \pi/2) \cdot \sigma^2$$

and

$$m_R = \sqrt{2} \cdot \sigma \cdot \sqrt{\pi}/2 = \sigma\sqrt{\pi/2},$$

respectively. Clearly, the Rayleigh distribution's variance is not twice that of the composite Gaussian processes', since we are adding the squares of the Gaussian processes, not the processes themselves.

The Rician CDF takes the shape of [9]

$$C_{\text{Rice}}(a) = 1 - e^{-\left(K + \frac{a^2}{2\sigma^2}\right)} \sum_{m=0}^{\infty} \left(\frac{s}{a}\right)^m \cdot I_m\left(\frac{a\,s}{\sigma^2}\right)$$

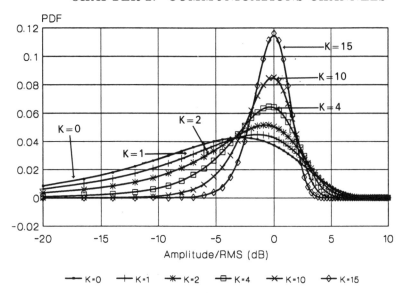

Figure 2.16: Rician PDFs

$$= 1 - e^{-\left(K + \frac{a^2}{2\sigma^2}\right)} \sum_{m=0}^{\infty} \left(\frac{\sigma\sqrt{2K}}{a}\right)^m \cdot I_m \left(\frac{a\sqrt{2K}}{\sigma}\right). \tag{2.49}$$

Clearly, this formula is more difficult to evaluate than the PDF of Equation 2.47 due to the summation of an infinite number of terms, requiring double or quadruple precision and it is avoided in numerical evaluations, if possible. However, in practical terms it is sufficient to increase m to a value, where the last term's contribution becomes less than 0.1 %.

A range of Rician CDFs evaluated from Equation 2.49 are plotted on a linear probability scale in Figure 2.17 for $K = 0, 1, 2, 4, 10$ and 15. Figure 2.18 shows the same Rician CDFs plotted on a more convenient logarithmic probability scale, which reveals the enormous difference in terms of deep fades for the K values considered. When choosing the fading margin overload probability, Figure 2.18 is more useful as it expands the tails of the CDFs, where for example for a Rician CDF with $K = 1$ the $15dB$ fading margin overload probability is seen to be approximately 10^{-2}.

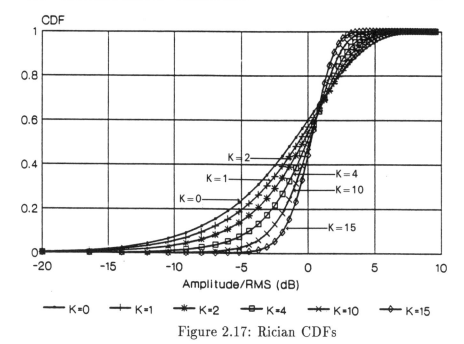

Figure 2.17: Rician CDFs

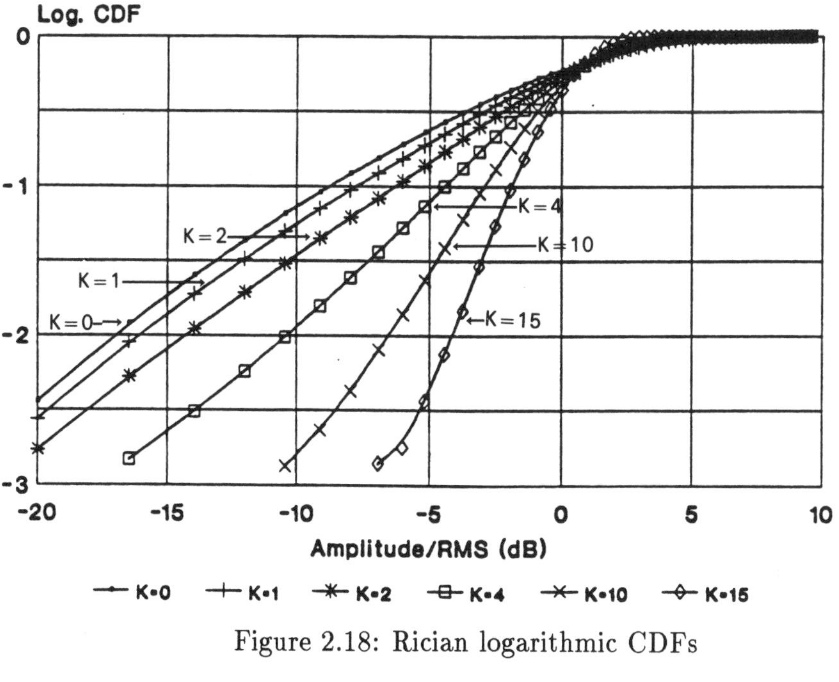

Figure 2.18: Rician logarithmic CDFs

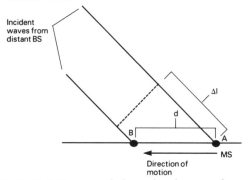

Figure 2.19: Relative path-length change due to the MS's movement

2.3.4.4 Doppler Spectrum

Having described the fading statistics let us now concentrate on the effects of the Doppler shift and consider again the transmission of an unmodulated carrier frequency f_c from a BS. A MS travelling in a direction making an angle α_i with respect to the signal received on the i-th path as seen in Figure 2.19 advances a distance of $d = v \cdot \triangle t$ during $\triangle t$, when travelling at a velocity of v. This introduces a relative carrier phase change of $\triangle \Phi = 2\pi$, if the flight of the wave is shortened by an amount of $\triangle l = \lambda$, where the wavelength can be computed from $\lambda = c/f_c$ with c being the velocity of light. For an arbitrary $\triangle l$ value we have $\triangle \Phi = -2\pi \cdot \triangle l / \lambda$, where the negative sign implies that the carrier wave's phase delay is reduced, if the MS is travelling towards the BS. From the simple geometry of Figure 2.19 we have $\triangle l = d \cdot \cos \alpha_i$ and therefore the phase change becomes:

$$\triangle \Phi = -\frac{2\pi v \triangle t \cos \alpha_i}{\lambda}. \tag{2.50}$$

The Doppler frequency can be defined as the phase change due to the movement of the MS during the infinitesimal interval $\triangle t$:

$$f_D = -\frac{1}{2\pi} \frac{\triangle \Phi}{\triangle t}. \tag{2.51}$$

When substituting Equation 2.50 into 2.51 we get:

$$f_D = \frac{v}{\lambda} \cos \alpha_i = f_m \cos \alpha_i, \tag{2.52}$$

where $f_m = v/\lambda = vf_c/c$ is the maximum Doppler frequency deviation from the transmitted carrier frequency due to the MS's movement. Notice that a Doppler frequency can be positive or negative depending on α_i, and that the maximum and minimum Doppler frequencies are $\pm f_m$. These extreme frequencies correspond to the $\alpha_i = 0°$ and $180°$, when the ray is aligned with the street that the MS is travelling along, and corresponds to the ray coming towards or from behind the MS, respectively. It is analogous to the change in the frequency of a whistle from a train perceived by a person standing on a railway line when the train is bearing down or receding from the person, respectively.

According to Equation 2.52 and assuming that α_i is uniformly distributed, the Doppler frequency has a so-called random cosine distribution. The received power in an angle of $d\alpha$ around α_i is given by $p(\alpha_i)d\alpha$, where $p(\alpha_i)$ is the probability density function (PDF) of the received power, which is assumed to be uniformly distributed over the range of $0 \le \alpha_i \le 2\pi$, giving $p(\alpha_i) = 1/(2\pi)$. The Doppler power spectral density $S(f_D)$ can be computed using Parseval's theorem by equating the incident received power $p(\alpha_i)d\alpha$ in an angle $d\alpha$ with the Doppler power $S(f_D)df_D$, yielding $S(f_D) = d\alpha_i/(2\pi \cdot df_D)$. Upon expressing α_i from $f_D = f_m \cos \alpha_i$ and exploiting that

$$\frac{d \cos^{-1} x}{dx} = -\frac{1}{\sqrt{1 - x^2}}$$

we then have:

$$S(f_D) = \frac{d\alpha_i}{2\pi df_D} = \frac{d(\cos^{-1} f_D/f_m)}{2\pi df_D} = -\frac{1}{2\pi f_m \sqrt{1 - (f_D/f_m)^2}}$$

$$(2.53)$$

The incident received power at the MS depends on the power gain of the antenna and the polarisation used. Thus the transmission of an unmodulated carrier is received as a 'smeared' signal whose spectrum is not a single carrier frequency f_c, but contains frequencies up to $f_c \pm f_m$. In general we can express the received RF spectrum $S(f_D)$ for a particular MS speed, propagation frequency, antenna design and polarisation as,

$$S(f_D) = \frac{C}{\sqrt{1 - (f_D/f_m)^2}} \qquad (2.54)$$

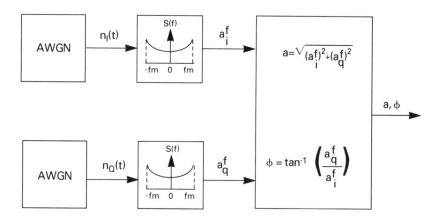

Figure 2.20: Baseband Rayleigh fading simulation model

where C is a constant that absorbs the $1/2\pi f_m$ multiplier in Equation 2.53. Notice that the Doppler spectrum of Equation 2.54 becomes $S(f_D = 0) = C$ at $f_D = 0$, while $S(f_D = f_m) = \infty$, when $f_D = f_m$. Between these extreme values $S(f)$ has a U-shaped characteristic, as it is portrayed in a stylized form in the simulation model of Figure 2.20, which will be developed in the next Subsection.

2.3.4.5   Simulation of Narrowband Channels

The Rayleigh fading channel model used in the previous subsection can be represented by the quadrature arrangement shown in Figure 2.20, where the distribution of both received quadrature components (a_i, a_q) is normal due to the central limit theorem. These can be modelled as uncorrelated normally distributed AWGN sources. The outputs from the AWGN sources are applied to low-pass-type filters having U-shaped frequency-domain transfer functions that represent the effects of Doppler frequency shifts, as will be demonstrated.

Observe that the maximum Doppler frequency $f_m = v/\lambda = v \cdot f_c/c$ depends on the product of the speed v of the MS and the propagation frequency f_c. Therefore, the higher the speed or the propagation frequency, the wider the frequency band over which the received carrier is 'smeared'. The effect of deploying the Doppler filter in Figure 2.20 is that the originally uncorrelated quadrature components (a_i, a_q) are now effectively low-pass filtered, which introduces some inter-sample correlation by restricting the maximum rate of change of (a_i, a_q), without altering the Rayleigh distributed envelope fading. This is true, because passing an AWGN process through a linear system, such as a low-pass filter, will reduce the variance of the signal, but retains the Gaussian nature of the distribution for both quadrature components. Having no low-pass Doppler filter at all would be equivalent to $f_m = \infty$ implying an infinitely high vehicular speed and hence allowing the reception of arbitrary uncorrelated frequencies, when transmitting the unmodulated carrier frequency of f_c.

The simulation of the Rayleigh distributed fast fading envelope is based on the concept portrayed in Figure 2.20, but it can be implemented in both time and frequency domain.

2.3.4.5.1   Frequency-domain fading simulation   In the frequeny domain approach one could exploit the fact that the Fourier transform of an AWGN process is another AWGN process. Hence the frequency-domain AWGN sequence generated by the Box-Müller algorithm to be described below can be multiplied by the frequency-domain Doppler transfer function of Equation 2.54 and then transformed back by IFFT to the time-domain in order to generate the I and Q components (a_i^f, a_q^f) of the filtered complex Gaussian process. Then the Rayleigh-distributed magnitude a is given by

$$a = \sqrt{(a_i^f)^2 + (a_q^f)^2},$$

while the uniformly distributed phase ϕ is computed as

$$\phi = \arctan \left[\frac{a_q^f}{a_i^f} \right].$$

The main difficulty associated with this frequency domain approach is that the Doppler filter's bandwidth f_m is typically much lower than the sampling frequency, at which the faded samples are produced. The faded samples have to be generated exactly at the signaling rate at which modulation symbols are transmitted in order to supply a fading envelope and phase rotation value for their corruption.

A typical Doppler bandwidth f_m at a carrier frequency of $f_c = 1.8GHz$ and vehicular speed of $v = 30mph = 13.3m/s$ is given by

$$f_m = \frac{v \cdot f_c}{c} = \frac{13.3\frac{m}{s} \cdot 1.8 \cdot 10^9 \frac{1}{s}}{3 \cdot 10^8 \frac{m}{s}} \approx 80Hz,$$

where $c = 3 \cdot 10^8 m/s$ is the speed of light. This f_m value becomes about 40 Hz at $f_c = 900MHz$ and 8 Hz at a pedestrian speed of 3 mph. Typical multi-user signaling rates in state-of-arts Time Division Multiple Access (TDMA) systems are in excess of $f_s = 40KHz$. Therefore the pedestrian relative Doppler bandwidth D_r becomes $D_r = 8Hz/40KHz = 2 \cdot 10^{-4}$ suggesting that only a negligible proportion of the input samples will fall in the Doppler filter's pass band. This fact may severely affect the statistical soundness of this approach, unless a very long IFFT is invoked, which will retain a sufficiently high number of frequency domain AWGN samples after removing those outside the Doppler filter's bandwidth.

2.3.4.5.2   Time-domain fading simulation   When using the time-domain approach the AWGN samples generated by the Box-Müller algorithm must be convolved with the impulse response $h_D(t)$ of the Doppler filter $S(f)$ of Equation 2.54 in both quadrature arms of Figure 2.20. Similarly to the frequency-domain method, we are faced with a difficult notch-filtering problem. Since the filter bandwidth is typically very narrow in comparision to the sampling frequency, the impulse response $h_D(t)$ will be very slowly decaying, requiring tens of thousands of tap values to be taken into account in the convolution in case of a low Doppler bandwidth. This problem is aggravated by the non-decaying U-shaped nature of the Doppler's transfer function $S(f)$. The consequence of these difficulties is that the confidence measures delivered by rigorous goodness-of-fit techniques such as the χ^2-test or the Kolmogorov-Smirnov test described for example in Chapter 2 of reference [3] might become low, although the resulting fading envelope and phase trajectories are appropriate for simulation studies of mobile radio systems.

2.3.4.5.3   Box-Müller Algorithm of AWGN generation   The previously mentioned Box-Müller algorithm is formulated as follows:

1. Generate two random variables u_1, u_2 and let:

$$s = u_1^2 + u_2^2.$$

2. While $s \geq 1$, discard s and re-compute u_1, u_2 and s.

3. If $s < 1$ is satisfied, compute the I and Q components of the noise as follows:

$$u_I = u_1 \sqrt{-\frac{2\sigma^2}{s} \cdot \log_e s}$$

$$u_Q = u_2 \sqrt{-\frac{2\sigma^2}{s} \cdot \log_e s},$$

where σ is the standard deviation of the AWGN. This algorithm can be used both for the generation of the Rayleigh-faded signal envelope as well as for generating the thermal AWGN.

2.3.5 Wideband Channels

2.3.5.1 Modelling of Wideband Channels

The impulse response of the flat Rayleigh fading mobile radio channel consists of a single delta function whose weight has a Rayleigh PDF. This occurs because all the multipath components arrive almost simultaneously and combine to have a Rayleigh PDF. If the signal's transmission bandwidth is narrower than the channel's so-called coherence bandwidth $B_c = 1/(2 \cdot \pi \cdot \Delta)$, where Δ represents the time-dispersion interval over which significant multipath components are received, then all transmitted frequency components encounter nearly identical propagation delays. Therefore the so-called narrow band condition is met and the signal is subjected to non-selective or flat envelope fading. The channel's coherence bandwidth (B_c) is defined as the frequency separation, where the correlation of two received signal components' attenuation becomes less than 0.5.

The effect of multipath propagation is to spread the received symbols. If the path delay differences are longer than the symbol duration, several echoes of the same transmitted modulated symbol are

received over a number of symbol periods. This is equivalent to saying that in wideband channels the symbol rate is sufficiently high
that each symbol is spread into adjacent symbols causing intersymbol interference (ISI). In order for the receiver to remove the ISI
and regenerate the symbols correctly it must determine the impulse
response of the mobile radio channel by channel sounding. This response must be frequently measured, since the mobile channel may
change rapidly both in time and space.

The magnitude of a typical impulse response is a continuous waveform when plotting received amplitude against time delay. If we partition the time delay axis into equal delay segments, usually called
delay bins, then there will be, in general, a number of received signals in each bin corresponding to the different paths whose times of
arrival are within the bin duration. These signals when vectorially
combined can be represented by a delta function occurring in the
centre of the bin having a magnitude that is Rayleigh distributed.
Impulses which are sufficiently small that they are of not significance
to the receiver can then be discarded.

As an example here we describe a set of frequently used typical
wideband channel impulses specified by the Group Speciale Mobile
committee during the definition of the Pan-European mobile radio
system known as GSM. These impulse responses describe typical
urban, rural and hilly terrain environments, as well as an artificially
contrived equaliser test response.

The wideband propagation channel is the superposition of a number of dispersive fading paths, suffering from various attenuations
and delays, aggravated by the phenomenon of Doppler shift caused
by the MS's movement. The maximum Doppler shift (f_m) is given
by $f_m = v/\lambda = v \cdot f_c/c$, where v is the vehicular speed, λ is the
wavelength of the carrier frequency f_c and c is the velocity of light.
The momentary Doppler shift f_D depends on the angle of incidence
α_i, which is uniformly distributed, i.e., $f_D = f_m \cdot \cos \alpha_i$, which has
hence a so-called random cosine distribution with a Doppler spec-
trum limited to $-f_m < f_D < f_m$. Due to time-frequency duality, this
"frequency dispersive" phenomenon results in "time-selective" behaviour and the wider the Doppler spread, i.e., the higher the vehicular

speed, the faster is the time-domain impulse response fluctuation.

The set of 6-tap GSM impulse responses is depicted in Figure 2.21. In simple terms the wideband channel's impulse response is measured by transmitting an impulse and detecting the received echoes at the channel's output in every D-spaced so-called delay bin. In some bins no delayed and attenuated multipath component is received, while in others significant energy is detected, depending on the typical reflecting objects and their distance from the receiver. The path-delay can be easily related to the distance of the reflecting objects, since radio waves are travelling at the speed of light. For example, at a speed of 300 000 km/s a reflecting object situated at a distance of 0.15 km yields a multipath component at a round-trip delay of 1 μs.

The Typical Urban (TU) impulse response spreads over a delay interval of 5 μs, therefore it definitely spills energy into adjacent signalling intervals for signalling rates in excess of 200 ksymbols/s, resulting in serious ISI. In practical terms the transmissions can be considered non-dispersive, if the so-called excess path delay does not exceed 10 % of the signalling interval, which in our example would correspond to 20 ksymbols/s or 20 kBaud. The Hilly Terrain (HT) model has a sharply decaying short-delay section due to local reflections and a long-delay part around 15 μs due to distant reflections. Therefore in practical terms it can be considered a two- or three-path model having reflections from a distance of $3 \cdot 10^8$ m/s $\cdot$ 15 μs = 2.25 km. The Rural Area (RA) response seems the least hostile amongst all standardised responses, decaying fast within 1 μs and hence up to signalling rates of 100 kBaud can be treated as a flat-fading narrow-band channel.

The last standardised GSM impulse response is artificially contrived to test the channel equaliser's performance and is constituted by six equidistant unit-amplitude impulses representing six equal-powered independent Rayleigh-fading paths with a delay-spread over 16 μs. With these impulse responses in mind the required channel is simulated by summing the appropriately delayed and weighted received signal components. In all but one cases the individual components are assumed to have Rayleigh amplitude distribution. In

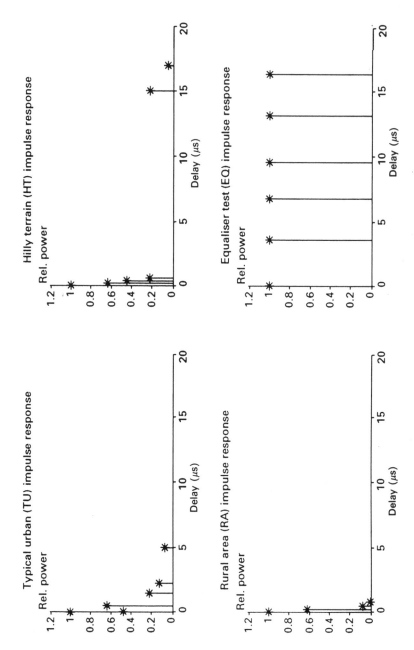

Figure 2.21: GSM specified impulse responses

the RA model the main tap at zero delay is supposed to have Rician distribution with the presence of a dominant path.

We can model a wideband impulse response using the algorithm shown in Figure 2.22. The inphase modulated signal $s_I(t)$ is applied to a series of delays equal to the width of a delay bin. At each delay it is multiplied by the magnitude of the wideband channel at that delay. However, as the wideband channel will be changing as the mobile moves, it is necessary to superimpose fading on each of the wideband responses. This is done using a noise generator and Doppler filter as described earlier. An identical arrangement to that in Figure 2.22 is used for the quadrature component $s_Q(t)$, and the appropriate convolutional terms are combined to obtain the received signal's quadrature components $r_I(t)$ and $r_Q(t)$.

2.4 Mobile Satellite Propagation

2.4.1 Fixed-link satellite channels

These links are normally between geostationary satellites and fixed, dish-type receivers on the ground. With the spread of satellite broadcasting systems to home users, such links have become widespread. Because of the stationary nature of both ends of the link, the channel itself is normally modelled by a stationary process. Furthermore, because of the high directivity of the antennas used, there is little likelihood of reflected rays being received. To a first order, such channels can be modelled as Gaussian channels.

More precise channel models take into account rain-fading. This is a reduction in signal level caused by the signal being absorbed by moisture present in the atmosphere. It is dependent on the meterological conditions at the time of the transmission. Rain-fading is also dependent on the transmission frequency. A general guideline is that rain-fading starts to become significant at frequencies above 10GHz, with a typical fade margin at 20GHz being 10dB [18].

Satellite channels are often power limited as the satellite only has a limited amount of power available to it. This has often discouraged the use of power inefficient modulation schemes such as QAM. However, techniques are continually emerging to increase the power

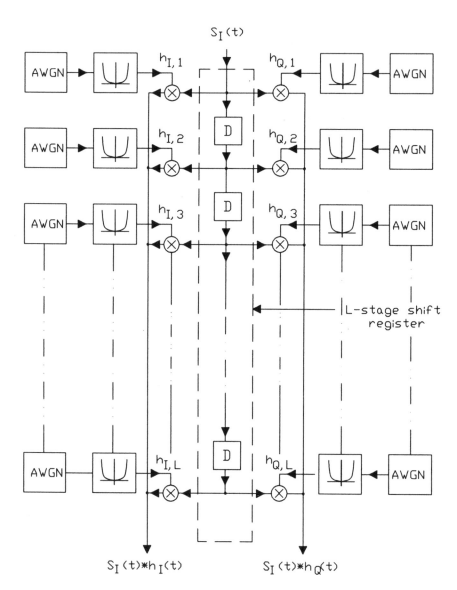

Figure 2.22: Generation of the baseband inphase received signal via wide-band channels [3]©1992, Steele

efficiency of QAM, making it increasingly attractive for satellite applications.

2.4.2 Satellite-to-mobile channels

Satellite-to-mobile communications is still relatively little used due to the difficulties of this particular environment [19]-[22]. Mobiles are generally unable to deploy highly directional dish antennas and satellites are normally unable to transmit at high power levels. Some satellite communication systems are restricted to LOS transmission. Because of the elevation of the satellite, LOS transmission will be more frequent than in a conventional cellular system, especially in suburban and rural areas. However, LOS is often masked by trees in rural areas, and by tall buildings in urban areas. Furthermore, the user may be inside a building, further increasing the path loss of the communications link. Once the LOS path is obscured, the signal may arrive at the receiver via a number of reflected paths. The differing phase of these paths will ensure Rician fading.

Few models have been suggested for this channel. Loo [23] suggests that the channel should be modelled as a LOS component with lognormally distributed shadow fading and a multipath component with Rayleigh distribution. This leads to the channel model that

$$p(r) = r/(b_0\sqrt{2\pi d_0}) \int_0^\infty 1/z I_0(rz/b_0) \qquad (2.55)$$
$$\cdot \exp[-(ln\ z - mu)^2/2d_0 - (r^2 + z^2)/2b_0)]dz$$

where b_0 is the average scattered power due to multipath, d_0 and μ are the variance and mean due to shadowing, respectively, I_0 is the modified Bessel function, and r is the received signal envelope. The shadowing parameters depend not only on the local environment, but also the satellite elevation, with higher elevations tending to produce lower shadowing losses due to the reduced likelihood of having an obscured LOS path between mobile and satellite.

Because of the hostility of these channels, it is unlikely that the use of multilevel modulation will be widespread.

2.5   Summary

In this Chapter we have briefly reviewed the properties of various fixed and mobile communications channels and have shown the equivalence of baseband and passband channels. This allows us to carry out simulations and theoretical analysis in the baseband. In the case of fixed channels the dominant impairment is typically AWGN and linear distortions, as we have seen for example in case of the CCITT standard channels M1020 and M1025 in Figures 2.5-2.8. Narrowband mobile radio channels were characterised in terms of pathloss, lognormal slow fading and Rician fast fading, as seen in Figure 2.13. The best- and worst-case Rician channels associated with K-factors of $K=\infty$ and $K=0$ are the Gaussian and Rayleigh-fading channels, characteristic of the strong LOS and no LOS scenarios, respectively. The phenomenon of Doppler shift was introduced, which yielded a smeared spectrum, when a single tonal frequency corresponding to an unmodulated carrier was transmitted. A simple simulation model was derived for narrowband channels, which was later extended to dispersive channels. The concept of dispersive wide-band channels was portrayed in the context of the GSM wideband channels.

Having considered the non-ideal transmission medium we now embark upon a rudimentary introduction to modems, and review how modems can counteract the channel impairments and facilitate reliable information transmission in a finite bandwidth.

Bibliography

[1] **W.C.Jakes**, "Microwave mobile communications", *John Wiley & Sons*, New York, 1974.

[2] **W.Y.C.Lee**, "Mobile cellular communications", *McGraw Hill*, New York, 1989.

[3] **R.Steele (Ed.)**, "Mobile radio communications", *Pentech Press 1992*

[4] J. D. Parsons: The mobile radio channel, Pentech Press, London, 1992

[5] D. Greenwood, L. Hanzo: Characterisation of mobile radio channels, pp 92-185, Chapter 2 in R. Steele (Ed.) - Mobile radio communications, Pentech Press, London, 1992

[6] **J.C.S. Cheung**: Adaptive equalisers for wideband time division multiple access mobile radio, *Phd Thesis, Dept. of Electr. and Comp. Sc., Univ. of Southampton*, 1991

[7] **R.Steele and V.K.Prabhu**, "Mobile radio cellular structures for high user density and large data rates", *Proc. of the IEE*, Pt F, No.5, pp.396-404, August 1985.

[8] **R.Steele**, "The cellular environment of lightweight hand-held portables", *IEEE Communications Magazine*, pp.20-29, July 1989.

[9] **J.G.Proakis** "Digital communications" *McGraw Hill, 1989*

[10] **J.D.Parson** "The mobile radio propagation channel", *Pentech Press*, London, 1992.

[11] **K.Bullington**, "Radio propagation at frequencies above 30 Mc/s", *Proc. IRE 35*, pp.1122-1136, (1947).

[12] **R.Edwards and J.Durkin**, "Computer prediction of service area for VHF mobile radio networks", *Proc IRE 116 (9)* pp.1493-1500, 1969.

[13] **W.T.Webb**, "Sizing up the microcell for mobile radio communications", *IEE Electronics and communications Jnl.*, Vol.5, No.3, June 1993, pp133-140.

[14] **M. Hata.**, "Empirical Formula for Propagation Loss in Land Mobile Radio", *IEEE Trans. VT-29*, pp. 317-325, August 1980

[15] **Y. Okumura, E. Ohmori, T. Kawano and K. Fukuda**, "Field Strength and its Variability in VHF and UHF Land Mobile Service", *Review of the Electrical Communication Laboratory, Vol 16*, pp. 825-873, Sept.-Oct. 1968

[16] **E.Green**, "Radio link design for microcellular systems", *British Telecom Technology J*, Vol 8, No.1, pp.85-96 January 1990.

[17] **A. Rustako, N. Amitay, G.J. Owens and R.S. Roman.** "Propagation Measurements at Microwave Frequencies for Microcellular Mobile and Personal Communications". *Proc. of 39th IEEE VTC*, pp. 316-320, 1989

[18] **J.W.Kiebler**, "The design and planning of feeder links to broadcasting satellites", *IEEE J-SAC* Vol.SAC-3, No.1, Jan 1985, pp181-185.

[19] **C. Loo**, "A statistical model for a land mobile radio satellite link", *IEEE Tr. on VT*, Vol. VT-34. No. 3, Aug. 1985, pp 122-127

[20] **C. Loo**, "Digital transmission through a land mobile satellite channel", *IEEE Tr. on Comms.*, Vol. 38, No. 5, May 1990, pp 693-697

[21] **E. Lutz, D. Cygan, M. Dippold, F. Dolainsky and W. Papke**, "The land mobile satellite communications channel - Recording, statistics and channel model", *IEEE Tr. on VT.*, Vol. 40, No.2, May 1991, pp 375-386

[22] **J. Hagenauer, F. Dolainsky, E. Lutz, W. Papke and R. Schweikert**, "The maritime satellite communication channel- Channel model, performance of modulation and coding", *IEEE JSAC., Vol. SAC-5*, No 4., May 1987, pp 701-713

[23] **C.Loo**, "Measurements and models of a land mobile satellite channel and their application to MSK signals", *IEEE Trans. Vehicular Tech.*, Vol.VT-35, No.3, Aug 1987, pp114-121.

Chapter 3

Introduction to modems

In this chapter we expand upon our introduction in Chapter 1 by looking in more detail at the basic constituent parts of a modem and considering filtering in more detail.

A typical communications system will input data, perform some form of processing and frequency translation, transmit the data, and perform the converse operations at the receiver. The basic block diagram of such a system employing QAM is shown in Figure 3.1. In a digital communications system the modem's input signal will be a digital signal stream from a digital source or channel encoder. If, however the modem's input signal is generated by an analogue information source, the signal must be first bandlimited to a bandwidth of B, before sampling takes place. According to Nyquist's fundamental theory [1] the sampling frequency must be equal to or higher than twice the bandwidth B, i.e. $f_s \geq 2B$. If this condition is met, the original bandlimited signal can be recovered from its $1/(2B)$-spaced sampled representation with the aid of a low-pass filter having a cut-off frequency of B.

For example, most of the energy of a voice signal is concentrated at frequencies below 4 kHz, and hence speech signals are typically low-pass filtered to 4 kHz. As a result, a sampling rate of 8 kHz or higher would be required in order to accurately reconstruct such a signal. In practice, most voice communication systems use a sampling rate of 8 kHz.

We now describe the operation of each of the blocks in the block

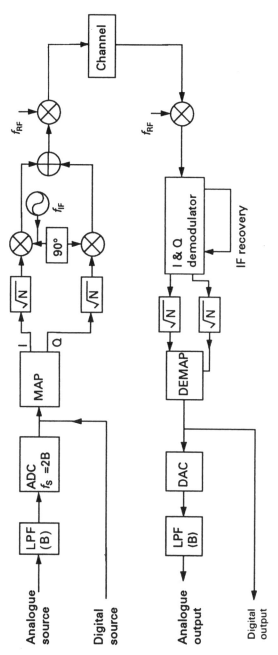

Figure 3.1: Basic QAM modem schematic

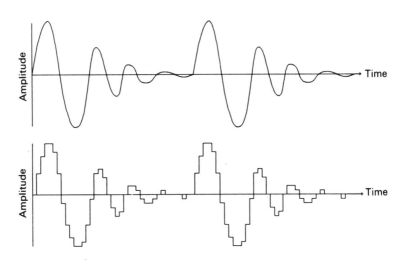

Figure 3.2: Typical ADC input- and output-waves

diagram of Figure 3.1.

3.1 Analogue to digital conversion

The analogue to digital convertor (ADC) takes the bandlimited signal to be transmitted and digitizes it by converting the analogue
level of each sample to a discrete level. For example, in an 8-bit
ADC each discrete level is represented by eight binary output bits.
This provides a resolution of 256 distinct digital levels. The action
of the ADC is shown in Figure 3.2, where a typical analogue signal
is depicted along with its digitised counterpart using only a small
number of quantised bits.

The key difference between digital communication systems and the
more traditional analogue systems is the signal transmission techniques employed. In an analog radio, the signal to be transmitted is
modulated directly, often by simple multiplication, onto the carrier.
On the other hand, digital systems must incorporate modulation
schemes which can map the input data onto the carrier in an efficient and readily decoded manner. The benefit gained from using
the more sophisticated digital techniques is that the digital link can

be rendered error-free by means of signal processing, while in analogue systems the inherent thermal device noise causes always some impairment and hence loss of information.

3.2 Mapping

The process of mapping the information bits onto the streams modulating the I and Q carriers plays a fundamental role in determining the properties of the modem and this is discussed in Chapter 5. The mapping can be represented by the so-called constellation diagram. A constellation is the resulting two-dimensional plot when the amplitudes of the I and Q levels of each of the points which could be transmitted (the constellation points) are drawn in a rectangular coordinate system. For a simple binary amplitude modulation scheme, the constellation diagram would be two points both on the positive x axis. For a binary PSK (BPSK) scheme the constellation diagram would consist again of two points on the x axis, but both equidistant from the origin, one to the left and one to the right, as we have seen in Figure 1.2. The "negative amplitude" of the point to the left of the origin represents a phase shift in the transmitted signal of 180 degrees. If we allow phase shifts of angles other than 0 and 180 degrees, then the constellation points move off the x axis. They can be considered to possess an amplitude and phase, the amplitude representing the magnitude of the transmitted carrier, and the phase representing the phase shift of the carrier relative to the local oscillator in the transmitter. The constellation points may also be considered to have cartesian, or complex co-ordinates, which are normally referred to as inphase (I) and quadrature (Q) components corresponding to the x and y axes, respectively.

In the 16-QAM square constellation of Figure 3.3 each phasor is represented by a four-bit symbol, constituted by the in-phase bits i_1, i_2 and quadrature bits q_1, q_2, which are interleaved to yield the sequence i_1, q_1, i_2, q_2. The quaternary quadrature components I and Q are Gray encoded by assigning the bits *01, 00, 10* and *11* to the levels *3d, d, -d* and *-3d*, respectively. This constellation is widely used because it has equidistant constellation points arranged in a

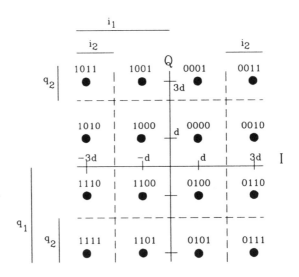

Figure 3.3: 16-QAM square constellation

way that the average energy of the phasors is maximised. Using the geometry of Figure 3.3 the average energy is computed as

$$E_0 = (2d^2 + 2 \times 10d^2 + 18d^2)/4 = 10 \times d^2 \qquad (3.1)$$

For any other phasor arrangement the average energy will be less and therefore, assuming a constant noise energy, the signal to noise ratio required to achieve the same bit error rate (BER) will be higher.

Notice from the mapping in Figure 3.3 that the Hamming distance amongst the constellation points, which are "closest neighbours" with a Euclidean distance of $2d$ is always one. The Hamming distance between any two points is the difference in the mapping bits for those points, so points labelled 0101 and 0111 would have a Hamming distance of 1, and points labelled 0101 and 0011 would have a Hamming distance of 2. This is a fundamental feature of the Gray coding process and ensures that whenever a transmitted phasor is corrupted by noise sufficiently that it is incorrectly identified as a neighbouring constellation point, the demodulator will choose a phasor with a single bit error. This minimises the error probability.

In Figure 3.4 we plot a typical quaternary I component sequence

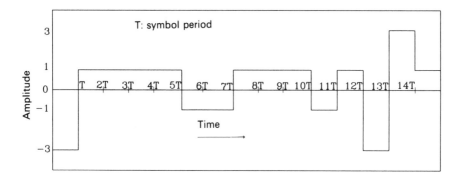

Figure 3.4: Typical I or Q component time-domain representation

generated by the Mapper. Because of the instantaneous transitions in the time domain this I-sequence has an infinite bandwidth and hence would require an infinite channel bandwidth for transmission. The Q-component has similar time- and frequency-domain representations. These signals must be bandlimited before transmission in order to contain the spectrum within a limited band and so minimise interference with other users or systems sharing the spectrum.

3.3 Filtering

An ideal linear-phase low pass filter (LPF) with a cut-off frequency of $f_N = f_s/2$, where $f_s = 1/T$ is the signaling frequency, T is the signaling interval duration and f_N is the so-called Nyquist frequency would retain all the information conveyed by the quadrature components I and Q within a compact frequency band. Due to the linear phase response of the filter all frequency components would exhibit the same group-delay. Because such a filter has a sinc function shaped impulse response with equidistant zero-crossings at the sampling instants, it does not result in inter-symbol-interference (ISI). This ideal transfer function is referred to as a Nyquist characteristic and is shown in

Figure 3.5 along with its impulse response. However, such a filter is unrealisable, as all practical lowpass (LP) filters exhibit amplitude and phase distortions, particularly towards the transition between the pass- and stop-band. Conventional Butterworth, Chebichev or inverse-Chebichev LP filters have impulse responses with non-zero values at the equi-spaced sampling instants and hence introduce ISI. They therefore degrade the bit error rate (BER) performance.

Nyquist's fundamental theoretical work [1] suggested that special pulse shaping filters must be deployed, ensuring that the total transmission path, including the channel, has an impulse response with a unity value at the correct signalling instant and zero-crossings at all other sampling instants. He showed that any odd-symmetric frequency-domain extension characteristic fitted to the ideal LPF amplitude spectrum yields such an impulse response, and is therefore free from ISI.

A practical odd-symmetric extension characteristic is the so-called raised-cosine (RC) characteristic fitted to the ideal LPF of Figure 3.5. The parameter controlling the bandwidth of the Nyquist filter is the so-called roll-off factor α, which is one if the ideal LPF bandwidth is doubled by the extension characteristic. If $\alpha = 0.5$ a total bandwidth of $1.5 \times B$ results, and so on. The lower the value of the roll-off factor, the more compact the spectrum becomes but the higher the complexity of the required filter. The frequency response of these filters is shown in Figure 3.6 for $\alpha = 0.9$ and $\alpha = 0.1$.

Observe in Figures 3.7 and 3.8 how the roll-off factor's value affects the time-domain signal in case of 16-QAM for $\alpha = 0.9$ and $\alpha = 0.1$, respectively. In the former case the signal is less sharply filtered and in time-domain it strongly resembles the unfiltered I component of Figure 3.4. The high-frequency signal components are removed and hence the sharp time-domain transitions are smoothed. For $\alpha = 0.9$ the spectrum extends to $1.9 \times B$, i.e. it is virtually doubled when compared to the minimum requirement of B. Waveforms for $\alpha = 0.1$ are shown in Figure 3.8 where it can be seen that the spectrum is confined to $1.1 \times B$, and due to the sharper filtering the time-domain waveform is highly smoothed, exhibiting a lesser resemblance to the unfiltered I component of Figure 3.4.

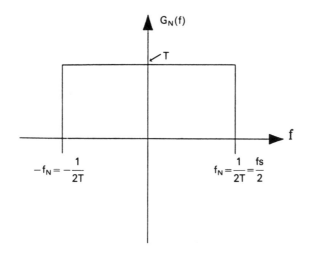

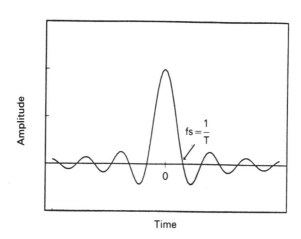

Figure 3.5: Ideal Nyquist filter characteristic and its ISI free
impulse response

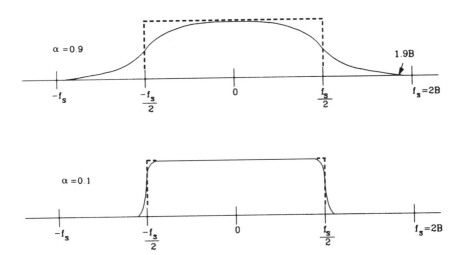

Figure 3.6: Stylised frequency response of two filters with $\alpha = 0.9$ and 0.1

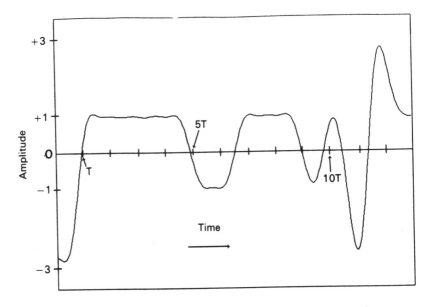

Figure 3.7: Typical filtered I component $\alpha = 0.9$

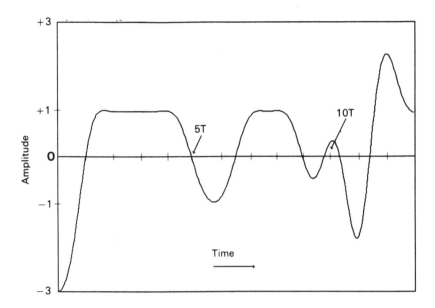

Figure 3.8: Typical filtered I component for $\alpha = 0.1$

In case of additive white gaussian noise (AWGN) with a uniform power spectral density (PSD) the noise power admitted to the receiver is proportional to its bandwidth. Therefore it is also necessary to limit the received signal bandwidth at the receiver to a value close to the transmitter's bandwidth. Optimum detection theory [2] shows that the SNR is maximised, if so-called matched filtering is used, where the Nyquist characteristic is divided between two identical filters, each characterised by the square root of the Nyquist shape, as suggested by the filters $\sqrt{N}$ in Figure 3.1.

3.4 Modulation and demodulation

Once the analogue I and Q signals have been generated and filtered, they are modulated by an I-Q modulator as shown in Figure 3.1. This modulator essentially consists of two mixers, one for the I channel and another for the Q channel. The I channel is mixed with an intermediate frequency (IF) signal that is in phase with respect to the

Transmitted RF spectrum

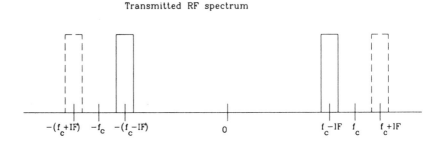

Received RF spectrum at SNR=10dB

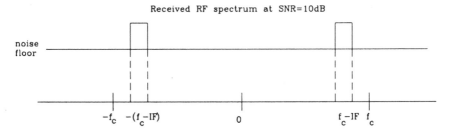

Figure 3.9: Typical transmitted and received RF spectra

carrier, and the Q channel is mixed with an IF that is 90 degrees out of phase. This process allows both signals to be transmitted over a single channel within the same bandwidth using quadrature carriers. In a similar fashion, the signal is demodulated at the receiver. Provided signal degradation is kept to a minimum, the orthogonality of the I and the Q channels will be retained and their information sequences can be demodulated.

Following I-Q modulation, the signal is modulated by a radio frequency (RF) mixer, increasing its frequency to that used for transmission. Since the IF signal occurred at both positive and negative frequencies, it will occur at both the sum and difference frequencies when mixed up to the RF. Since there is no reason to transmit two identical sidebands, one is usually filtered out, as seen plotted in dashed lines in Figure 3.9.

The transmission channel is often the most critical factor influencing the performance of any communications system. Here we consider only the addition of noise based on the signal to noise ratio

(SNR). The noise is often the major contributing factor to signal degradation and its effect exhibits itself as a noise floor, as portrayed in the received RF spectrum of Figure 3.9.

The RF demodulator mixes the received signal down to the IF for the I-Q demodulator. In order to accurately mix the signal back to the appropriate intermediate frequency, the RF mixer operates at the difference between the IF and RF frequencies. Since the I-Q demodulator includes IF recovery circuits, the accuracy of the RF oscillator frequency is not critical. However, it should be stable, exhibiting a low phase noise, since any noise present in the down-conversion process will be passed on to the detected I and Q baseband signals, thereby adding to the possibility of bit errors. The recovered IF spectrum is similar to the transmitted one but with the additive noise floor seen in the RF spectrum of Figure 3.9.

Returning to Figure 3.1, I-Q demodulation takes place in the reverse order to the modulation process. The signal is split into two paths, with each path being mixed down with IF's that are 90 degrees apart. Since the exact frequency of the original reference must be known to determine absolute phase, IF carrier recovery circuits are used to reconstruct the precise reference frequency at the receiver. The recovered I component should be near identical to that transmitted, with the only differences being caused by noise.

3.5 Data recovery

Once the analogue I and Q components have been recovered, they must be digitised. This is done by the bit detector. The bit detector determines the most likely bit transmitted by sampling the I and Q signals at the correct sampling instants and comparing them to the legitimate I and Q values of $-3d, -d, d, 3d$ in the case of a square QAM constellation. From each I and Q decision two bits are derived, leading to a 4-bit 16-QAM symbol. The four recovered bits are then passed on to the DAC. Although the process might sound simple, it is complicated by the fact that the "right time" to sample is a function of the clock frequency at the transmitter. The data clock must be regenerated upon recovery of the carrier. Any error in clock recovery will increase the BER.

If there is no channel noise or the SNR is high, the reconstructed digital signal is identical to the original input signal. Provided the DAC operates at the same frequency and with the same number of bits as the input ADC, then the analogue output signal after low-pass filtering with a cut-off frequency of B, is also identical to the output signal of the LPF at the input to the transmitter. Hence it is a close replica of the input signal.

3.6 Summary

In this short Chapter we have described the fundamental structure of modems using the basic schematic shown in Figure 3.1. The concept of Gray coding was highlighted, which assigns bit patterns having a Hamming distance of one to nearest neighbours in the phasor constellation in order to minimize the bit error probability. Furthermore, a rudimentary introduction to Nyquist filtering was offered, which is an essential pre-requisite for intersymbol interference (ISI) free communications over bandlimited channels, as we will show in the next Chapter.

Accordingly, Chapter 4 will focus on a range of further QAM techniques, including the design of various phasor constellations for channels having a range of impairments. Then an indepth treatment of ISI-free signaling using Nyquist filtering will be given, which is followed by a detailed discussion on various QAM detection methods, such as threshold detection, matched filtering and correlation receivers. Finally, Chapter 4 will incorporate a Subsection on the linearisation problems of power amplifiers and it will be concluded by a discussion on non-differential versus differential coding of QAM signals.

Bibliography

[1] **H. Nyquist**, "Certain factors affecting telegraph speed", *Bell System Tech Jrnl*, Apr. 1928, p 617

[2] **H.R. Raemer**, "Statistical communication theory and applications", Prentice Hall, Inc., Englewood Cliffs, New Jersey, 1969

Chapter 4

Basic QAM Techniques

In this chapter we consider some of the details of QAM modems in more depth than Chapter 3. We are specifically concerned with constellation types for various channels having different dominant impairments, encoding techniques and suitable forms of pulse shaping for QAM transmission. We will also present a short theoretical discourse on the necessary conditions for interference free communications over bandlimited channels and derive the optimum transmitter and receiver filters. Methods of QAM detection, such as threshold detection, matched filtering and correlation receivers are also the subject of this Chapter, which is concluded with a brief discussion on differential versus non-differential coding of QAM signal.

4.1 Constellations for Gaussian channels

As discussed in Chapter 1, a large number of different constellations have been proposed for QAM transmissions over Gaussian channels. However, the three constellations shown in Figure 4.1 are often preferred. The essential problem is to maintain a high minimum distance, d_{min}, between points whilst keeping the average power required for the constellation to a minimum. Calculation of d_{min} and the average power is a straightforward geometric procedure, and has been performed for a range of constellations by Proakis [1]. The results show that the square constellation is optimal for Gaussian channels. The Type I and Type II constellations require a higher en-

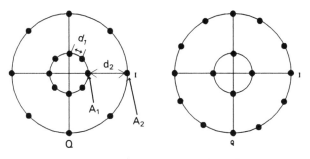

Type I QAM Constellation   Type II QAM Constellation

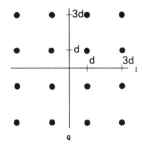

Type III QAM Constellation

Figure 4.1: Variety of QAM constellations

ergy to achieve the same d_{min} as the square constellation and so are generally not preferred for Gaussian channels. However, there may be implementational reasons for favouring circular constellations over the square ones.

When designing a constellation, consideration must be given to:

1. The minimum Euclidean distance amongst phasors, which is characteristic of the noise immunity of the scheme.

2. The minimum phase rotation amongst constellation points, determining the phase jitter immunity and hence the scheme's resilience against clock recovery imperfections and channel phase rotations.

3. The ratio of the peak-to-average phasor power, which is a measure of robustness against non-linear distortions introduced by the power amplifier.

It is quite instructive to estimate the optimum ring ratio RR for the Type I constellation of Figure 4.1 in AWGN under the constraint

of a constant average phasor energy E_0. Accordingly, a high ring
ratio value implies that the Eucledian distance amongst phasors on
the inner ring is reduced, while the distance amongst phasors on
different rings is increased. In contrast, upon reducing the ring ratio
the cross-ring distance is reduced and the distances on the inner ring
become larger.

Intuitively, one expects that there will be an optimum ring ratio,
where the overall bit error rate (BER) constituted by detection errors
on the same ring plus errors between rings is minimised. This problem will be revisited in Figure 11.9 for transmissions over Rayleigh
fading channels using simulation experiments. Suffice to say here
that the minimum Euclidean distance amongst phasors is maximised if $d_1 = d_2 = A_2 - A_1$ in the Type I constellation of Figure 4.1.
Using the geometry of Figure 4.1 we can write that:

$$\cos 67.5^o = \frac{d_1}{2} \cdot \frac{1}{A_1}$$
$$d_1 = 2 \cdot A_1 \cdot \cos 67.5^o$$

and hence

$$A_2 - A_1 = d_1 = d_2 = 2 \cdot A_1 \cdot \cos 67.5^o.$$

Upon dividing both sides by A_1 and introducing the ring ratio RR
we arrive at:

$$RR - 1 = 2 \cdot \cos 67.5^o$$
$$RR \approx 1.77.$$

Simulation results using $1.5 < RR < 3.5$ both over Rayleigh and
AWGN channels showed [14] that the BER depends on the channel
SNR and has a very flat minimum in the above range, hence in Parts
III and IV of this book from Chapter 11 onwards over Rayleigh fading
channels we often opted for $RR = 3$.

Under the constraint of having identical distances amongst constellation points, when $d_1 = d_2 = d$, the average energy E_0 of the
Type I constellation can be computed as follows:

$$E_0 = \frac{8 \cdot A_1^2 + 8 \cdot A_2^2}{16} = \frac{1}{2}(A_1^2 + A_2^2)$$

Type	θ_{min}	d_{min}	r
I	$45°$	$0.43\sqrt{E_0}$	1.7
III	$< 45°$	$0.63 \cdot \sqrt{E_0}$	1.8

Table 4.1: Comparison of Type I and III constellations

where

$$A_1 = \frac{d}{2 \cdot \cos 67.5°} \approx \frac{d}{0.765} \approx 1.31d$$

and

$$A_2 \approx 1.77 \cdot A_1 \approx 3.01d$$

yielding

$$E_0 \approx 0.5 \cdot (9.07 + 1.72)d^2 \approx 5.4d^2.$$

The minimum distance of the constellation for an average energy of E_0 becomes:

$$d_{min} \approx \sqrt{E_0/5.4} \approx 0.43 \cdot \sqrt{E_0},$$

while the peak-to-average phasor energy ratio is:

$$r \approx \frac{(3.01d)^2}{5.4d^2} \approx 1.7.$$

The minimum phase rotation θ_{min}, the minimum Euclidean distance d_{min} and the peak-to-average energy ratio r are summarised in Table 4.1 for both the Type I and Type III constellations .

Let us now derive the above characteristic parameters for the Type III constellation . Observe from Figure 4.1 that $\theta_{min} < 45°$, while the distance between phasors is $2 \cdot d$. Hence the average phasor energy becomes:

$$
\begin{aligned}
E_0 &= \frac{1}{16} [4 \cdot (d^2 + d^2) + 8(9d^2 + d^2) + 4 \cdot (9d^2 + 9d^2)] \\
&= \frac{1}{16}(8d^2 + 80 \cdot d^2 + 72d^2) \\
&= 10d^2.
\end{aligned}
$$

Hence, assuming the same average phasor energy E_0 as for the Type

I constellation we now have a minimum distance of

$$d_{min} = 2d = 2 \cdot \sqrt{E_0/10} = \sqrt{E_0/2.5} \approx 0.63 \cdot \sqrt{E_0}.$$

Lastly, the peak-to-average energy ratio r is given by:

$$r = \frac{18d^2}{10d^2} = 1.8.$$

The Type III constellation's characteristics are also summarised in Table 4.1. Observe that the Type I constellation has a higher jitter immunity and a slightly lower peak-to-average energy ratio than the Type III scheme. However the Type III phasor constellation has an almost 50 % higher minimum distance at the same average phasor energy and hence it is very attractive for AWGN channels, where noise is the dominant channel impairment.

The Type III square constellation can only be implemented, when there are N bits per symbol, where $N = 2M$ and M is an integer. If an odd number of bits is to be encoded then the optimum constellation shape is less obvious. This issue was investigated by Smith [2] who determined that the best constellations were those which have come to be known as cross-QAM. An example of such a constellation is shown in Figure 4.2. It is not possible to Gray encode such a cross constellation so that all nearest neighbour points separated by d_{min} have a Hamming distance of one, and so a small Gray coding penalty must be accepted along with an increased encoding and decoding complexity. For these reasons, even-bit square constellations are significantly more common than odd-bit constellations.

4.2 General Pulse-Shaping Techniques

4.2.1 Baseband Equivalent System

In this section we follow the approach proposed by Lucky, Salz and Weldon [6] using the simplified system model of Figure 4.3, which is essentially a simplified version of Figure 3.1, ignoring the frequency translation or mixing sections of the modem schematic, which do not influence the shape of the signal's spectrum or the signal detection process. In the Figure only one of the quadrature arms is portrayed,

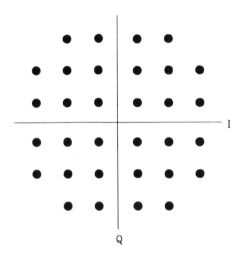

Figure 4.2: 5-bit QAM cross constellation

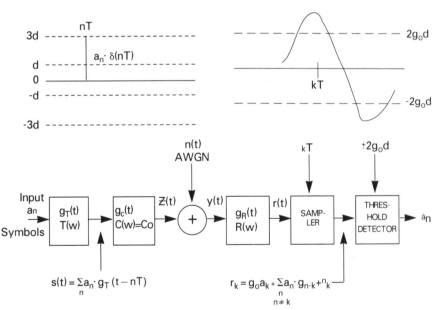

Figure 4.3: Baseband equivalent system model for the I or Q component of square 16-QAM

but we consider a 2^m-ary QAM system, where the I and Q components are $2^{m/2}$-ary. The information to be conveyed is encoded as amplitude values of the signalling pulse shape $g_T(t)$, and these values change at the signalling intervals nT, $n = 1, 2 \ldots \infty$. Thus the baseband transmitted signal on one of the quadrature channels is

$$s(t) = \sum_n a_n g_T(t - nT) \qquad (4.1)$$

where $g_T(t)$ is the transmitter filter's impulse response, implying that the information symbols a_n are idealised zero-width pulses. The demodulator has to infer the transmitted information a_n from the received signal.

We continue to use the baseband equivalent system model introduced in Chapter 2, and try and find that transmitter and receiver filter pair $T(\omega)$ and $R(\omega)$, respectively, which minimises the intersymbol interference (ISI). The legitimate QAM levels are $\pm d$, $\pm 3d$, $\ldots \pm (2^{m/2} - 1)$, as seen, for example, in the Type III phasor constellation of Figure 4.1. The transmitted signal is contaminated by AWGN $n(t)$ and may suffer multipath dispersion (see Chapter 2) via the channel whose transfer function is $C(\omega)$. The receiver filters the signal and after sampling at instants $kT + \tau$, where τ is the channel delay, infers the transmitted information by threshold detection. The signal $r(t)$ at the output of the receiver filter for one quadrature arm is given by:

$$r(t) = \sum_n a_n g(t - nT) + n(t), \qquad (4.2)$$

where $g(t)$ represents the impulse response of the total transmission path constituted by the transmitter, receiver and channel transfer functions $T(\omega)$, $R(\omega)$ and $C(\omega)$, respectively. Using their impulse responses of $g_T(t)$, $g_R(t)$ and $g_C(t)$, respectively, we have

$$g(t) = g_T(t) * g_C(t) * g_R(t), \qquad (4.3)$$

where $*$ means convolution. The received signal at the receiver's sampling instants is written as:

$$r(kT + \tau) = \sum_n a_n g(kT - nT + \tau) + n(kT + \tau), \qquad (4.4)$$

or using a convenient short-hand we have:

$$r_k = \sum_n a_n g_{k-n} + n_k, \qquad (4.5)$$

where the system delay τ has been absorbed in the signalling interval index. Equation 4.5 can be rewritten to emphasise the effect of the current symbol of index $k = n$ as:

$$r_k = g_0 a_k + \sum_{\substack{n \\ n \neq k}} a_n g_{n-k} + n_k, \qquad (4.6)$$

where g_0 is the main tap of the system's impulse response, while the second and third terms represent the ISI and AWGN, respectively. The receiver compares the signal r_k to the appropriately scaled decision levels of $0, \pm 2 g_0 d, \ldots \pm (2^{m/2} - 2) g_0 d$, and decides which of the legitimate a_k values is most likely to have been transmitted. An erroneous decision occurs when the (ISI+AWGN) term becomes larger than $g_0 d$, i.e.:

$$\left| \sum_{\substack{n \\ n \neq k}} a_n g_{n-k} + n_k \right| > g_0 d. \qquad (4.7)$$

Minimising the left-hand side (LHS) term of Equation 4.7, will minimise the BER. Since the channel's transfer function may be varying with time, we assume a linear-phase, distortion-free, equalised channel with $C(\omega) = C_0$ and $\phi_C = \omega T$ within the transmission band. Then the problem is that of finding the filter characteristics $T(\omega)$ and $R(\omega)$ minimising the LHS of Equation 4.7.

4.2.2 Nyquist Filtering

From Equation 4.7 the BER performance of one channel of the QAM system depends on the samples g_{n-k}, $n \neq k$ of the system's impulse response and the noise n_k. It is Nyquist's sampling theorem [5] that enables us to relate these time domain samples to the spectral domain filter characteristic $G(\omega) = T(\omega) R(\omega)$, where $G(\omega)$ is the Fourier transform pair of g_{n-k}. If the system is band limited to

$[-B, B]$, its behaviour is determined by its samples spaced apart by $T = (1/2B)$. Hence,

$$g(nT) = g\left(\frac{n}{2B}\right).$$ (4.8)

The system's transfer function $G(\omega)$ is given in terms of these samples by the Fourier series expansion of

$$G(\omega) = \begin{cases} \frac{1}{2B}\sum_n g\left(\frac{n}{2B}\right) e^{-j\omega n/2B} & \text{if } |\omega| \leq 2\pi B \\ 0 & \text{otherwise.} \end{cases}$$ (4.9)

Nyquist's sampling theorem also states that the original signal $g(t)$ can be perfectly recovered from its samples by low-pass filtering (LPF) the signal with a filter having a cut-off frequency of B. In time domain this filtering corresponds to convolution with the impulse response

$$h_{LPF}(t) = 2B\frac{\sin(2\pi Bt)}{2\pi Bt} = 2B sinc(2\pi Bt)$$ (4.10)

of the LPF. The sampling interval given by $T = 1/2B$ is often referred to as Nyquist interval and the associated frequency of $f_N = 1/2T$ is known as the Nyquist frequency.

The ISI term of Equation 4.7 can only be eliminated if $g_{n-k} = 0$ is met for $n \neq k$, which requires g_n to have zero-crossings at $nT \neq 0$. Since we are only using the T-spaced samples of $g(n)$, this requirement can be formulated by the help of the Fourier transform as:

$$g_n = \int_{-\infty}^{\infty} G(f)e^{j2\pi f nT} df = \delta_n.$$ (4.11)

where δ_n is the Kronecker delta. The above integration can be carried out in segments of Nyquist bandwidths given by $f_N = 1/2T$, as seen in Figure 4.4. Then we have:

$$g_n = \sum_k \int_{(2k-1)/2T}^{(2k+1)/2T} G(f)e^{j2\pi f nT} df = \delta_n,$$ (4.12)

Instead of integrating $G(f)$ piece-wise over the Nyquist frequency segments, as k is increased we can integrate over $[-1/2T, 1/2T]$ and shift $G(f)$ along the frequency axis by $2f_N = 1/T$, as k is increased, giving:

$$g_n = \sum_k \int_{-1/2T}^{1/2T} G\left(f + \frac{k}{T}\right) e^{j2\pi f nT} df = \delta_n.$$ (4.13)

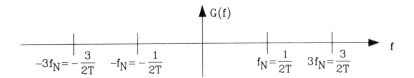

Figure 4.4: Nyquist Frequency Segments

Upon interchanging the summation with the integration, g_n can be expressed by the equivalent Nyquist characteristic $G_N(f)$ as follows:

$$g_n = \int_{-1/2T}^{1/2T} G_N(f)e^{j\omega nT} df = \delta_n \,, \qquad (4.14)$$

where

$$G_N(f) = \begin{cases} \sum_k G\left(f + \frac{k}{T}\right) & \text{if } |f| \le \frac{1}{2T} \\ 0 & \text{otherwise.} \end{cases} \qquad (4.15)$$

Equation 4.15 reveals that the equivalent Nyquist characteristic $G_N(f)$ is the superposition of all the $1/T$ wide frequency domain slices of $G(f)$ within the band $[-1/2T, 1/2T]$, while it is zero outside this band. Since Equation 4.14 fully specifies $g_n = \delta_n$ in terms of its $T = 1/2B$-spaced samples represented by the Kronecker delta, it also describes $G_N(f)$. The *sinc* function in Equation 4.10 fulfils the criterion of ISI-free signalling and constrains $G_N(f)$ to be an ideal LPF characteristic with zero phase, as seen in Figure 4.5 and given by

$$G_N(f) = \begin{cases} T & \text{if } |f| \le \frac{1}{2T} \\ 0 & \text{if } |f| > \frac{1}{2T}. \end{cases} \qquad (4.16)$$

The simplest implementation of the ISI-free Nyquist equivalent characteristic would be then the ideal LPF of Equation 4.16 plotted in Figure 4.5. Unfortunately, this filter characteristic is unrealisable and any approximation to it results in serious ISI penalty. Any practical Nyquist filter must have a wider bandwidth than $f_N = 1/2T$, but a bandwidth in excess of $2f_N$ is usually unacceptable in terms of bandwidth efficiency. This situation is depicted in Figure 4.6, where

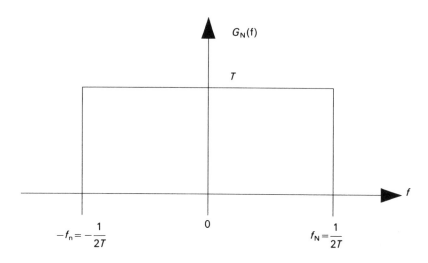

Figure 4.5: Baseband Equivalent Nyquist Characteristic for ISI-Free Transmission

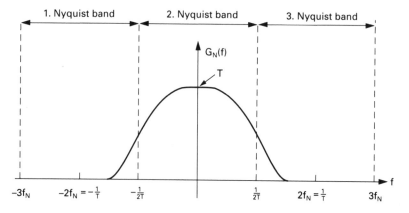

Figure 4.6: Sketch of a Practical Nyquist Filter Characteristic

$G(f)$ is limited to $[-2f_N, 2f_N]$ and hence has only three Nyquist segments. Then Equation 4.15 has only three terms as seen below:

$$G_N(f) = G\left(f - \frac{1}{T}\right) + G(f) + G\left(f + \frac{1}{T}\right) \qquad (4.17)$$

Observe from Figure 4.6 that the Nyquist segment overlaying specified by Equation 4.17 is equivalent to folding the 1. and 3. Nyquist segments back in the 2. segment around the frequencies $-f_N$ and f_N, respectively. This is due to the symmetry of the positive and negative wings of the spectrum. However, if the phase characteristic is non-zero, the spectrum's conjugate complex symmetry must be taken into account.

Equivalently, the folding process can be stated as follows. The Nyquist equivalent characteristic is constituted by an ideal LPF with a cut-off frequency of $f_N = 1/2T$ plus an overlaid characteristic having odd symmetry around f_N, but not extending beyond $2f_N$.

4.2.3 Raised-Cosine Nyquist Filtering

From the above discussion we know that there is a plethora of filters fulfilling the Nyquist criterion, having bandwidths between $f_N = 1/2T$ and $2f_N = 1/T$. In general, the higher the bandwidth efficiency, the better. A practical set of convenient Nyquist filters is the so-called raised-cosine (RC) characteristic, which fits a quarter period of a frequency-domain cosine shaped curve to the ideal LPF transfer characteristic, as seen in Figure 4.7.

The bandwidth is controlled by the so-called roll-off factor α, defined as the ratio of excess bandwidth above f_N to f_N. The RC characteristic is then defined as [6]

$$G(f) = \begin{cases} T & \text{for } 0 \leq |f| \leq \frac{1-\alpha}{2T} \\ \frac{T}{2}\left(1 - \sin\left[\frac{\pi T}{\alpha}\left(f - \frac{1}{2T}\right)\right]\right) & \text{for } \frac{1-\alpha}{2T} < |f| \leq \frac{1+\alpha}{2T}. \end{cases} \qquad (4.18)$$

4.2.4 The Choice of Roll-off Factor

The impulse response of the RC characteristic plays an important role in deciding upon the choice of α in a particular system. Namely, when the channel becomes non-ideal and hence the ISI is non-zero,

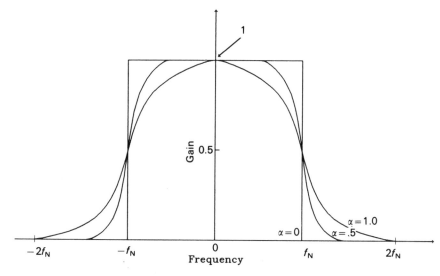

Figure 4.7: Sketch of Raised-Cosine Nyquist Filter Characteristics for Various Roll-off Factors

then the decay of the impulse response must be as rapid as possible to minimise the duration over which a previous transmitted symbol can influence the received signal.

The set of impulse responses corresponding to the RC curves in Equation 4.18 is given by [6]:

$$g(t) = \frac{\sin(\pi t/T)}{\pi t/T} \frac{\cos(\alpha \pi t/T)}{1 - 4\alpha^2 t^2/T^2} \tag{4.19}$$

These impulse responses are plotted in Figure 4.8 for roll-off factors of $\alpha = 0, 0.5$ and 1. Observe in Equation 4.19 that for $\alpha = 0$ we have:

$$g(t) = \frac{\sin(\pi t/T)}{\pi t/T}, \tag{4.20}$$

associated with the lowest bandwidth occupancy but also with the most slowly decaying impulse response. The fastest decay is ensured, when $\alpha = 1$, at the price of doubled bandwidth occupancy. In this case the impulse response exhibits an additional set of zero crossings between those stipulated by the Nyquist condition. A good compromise is represented by $\alpha = 0.5$ in terms of both bandwidth occupancy and impulse response decay. Notice that the impulse re-

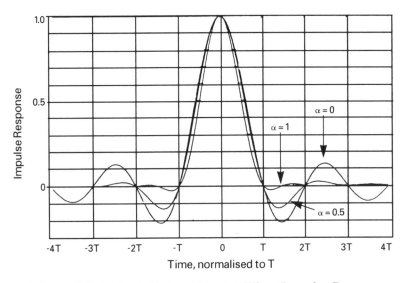

Figure 4.8: Raised-Cosine Nyquist Filter Impulse Responses for Various Roll-off Factors

sponse decay plays a crucial role in determining the system's robustness against ISI, because for slowly decaying responses the channel's ISI has a prolonged influence on future and past sampling instants. Therefore in high-ISI environments higher roll-off factors must be used, despite the lower bandwidth efficiency.

In summary, we determined the required transfer characteristic of the total transmission system, which must have an odd-symmetric roll-off around $f_N = 1/2T$. Lower roll-off factors yield spectral compactness, but they are also more vulnerable to ISI via non-ideally equalised channels. This makes clock recovery much more difficult to achieve.

4.2.5 Optimum Transmit and Receive Filtering

In this subsection we highlight briefly, how the transfer characteristic $G_N(f)$ must be split between the transmitter filter $G_T(f)$ and the receiver filter $G_R(f)$ in order to maximise noise immunity [6]. Recall from Equation 4.7 that we have minimised the effects of ISI by selecting an overall transfer characteristic $G_N(f)$. The BER due to AWGN is minimised by maximising the SNR at sampling instants for a given transmitted power.

Recall from Equation 4.1 that the transmitted signal was given by

$$s(t) = \sum_{n=-\infty}^{\infty} a_n g_T(t - nT),$$

where a_n represents the Dirac-shaped information symbols, while $g_T(t)$ is the transmitter filter's impulse response. Then the average transmitted power over an interval of $2 \cdot N \cdot T$ is given by the expectation value below:

$$P_T = \langle \lim_{N \to \infty} \frac{1}{2NT} \int_{-NT}^{NT} \left[\sum_{n=-N}^{N} a_n g_T(t - nT) \right]^2 dt \rangle. \qquad (4.21)$$

Upon interchanging the expectation and limit computation we have:

$$P_T = \lim_{N \to \infty} \frac{1}{2NT} \sum_{n=-N}^{N} \sum_{m=-N}^{N} \langle a_n a_m \rangle \int_{-NT}^{NT} g_T(t - nT) g_T(t - mT) dt. \qquad (4.22)$$

For uncorrelated input symbols we get:

$$\langle a_n a_m \rangle = \begin{cases} 0 & n \neq m \\ \bar{a}^2 & n = m \end{cases} \qquad (4.23)$$

and hence

$$\begin{aligned} P_T &= \lim_{N \to \infty} \frac{\bar{a}^2}{2NT} \sum_{n=-N}^{N} \int_{-NT}^{NT} g_T^2(t - nT) dt \\ &= \frac{\bar{a}^2}{T} \int_{-\infty}^{\infty} g_T^2(t) dt. \end{aligned} \qquad (4.24)$$

When exploiting Parseval's theorem given below:

$$\int_{-\infty}^{\infty} g_T^2(t) dt = \int_{-\infty}^{\infty} |G_T(f)|^2 df \qquad (4.25)$$

the channel's input power can also be expressed in terms of the spectral domain transmitter transfer function $G_T(f)$ as follows:

$$P_T = \frac{\bar{a}^2}{T} \int_{-\infty}^{\infty} |G_T(f)|^2 df = \frac{\bar{a}^2}{T} \int_{-\infty}^{\infty} \left| \frac{G_N(f)}{G_R(f)} \right|^2 df, \qquad (4.26)$$

where we exploited the fact that $G_N(f) = G_T(f) \cdot G_R(f)$. The received noise has a spectral density of $N(f)$ and after passing through the receiver filter it has a power of

$$P_N = \int_{-\infty}^{\infty} N(f)|G_R(f)|^2 df. \qquad (4.27)$$

The noise power P_N has to be minimised under the constraint of constant channel input power P_T so as to maximise the SNR. Using the technique of variational calculus [6] the functional F defined below must be minimised:

$$F = \lambda P_T + P_N , \qquad (4.28)$$

where λ is the so-called Lagrange multiplier.

The result of this minimisation problem is that for a flat noise spectral density N_0 and for a real Nyquist equivalent characteristic the transmitter and receiver filters must be identical in order to maximise the SNR, i.e.:

$$G_T(f) = G_R(f) = \sqrt{G_N(f)}. \qquad (4.29)$$

This important result was already implicitly exploited in Figure 3.1, where we represented the square root of the Nyquist filter by $\sqrt{N}$.

4.2.6 Characterisation of ISI by Eye-Diagrams

When a dispersive channel introduces ISI, previously transmitted symbols will cause non-zero contributions at subsequent sampling instants. The so-called eye-diagram is a simple and convenient tool to study the effects of ISI and other channel impairments both by simulation and in hardware experiments.

Let us imagine an ideal noiseless and ISI-free, infinite bandwidth communications system transmitting a binary data sequence having values of ± 1, at a bitrate of $R = 1/T$, as shown in Figure 4.9.

If this system's output signal is displayed on an analogue oscilloscope screen with persistence, when using external synchronisation having a frequency of $R = 1/T$, the beam starts its travel across the screen every $1/T$ sec and draws the adjacent signal sections on top of each other, as also shown in Figure 4.9.

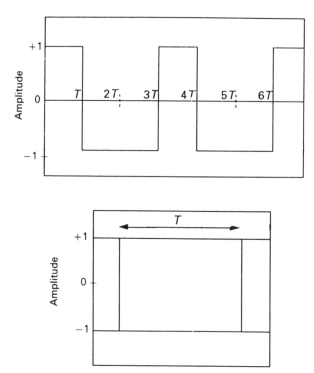

Figure 4.9: A Typical Binary Data Sequence and its Eye-Diagram

If this PRBS is now transmitted via a Nyquist-filtered, band-limited, but ISI-free channel, the corresponding signals are portrayed in Figure 4.10.

Observe that since no ISI and no noise are present, the eye is "clean" or "fully open" at the sampling instants and the zero crossings occur always at multiples of T, appearing at the same instant in the eye-diagram.

Let us now introduce ISI. The signalling waveforms will have typically non-zero values at all sampling instants and the received PRBS and its eye-diagram will typically resemble those in Figure 4.11. When AWGN is also superimposed, we expect waveforms similar to those in Figure 4.12.

As demonstrated by Figure 4.13, nearly all typical channel impairments become recognizable in the eye-diagrams, and hence eye diagrams are very useful in quick overall system evaluation. Observe

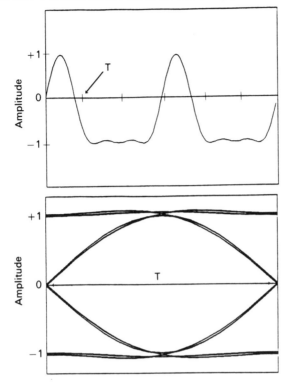

Figure 4.10: Received Signal and its Eye-Diagram via Band-Limited Channel with No Noise and ISI

that imperfectly timed sampling has a similar effect to increasing the AWGN. The zero-crossing jitter becomes very crucial in case of clock recovery circuits that operate by detecting zero-crossings (see Chapter 6) and using the time at which these occur to derive the optimal sampling point. When multilevel transmissions are used, the eye-diagram becomes much more complicated due to the increased number of possible transitions. The eye-opening is narrower, as demonstrated by Figure 4.14, where the transmitter's eye pattern is seen for a 16-QAM Nyquist-filtered modem having a roll-off factor of $\alpha = 1$.

This Nyquist filter with $\alpha = 1$ has the sharpest possible impulse response decay and hence minimises the effects of ISI. Lower α values result in smoother time domain transitions, yielding a more closed eye pattern. This increased sensitivity is the price paid for the higher spectral compactness of narrower Nyquist filters.

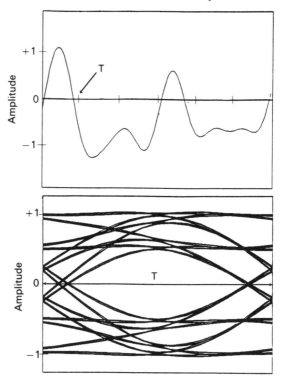

Figure 4.11: Received Signal and Eye-Diagram Impaired by ISI

4.2.7 Non-Linear Filtering

In 1982 Feher [7] suggested the use of non-linear filtering (NLF) for QAM satellite communications. This was a technique he had developed along with Huang in 1979 which simplified filter design by simply fitting a time-domain quarter period of a sine wave between two symbols for both of the quadrature carriers. This allowed the generation of jitter-free bandlimited signals, which had previously been a problem, improving clock recovery techniques. Furthermore, unlike partial-response filtering techniques which intentionally introduce ISI, NLF produces an ISI-free waveform since there is no contribution from previous symbols at any sample point, which is advantageous when complex high-level QAM constellations are transmitted. The disadvantage of this form of filtering is that it is less spectrally efficient than optimal partial-response filtering schemes.

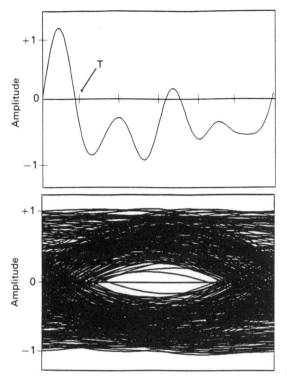

Figure 4.12: Received Signal and Eye-Diagram with ISI and AWGN

We performed some simulation work to compare their spectral efficiency, and our results suggested that whilst optimal partial-response schemes [4] necessitated an excess bandwidth of about 20% above the Nyquist frequency $f_N = 1/(2 \cdot T)$, the NLF scheme required an excess bandwidth of about 40%. Nevertheless, its implementational advantages often render this loss of efficiency acceptable. The power spectrum of a NLF signal is given by [7]

$$S(f) = T \left(\frac{\sin 2\pi fT}{2\pi fT} \frac{1}{1 - 4(fT)^2} \right)^2 \qquad (4.30)$$

and some sample waveforms are given in Figure 4.15 for one quadrature arm. The other quadrature arm is identical.

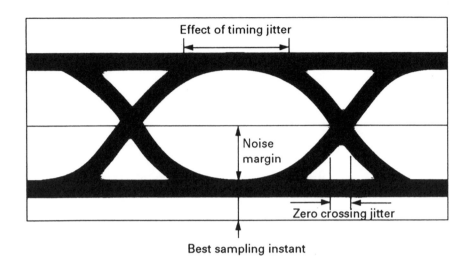

Figure 4.13: Effect of channel impairments on the eye-diagram

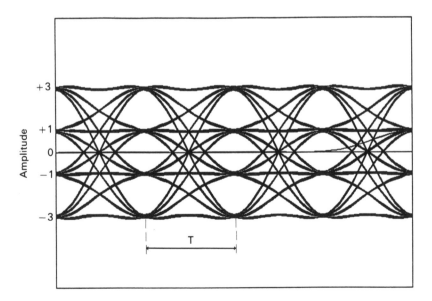

Figure 4.14: 16-QAM Transmitter Eye-Diagram using $\alpha = 1$

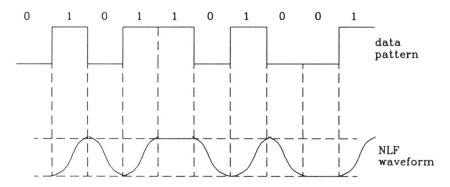

Figure 4.15: NLF **waveforms**

4.3 Methods of Generating QAM

4.3.1 Generating Conventional QAM

As discussed in Chapter 3 and shown in Figure 4.16, in a typical QAM modem the incoming binary data stream is passed through a serial-to-parallel convertor of an appropriate width. The data is then passed through a logic block which performs the translation between the binary input data and the constellation points, to allow Gray coding. Typically such a block would be implemented as a look-up table using a programmable memory device. In the case of square QAM the output from the serial-to-parallel convertor can be partitioned into two subsets, and each encoded onto a separate axis using identical mapping blocks. Digital-to-analogue (D/A) conversion is then required, followed by pulse-shaping, before up-converting the signal to the carrier frequency. It is often advantageous to perform the pulse-shaping prior to the D/A conversion by oversampling the transmitted data and using further look-up tables containing the pulse-shaping law in order to produce a digital representation of the smoothed signal. This will still need to be filtered after D/A conversion in order to remove aliasing errors caused by the oversampling ratio, but this filtering is substantially simpler than would otherwise

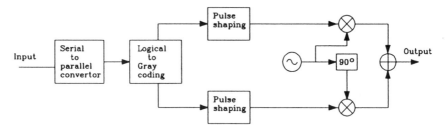

Figure 4.16: Standard QAM modulator

be required.

In order to demodulate the signal the reverse process is followed. The incoming waveform is sampled at the correct instants provided by the clock-recovery circuit, A/D converted and a decision is made as to the most likely constellation point to have been transmitted. The position of this constellation point is then passed through a logic block which performs the reverse operation to the one in the transmitter, leading to the encoded information. This is passed through a parallel to serial convertor leading to the output data stream.

Whilst this is by far the most common method for generating QAM signals, an alternative suggestion referred to as superposed QAM was made by Miyauchi *et al* [9], which will be considered in the next Subsection.

4.3.2   Superposed QAM

In superposed QAM modems the approach is to use a number of PSK modems in tandem as explained below. This had the advantage of being able to use circuitry already developed for PSK modems, allowing ease of implementation. This technique has not gained much popularity, since the conventional QAM generation method described in the previous Subsection has generally proved more efficient. Nevertheless, a brief description is included for completeness.

A diagram showing how a 16-level square QAM constellation could be constructed by this method is given in Figure 4.17. Essentially, the first two bits of the four-bit symbol are passed to a QPSK modulator operating at a certain power and the second two bits are passed to a second QPSK modulator operating at one quarter of the power of the first. The two QPSK modulated signals are then superimposed before transmission. At the receiver a similar philosophy can be employed.

Block diagrams of transmitter and receiver structures are given in Figure 4.18. At the receiver the signal is passed to a QPSK decoder. This essentially determines the quadrant of transmission, or the signal level produced by the first QPSK modulator within the transmitter. The decision is re-modulated and passed to a subtraction circuit. This forms the difference between the incoming signal and the re-modulated signal, giving the signal produced by the second QPSK modulator. This can also be demodulated to produce the remaining output bits.

4.3.3 Offset QAM

Offset, or staggered modulation, is a technique which evolved with PSK transmissions in an effort to reduce the envelope variations of the transmitted signal, and in particular to prevent the envelope of the transmitted signal passing through zero during transitions between symbols as this required the power amplifier to maintain linearity across a wide amplitude range. This was problematic as non-linearities in amplifiers, particularly those used for satellite applications, could cause considerable distortion of the transmitted waveform. Furthermore, large variations in the envelope could result in a requirement for tight filtering if out-of-band spillage was to be avoided. Offset modulation involves delaying one of the quadrature arms by half a symbol period with respect to the other arm. Therefore, when the maximum rate of change of level is taking place on one arm (i.e. in the centre of a transition between levels) then the other arm is near stationary. Offset QAM (O-QAM) can be expressed as:

$$s(t) = \left[\sum_k a_{2k} h(t - 2kT) \right] \cos(2\pi f_c t) \qquad (4.31)$$

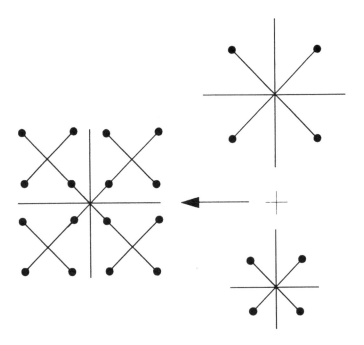

Figure 4.17: Constructing QAM with 2 PSK modulators

$$- \left[\sum_k a_{2k-1} h(t - (2k-1)T) \right] \sin(2\pi f_c t)$$

where f_c is the carrier frequency, $1/T$ is the symbol rate, a_k is the kth data symbol, for 16-level square QAM taking on values ± 1 and ± 3, and $h(t)$ is the signalling waveform corresponding to the impulse response of the transmitter's pulse shaping filter used. A diagram showing the structure of an O-QAM modulator is shown in Figure 4.19.

Offsetting the modulation can make clock recovery more problematic, and decoding more complex. Further uncertainty can exist within the receiver concerning which axis is delayed with respect to the other, and we consider differential coding to overcome this ambiguity in Section 4.7. Claims have been made for less out-of-band spillage for O-QAM compared to QAM [3], with a resulting increase in spectral efficiency due to tighter packing of adjacent channels.

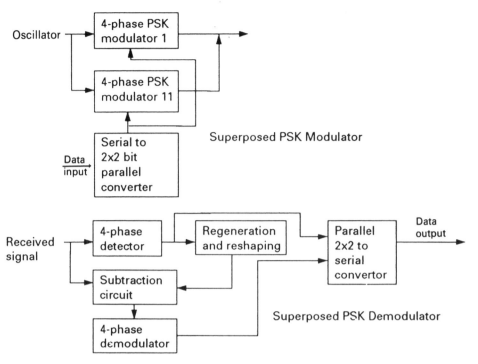

Figure 4.18: Superposed PSK modulator and demodulator

Malkamaki [3] performed a number of simulations where he compared the spectral efficiency of QAM with O-QAM. Spectral efficiency is defined in many ways, and we consider some of these definitions in Chapter 19 of this book. In the meantime, in this section we use Malkamaki's definition that the spectral efficiency is given by

$$S_r = \frac{R_m}{B_m} \left(\frac{C}{I_c}\right)^{-2/\alpha} \tag{4.32}$$

where R_m is the modulation rate, B_m is the channel spacing, C is the received carrier power, I_c is the interference power, and α is the assumed propagation exponent. Malkamaki performed a number of simulations and reported the relative efficiency results displayed in Table 4.2.

The results suggest that in terms of spectral efficiency O-QAM is only marginally better than QAM, and implementation difficulties may reduce this slight advantage. Furthermore, O-QAM requires a less efficient differential coding system than QAM, as discussed in

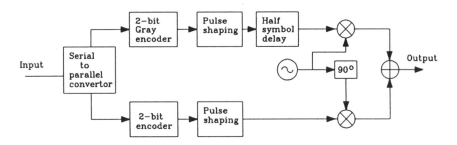

Figure 4.19: O-QAM modulator structure

C/I_c dB	S_r $(\alpha = 2)$	S_r $(\alpha = 4)$	S_r $(\alpha = 6)$
-9	1.07	1.07	1.06
-15	1.05	1.04	1.03
-20	1.04	1.03	1.03

Table 4.2: Relative efficiency of O-QAM compared to QAM

Section 4.7, and it is not clear whether Malkamaki has taken this into account. It would appear that O-QAM is only advantageous where large envelope variations must be avoided due to amplifier design considerations.

4.3.4 Non-Linear Amplification

QAM had been proposed for satellite applications in the late 1960s but a major implementational stumbling block was that of amplification. Because of limited power within satellites, power efficient non-linear class C amplifiers were preferred. QAM, being a non-constant envelope modulation, requires linear amplifiers. The increase in power required when using low-efficiency linear class A amplifiers precluded QAM from most satellite applications. Feher [10] suggested a new method of generation of QAM signals using highly non-linear amplifiers which he termed non-linearly amplified QAM (NLA-QAM) in order to overcome this problem. Two separate amplifiers for the 16-QAM case were used, one operating with quarter of the output power of the other. This is shown in Figure 4.20. The higher power amplifier processed the two most significant bits (MSBs) of the four bit symbol only, and the lower power amplifier processed only the two least significant bits (LSBs). The two MSBs and LSBs represented the high-power and low-power phasors, respectively, which always maintained a constant magnitude and hence were class-C amplified. The amplified processed signals were then summed at full output power to produce the QAM signal.

Again, in this arrangement each amplifier was producing a QPSK signal, therefore the scheme has certain similarities with that proposed by Miyauchi, except the latter performed summation of QPSK signals prior to amplification, whereas Feher sums the signals after amplification. Because both amplifiers were able to use constant envelope modulation they could be operated at a constant level with resulting high power efficiency. However, Feher's NLA scheme resulted in an increased complexity due to the need for two amplifiers and a hybrid combiner, compared to previous systems which used only a single amplifier. Nevertheless, in satellite applications, complexity was relatively unimportant compared to power efficiency, and this

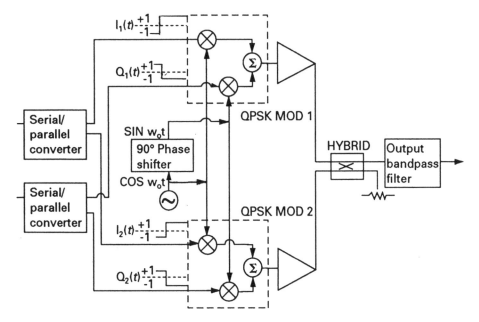

Figure 4.20: NLA structure

NLA technique offered a substantial 5dB power gain, considerably increasing the potential of QAM in severely power limited applications. This work was soon followed by a performance study of a NLA 64-state system [11] which extended the NLA scheme to 64 levels by using three amplifiers all operating at different power levels.

Non-linear amplification is rarely used in other applications due to the increase in hardware complexity.

4.4   Methods of Detecting QAM Signals

4.4.1   Threshold Detection of QAM

In most of this book we will be assuming that the filtered received waveform is sampled at the correct point by use of a clock recovery circuit (see Chapter 6) and subjected to threshold detection in

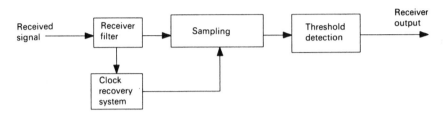

Figure 4.21: Receiver Structure using Threshold Detection

order to derive the received information symbol for that symbol instant. A generic receiver designed around these principles is shown in Figure 4.21. The optimum receiver filter maximising the signal-to-noise ratio (SNR) and minimising hence the bit error rate (BER) was derived in Section 4.2, while the BER using a perfectly coherent threshold detector will be analytically derived for 16-QAM and 64-QAM over AWGN channels in Chapter 5.

Unless stated to the contrary, throughout this book we will be assuming that the receiver of Figure 4.21, which is based on threshold detection is employed.

4.4.2   Matched Filtered Detection

In the previous Subsection we have briefly summarised the salient features of the low-complexity threshold detector receiver, which is constituted by a receiver filter followed by a sampler and threshold detector. In Section 4.2 we optimised the receiver filter under the constraint of constant channel input power or transmitted power P_T and minimised the amount of noise power P_N admitted to the threshold detector by appropriately designing the receiver filter. The result was that the Nyquist characteristic had to be split symmetrically between the transmitter and receiver filter, while the channel was assumed to be equalised.

When designing a so-called matched filter, the approach is to maximise the signal-to-noise ratio (SNR) at the output of the matched filter for a given received signal waveform [12]. The system's schematic is identical to that in Figure 4.3. Considering for example one of the quadrature components of a 2^m-ary QAM signal at the input of the receiver we have:

$$y(t) = \sum_n a_n \cdot h(t - nT) + n(t) = z(t) + n(t)$$

where a_n represents the $M = 2^{m/2}$-ary I or Q components, $n(t)$ is the AWGN and $h(t)$ is given by the convolution:

$$h(t) = g_T(t) * g_c(t),$$

with $g_T(t)$ and $g_c(t)$ being the transmitter filter's and the channel's impulse response, respectively. Clearly, signaling is carried out using the signaling waveforms $h(t)$ weighted by the $M = 2^{m/2}$-ary I and Q components. Assuming that there is no intersymbol-interference (ISI) the sampling circuit's output signal at time $t = T$ is the sum of a signal contribution r_k and a noise contribution n_k.

Our goal is then to maximise the following SNR term [1, 12, 13]:

$$SNR_T = \frac{r_k^2}{\sigma_0^2},$$

at $t = T$, where σ_0^2 is the noise variance, as a function of the filter transfer function $R(f)$. The information signal $r(t)$ at the filter's output can be formulated by the help of the Fourier transform as:

$$r(t) = \int_{-\infty}^{\infty} R(f)Z(f) \cdot e^{j2\pi ft} df,$$

where $Z(f)$ is the frequency domain representative of the received signal $z(t)$ and $R(f)$ is the transfer function of the filter $g_R(t)$ at the receiver's input.

Following Sklar's approach [12] and assuming a double-sided noise spectral density of $N_0/2$, the filter's output noise power is given by:

$$\sigma_0^2 = \frac{N_0}{2} \int_{-\infty}^{\infty} |R(f)|^2 df.$$

Then the SNR is expressed as

$$SNR_T = \frac{|\int_{-\infty}^{\infty} R(f) \cdot Z(f)e^{j2\pi fT} df|^2}{N_o/2 \int_{-\infty}^{\infty} |R(f)|^2 df}. \tag{4.33}$$

In order to find the optimum filter $R(f) = R_{opt}(f)$, Schwartz's inequality can be invoked, which is formulated in general as:

$$\left| \int_{-\infty}^{\infty} g_1(x) \cdot g_2(x) dx \right|^2 \leq \int_{-\infty}^{\infty} |g_1(x)|^2 dx \cdot \int_{-\infty}^{\infty} |g_2(x)| dx.$$

The equality is satisfied, if $g_1(x) = c \cdot g_2^*(x)$, where c is a constant and $*$ denotes the complex conjugate. If we let $g_1(x) = R(f)$ and $g_2(x) = Z(f) \cdot e^{j2\pi fT}$, we arrive at:

$$\left| \int_{-\infty}^{\infty} R(f) \cdot S(f) e^{j2\pi fT} df \right|^2 \leq \int_{-\infty}^{\infty} |R(f)|^2 df \cdot \int_{-\infty}^{\infty} |Z(f)|^2 df, \quad (4.34)$$

where equality is satisfied if

$$R(f) = c \cdot Z^*(f) e^{-j2\pi fT}. \quad (4.35)$$

Upon substituting Equation 4.34 into Equation 4.33 we have

$$SNR_T \leq \frac{\int_{-\infty}^{\infty} |R(f)|^2 df \cdot \int_{-\infty}^{\infty} |Z(f)|^2 df}{N_0/2 \int_{-\infty}^{\infty} |R(f)|^2 df}$$

giving

$$SNR_T \leq \frac{2}{N_0} \int_{-\infty}^{\infty} |Z(f)|^2 df.$$

If we denote the received signal's energy by E_z and exploit the Parseval theorem, we arrive at:

$$E_z = \int_{-\infty}^{\infty} |z(t)|^2 dt = \int_{-\infty}^{\infty} |Z(f)|^2 df$$

and hence the maximum SNR is given by:

$$SNR_T^{max} = \frac{2E_z}{N_0}. \quad (4.36)$$

Observe that the received signal's wave form shape does not appear in the above Equation, indicating that the SNR depends on the energy of $z(t)$, rather than its shape. Recall from Equations 4.35 and 4.36 that the equality condition ensured the maximum SNR and from Equation 4.35 this requires in the time domain that

$$\begin{aligned} g_R(t) &= \mathcal{F}^{-1}\{R(f)\} \\ &= \mathcal{F}^{-1}\{c \cdot Z^*(f) e^{-j2\pi fT}\}, \end{aligned}$$

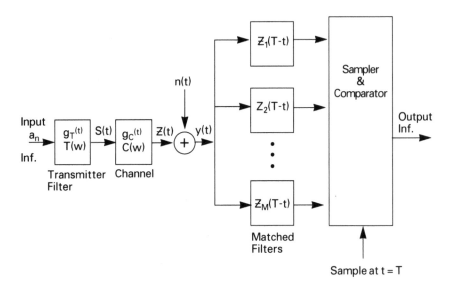

Figure 4.22: Matched filtered receiver

where $\mathcal{F}$ represents the Fourier transform. When taking into account that:

$$\mathcal{F}^{-1}\left\{Z^*(f)\right\} = z(-t)$$

and that the factor $e^{-j2\pi fT}$ corresponds to a time domain delay of T, we arrive at

$$g_R(t) = \begin{cases} c \cdot z(T-t) & 0 \le t \le T \\ 0 & \text{otherwise.} \end{cases} \qquad (4.37)$$

Explicitly, the impulse response of the filter maximising the SNR at $t = T$ must be the reflected and shifted version of the received signal $z(t)$. Observe from Equation 4.37 that the delay of T renders the impulse response causal or realisable, since $g_R(t) = z(-t)$ would not be realisable.

The matched filtered receiver will then have a bank of filters, each of which is matched to one of the possible $M = 2^{m/2}$ received I or Q waveforms $z_1(t), z_2(t) \ldots z_M(t)$, as portrayed in Figure 4.22. The received signal is filtered through all matched filters and the output signal of that specific filter will be the largest, which is adequately

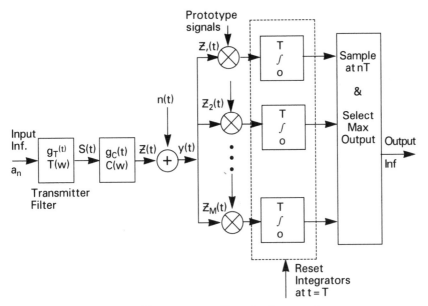

Figure 4.23: Correlation receiver

matched to the received signal. The output signal of the remaining filters will be significantly lower, and hence the comparator finally infers, which a_n $n = 1 \ldots M$ has been transmitted.

Having described the matched filtered receiver we now briefly focus our attention on an alternative implementation of it, the so-called *correlation receiver*.

4.4.3 Correlation receiver

Observe from Figure 4.22 that the causal filter's output signal can also be described by the help of the convolution:

$$r(t) = y(t) * g_R(t) = \int_0^t y(\tau) \cdot g_R(t - \tau) d\tau \qquad (4.38)$$

and setting arbitrarily $c = 1$ in Equation 4.37 as well as exploiting that:

$$g_R(t - \tau) = c \cdot z[T - (t - \tau)]$$

yields:

$$r(t) = \int_0^t y(\tau) \cdot z(T - t + \tau) d\tau.$$

For $t = T$ this can be written as:

$$r(t = T) = \int_0^{t=T} y(\tau) \cdot z(\tau) d\tau,$$

which allows us to interpret the matched filtered receiver as a *correlation receiver*.

Explicitly, in the correlation receiver of Figure 4.23 the received signal $y(t)$ is correlated with all legitimate prototype signals $z_n(t), n = 1 \ldots M$ using a bank of M correlators and that one is assumed to have been transmitted, which exhibits the highest correlation at $t = T$. It is important to emphasise however that the output of the matched filter is only equal to that of the correlator at $t = T$, which can be easily demonstrated using simple specific received signal waveforms.

Lastly, it is important to note that the channel's impulse response $g_c(t)$ can be determined by using channel sounding methods, which is briefly explained later in Section 7.6. If $g_c(t)$ is known, then the prototype signals $z_n(t), n = 1 \ldots M$ can be determined. Alternatively, the channel can be equalised initially in order to render $C(f) = C_0$, where C_0 is a constant. This constant transfer function is associated with an ideal Dirac-delta impulse response $g_c(t)$, in which case we have for the prototype signals $z_n(t) = s_n(t), n = 1 \ldots M = 2^{m/2}$ given by $z_n(t) = s_n(t) = a_n g_T(t - nT)$.

4.5 Linearisation of Power Amplifiers

4.5.1 The Linearisation Problem

A major problem with bandwidth efficient QAM schemes is that their performance is strongly dependent on the linearity of the transmission system. The system designer is faced with the choice of

(1) using a low-efficiency linear class-A amplifier,

(2) opting for Feher's non-linear amplification principle [15] relying on separate amplifiers for all amplitude levels, or

(3) deploying a power-efficient, weakly non-linear (NL) amplifier and use linearisation techniques to minimise the power amplifier's out-of-band emission and produce a waveform which can be accurately demodulated. Techniques for achieving this include active biasing

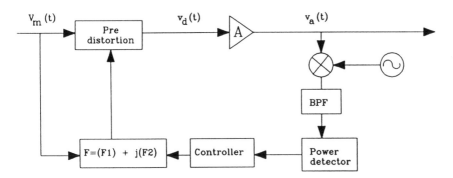

Figure 4.24: Basic Predistorter Block Diagram [21] ©IEEE, 1992, Stapleton et al

[16], the feed-forward method [17], the LINC technique [18], negative feedback [19, 20], predistortion [21, 22, 23] or postdistortion [24].

4.5.2 Linearisation by Predistortion[21]

4.5.2.1 The Predistortion Concept

This subsection concentrates on linearisation by predistortion following the approach proposed by Stapleton et al [21, 22, 23], [26]–[30] whereby a slowly adapting predistorter is used [21] to minimise the out-of-band spectral spillage due to power amplifier non-linear (NL) distortions. The simplest method would be to use a non-linear device in front of the power amplifier to produce intermodulation products in anti-phase to those of the amplifier in an open-loop configuration. However, this will not adapt to varying transmitter characteristics and needs to be set individually for each amplifier. Instead we use a slowly adapting feedback system, which is shown in Figure 4.24. This method monitors the out-of-band power produced by the non-linear amplifier (NLA) and adjusts the predistorter's parameters to minimise it.

As seen in this figure, the predistorter creates the distorted signal $v_d(t)$ from the undistorted modulated signal $v_m(t)$. Upon inputting

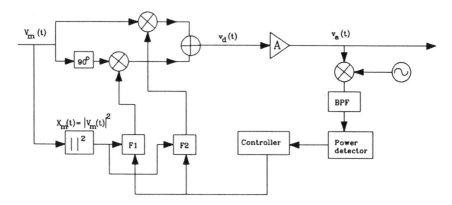

Figure 4.25: Detailed   Predistorter   Block   Diagram   [21]
©IEEE, 1992, Stapleton et al

this signal to the amplifier A, its output signal is given by $v_a(t)$. The adaptive feedback path down-converts the bandpass amplifier's output signal, which is then bandpass filtered (BPF) to separate the out-of-band (OOB) signal power from the wanted signal. The OOB signal power is then averaged by the power detector and used by the controller to adjust the predistorter's complex transfer characteristic to minimise the OOB power.

4.5.2.2   Predistorter Description

Based on the above concept Stapleton et. al. have shown [21] that using the in-phase and quadrature-phase second-order non-linear functions, F_1 and F_2, which are derived from the envelope of the predistorter's input signal $v_m(t)$, the inverse functions of the power amplifier's amplitude and phase responses can be interpolated. The predistorted signal $v_d(t)$ is derived by multiplying the I and Q components of the modulated signal $v_m(t)$ with the second-order non-linear functions F_1 and F_2, as portrayed in Figure 4.25. The magnitude and phase characteristics of a typical class–AB amplifier are depicted in Figure 4.26 as a function of the input power. Observe

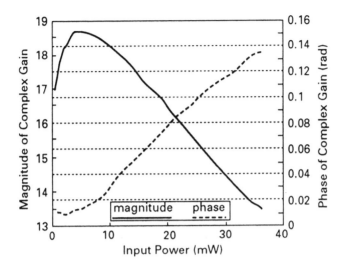

Figure 4.26: Magnitude and phase versus input power for a typical class AB amplifier [21] ©IEEE, 1992, Stapleton et al

the diagrammatic gain and phase variations due to the input power fluctuations. These amplitude characteristics, which depend exclusively on the input power level, must be linearised. It follows that the 2nd order functions F_1 and F_2 will also only have to depend on the magnitude of the modulated signal, i.e. on $x_m(t) = |v_m(t)|^2$, as shown below:

$$F_1\{x_m(t)\} = a_{11} + a_{13}x_m(t) + a_{15}x_m^2(t)$$
$$F_2\{x_m(t)\} = a_{21} + a_{23}x_m(t) + a_{25}x_m^2(t). \qquad (4.39)$$

Note that the coefficient indices have been chosen for later notational convenience. Observe also that the scalar gains a_{11} and a_{21} linearly weight the I and Q components, without introducing any dependency on $v_m(t)$.

The in-phase and quadrature-phase weighting functions F_1 and F_2 allow us to express the predistorter's complex gain as:

$$F\{x_m(t)\} = F_1\{x_m(t)\} + jF_2\{x_m(t)\}$$
$$= a_{11} + ja_{21} + (a_{13} + ja_{23})x_m(t) + (a_{15} + ja_{25})x_m^2(t)$$

$$= a_1 + a_3 x_m(t) + a_5 x_m{}^2(t), \tag{4.40}$$

where the complex coefficients are given below:

$$\begin{aligned}
a_1 &= a_{11} + j a_{21} \\
a_3 &= a_{13} + j a_{23} \\
a_5 &= a_{15} + j a_{25}.
\end{aligned} \tag{4.41}$$

Using the predistorter's complex transfer function F in Equation 4.40, the predistorted signal $v_d(t)$ is given by:

$$\begin{aligned}
v_d(t) &= v_m(t) F\{x_m(t)\} \tag{4.42}\\
&= a_1 v_m(t) + a_3 v_m(t) x_m(t) + a_5 v_m(t) x_m{}^2(t) \\
&= a_1 v_m(t) + a_3 v_m(t) |v_m(t)|^2 + a_5 v_m(t) |v_m(t)|^4.
\end{aligned}$$

Observe in the above Equation that $v_d(t)$ has a 1st, a 3rd and a 5th order $v_m(t)$-dependent term, which explains the choice of coefficient indices. Therefore, by appropriately choosing the coefficients a_3 and a_5 the amplifier's 3rd and 5th order intermodulation distortion can be reduced.

In a similar approach to our previous deliberations we introduce $x_d(t) = |v_d(t)|^2$ for the envelope of the pre-distorted signal and model the power amplifier also by a simple complex gain expression of the form:

$$G\{x_d(t)\} = G_1\{x_d(t)\} + j G_2\{x_d(t)\} = G\{|v_d(t)|^2\}, \tag{4.43}$$

giving the amplifier's output signal $v_a(t)$ in the following form:

$$v_a(t) = v_d(t) G\{|v_d(t)|^2\}. \tag{4.44}$$

The complex amplifier's gain can be modelled by the following complex power series:

$$G\{x_d(t)\} = g_1 + g_3 x_d(t) + g_5 x_d{}^2(t). \tag{4.45}$$

This simple model allows us to portray the whole system as shown in Figure 4.27. Observe that both $F\{|v_m(t)|^2\}$ and $G\{|v_d(t)|^2\}$ depend only on the power of their input signals, but not on their phases. The

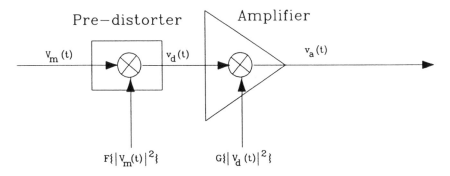

Figure 4.27: Simplified Predistorter Schematic

complex coefficients of G in Equation 4.45 describe both the amplitude modulation to amplitude modulation (AM-AM) and the amplitude modulation to phase modulation (AM-PM) conversion characteristics of the power amplifier.

The system model displayed in Figure 4.27 can be further simplified, as depicted in Figure 4.28, where the overall complex system gain $K\{|v_m(t)|^2\}$ can be derived as follows. First the amplifier's output signal is expressed as:

$$\begin{aligned} v_a(t) &= v_d(t).G\{x_d(t)\} \\ &= v_m(t).F\{x_m(t)\}.G\{x_m(t).|F[x_m(t)]|^2\}, \qquad (4.46) \end{aligned}$$

where we exploited the relationships that $x_d(t) = x_m(t).|F\{x_m(t)\}|^2$ and $v_d = v_m.F\{x_m(t)\}$. From Equation 4.46 the complex system gain is given by:

$$K\{|v_m(t)|^2\} = \frac{v_a(t)}{v_m(t)} = F\{x_m(t)\}.G\{x_m(t).|F[x_m(t)]|^2\}. \qquad (4.47)$$

Similarly to the amplifier, the whole system can be modelled by a complex power series, truncated after the 5th order term, given by:

$$\begin{aligned} K\{x_m(t)\} &= K_1\{x_m(t)\} + jK_2\{x_m(t)\} \\ &= k_1 + k_3 x_m(t) + k_5 x_m{}^2(t). \qquad (4.48) \end{aligned}$$

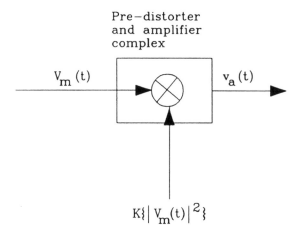

Figure 4.28: Block Diagram of Predistorter and Amplifier Complex

Then, in accordance with Equation 4.42 we can write:

$$\begin{aligned}
v_a(t) &= v_m(t)K\{x_m(t)\} \\
&= k_1 + k_3 v_m(t)x_m(t) + k_5 v_m(t)x_m{}^2(t) \qquad (4.49) \\
&= k_1 + k_3 v_m(t)|v_m(t)|^2 + k_5 v_m(t)|v_m(t)|^4,
\end{aligned}$$

which shows the 3rd and 5th order dependence of $v_a(t)$ on $v_m(t)$.

The computation of the coefficients k_1, k_3 and k_5 proceeds by equating the right hand sides of Equations 4.47 and 4.48 and substituting the appropriate expressions for $F\{\ \}$ and $G\{\ \}$ to yield:

$$k_1 + k_3 x_m(t) + k_5 x_m{}^2(t)$$
$$= [a_1 + a_3 x_m(t) + a_5 x_m{}^2(t)][g_1 + g_3 x_m(t)|F\{x_m(t)\}|^2$$
$$+ g_5 x_m{}^2(t)|F\{x_m(t)\}|^4]. \qquad (4.50)$$

Performing the required multiplications gives:

$$k_1 + k_3 x_m(t) + k_5 x_m{}^2(t)$$
$$= [a_1 + a_3 x_m(t) + a_5 x_m{}^2(t)][g_1 + g_3 x_m(t)|a_1 + a_3 x_m(t) +$$
$$a_5 x_m{}^2(t)|^2 + g_5 x_m{}^2(t)|a_1 + a_3 x_m(t) + a_5 x_m{}^2(t)|^4].$$

$$(4.51)$$

After collecting the 0, 1st and 2nd order terms of $x_m(t)$ on the right hand side of Equation 4.51 we get the following relationships:

$$
\begin{aligned}
k_1 &= a_1 g_1 \\
k_3 &= a_3 g_1 + a_1 g_3 |a_1|^2 \\
k_5 &= a_5 g_1 + a_3 g_3 |a_1|^2 + a_1 g_5 |a_1|^4 + 2a_1 g_3 Re\{a_1 a_3^*\}.
\end{aligned}
\tag{4.52}
$$

Observe that the 3rd order distortion depends on the a_1 and a_3 coefficients of the pre-distorter (PD), while the 5th order distortion can be controlled by a_1, a_3 and a_5. This suggests that both the 3rd and 5th order intermodulation products can be efficiently reduced by the appropriate choice of the coefficients a_1, a_3 and a_5.

4.5.2.3 Predistorter Coefficient Adjustment

The multiplicative second-order non-linear functions F_1 and F_2 to be used by the pre-distorter are derived from the amplifier's AM-AM and AM-PM characteristics. A specific 5 W class–AB amplifier's characteristics operating in the 800 MHz frequency band have been measured by Stapleton et al. [21] and are shown in Figure 4.29. The inverses of these characteristics are the required F_1 and F_2 non-linear functions, which can be inspected in Figure 4.30 along with the minimum mean squared error (mmse) fitted second-order curves. The exact coefficients for the initial F_1 and F_2 functions for this particular amplifier were provided by Stapleton et. al. [21]:

$$
\begin{aligned}
F_1\{x_m(t)\} &= 0.58315 - 0.08498 x_m(t) + 0.05169 x_m^2(t) \\
F_2\{x_m(t)\} &= -0.00395 + 0.0214 x_m(t) - 0.01887 x_m^2(t).
\end{aligned}
\tag{4.53}
$$

These coefficients represent the initial values for the adaptive system. The functions F_1 and F_2 can be implemented for example by the help of operational amplifiers and linear four-quadrant multipliers, using the block diagram of Figure 4.31, where $F\{x_m^2(t)\} = a_1 + x_m^2(t)[a_3 + a_5 x_m^2(t)]$. The function $x_m(t) = |v_m(t)|^2$ can be realised by means of an envelope detector, which must exhibit good linearity across the range of input signal magnitudes.

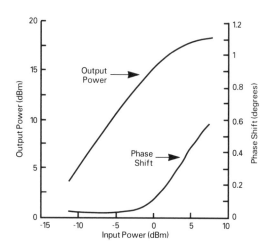

Figure 4.29: AM-AM and AM-PM Characteristics of Class–
AB Power Amplifier [21]©IEEE 1992, Stapleton
et al

The adaptive PD coefficient adjustment is based on measuring the
OOB signal power at the frequency of the 3rd and 5th upper harmonics. To render this power measurement practical, the output signal
of the power amplifier (PA) must be down-converted to a frequency,
where the 3rd and 5th harmonics can be filtered out. The power of
these components must be measured by a peak power-detector and
then averaged. As seen in Figure 4.24, the power detector's output
drives the predistorter's controller, which adjusts the coefficients a_1,
a_3 and a_5 adaptively to minimise the OOB signal power and hence
minimise the detrimental effects of the non-linearity of the power
amplifier (PA).

4.5.2.4   Predistorter Performance

In general the choice of a specific minimisation algorithm will depend on the initial convergence, tracking accuracy and computational complexity requirements. In our application the initial conver-

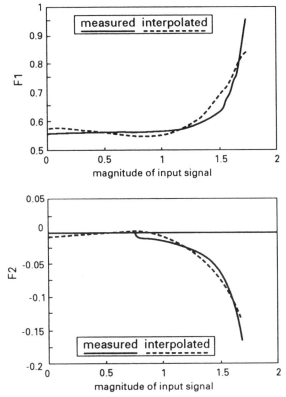

Figure 4.30: Interpolated F_1 and F_2 Functions [21]©IEEE 1992, Stapleton et al

gence requirement is not particularly crucial, but low complexity and good tracking accuracy are desirable. Direct search algorithms, such as the Hooke-Jeeve method [25] are attractive in terms of both low complexity and high noise immunity, but converge generally more slowly than gradient techniques.

Stapleton et al. [31] studied the performances of three different coefficient PD adaptation methods, namely, that of the Hook-Jeeve direct search technique, the Steepest Descent (SD) gradient algorithm [25] and the Davidson–Fletcher–Powell (DFP) surface-fit method [25]. Their convergence results are displayed in Figure 4.32. As demonstrated by the figure, the DFP method has the fastest convergence at somewhat higher computational complexity. The initial convergence of the SD algorithm appears to be identical to that of the DFP method. However, after the rapid initial intermodulation

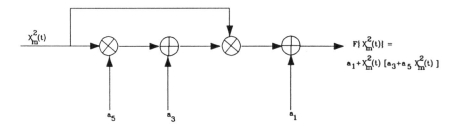

Figure 4.31: F-function implementation [21] ©IEEE, 1992,
Stapleton et al

decay its performance gradually tails off, exhibiting finally similar tracking performance to its other two counterparts.

The overall performance of the predistorter can be characterised by the spectral plot of Figure 4.33 [31], where the PA's input spectrum was plotted along with its output spectrum both with and without the PD. In the underlying experiment the previously portrayed 5 W class–AB amplifier was used with a back-off power of 6 dB. The modulated signal was generated by a 64 kbps 16–QAM modem having a tight roll-off factor of $\alpha = 0.33$. The spectrally compact sharp roll-off yields slow impulse response decay and increased ISI sensitivity. The PD coefficients were adjusted using the DFP method and the spectrum depicted was generated after a convergence time of 9.6 sec.

In conclusion, predistortion is an efficient technique to reduce the non-linear power amplifier's intermodulation distortion and hence out-of-band spectral spillage, which appears in adjacent channels in frequency division multiplex systems. Stapleton et al. demonstrated that the out-of-band emissions of a specific 5 W class–AB amplifier deployed in a 16–QAM system can be reduced by some 10 dB, while maintaining high power efficiency in the amplifier. The complexity of the predistorter is moderate.

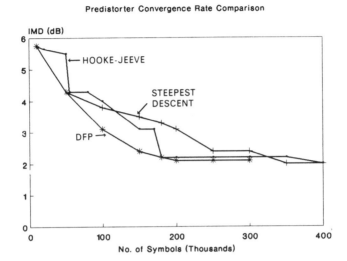

Figure 4.32: Predistorter Convergence Rate Comparison [31]©IEEE 1992, Stapleton et al

4.5.3 Postdistortion of NLA-QAM[33]

4.5.3.1 The Postdistortion Concept

In the previous section we considered cancelling the 3rd and 5th order OOB intermodulation distortions (IMD) of non-linearly amplified (NLA) QAM signals by predistortion. The OOB spectral spillage was reduced by about 15 dB, when using a power-efficient class-AB power amplifier. However, the predistorter's complexity and power consumption is not negligible.

It may prove more attractive to relax the OOB emission requirement, for instance, from -60 dBc to -45 dBc and remove the resulting unwanted adjacent channel interference at the base station (BS). This eliminates the predistorter in front of the QAM modulator and hence reduces the complexity of the hand-held mobile station (MS). The undesirable IMD is reduced at the BS by a postdistorter. The BS transmits the signal to the receiving MS using power-inefficient class-A linear amplification, since the BS's complexity and power

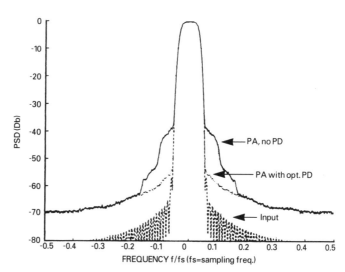

Figure 4.33: Simulated Power Spectrum after DFP Optimization of PD coefficients [31]©IEEE 1992

consumption constitutes a less severe limitation than that of the MS, and so no post-distortion is required in the mobile.

Best IMD cancellation is achieved using an adaptive postdistorter, which accounts for time-variant IMD caused by amplifier aging, supply voltage variations, temperature fluctuations or other slowly drifting time-variant IMD sources. The basic principle of the postdistorter is fairly similar to that of the predistorter, in that the AM-AM and AM-PM non-linearities of the power amplifier are adaptively measured and compensated. The postdistorter measures the envelope of the received signal and generates a non-linear signal, which models the MS power amplifier's 3rd and 5th order IMD. Then the postdistorter's output signal is subtracted from the distorted QAM signal in order to cancel the IMD and hence the adjacent channel interference is significantly reduced.

The block diagram of a three-channel, QAM-based, frequency division multiple access (FDMA) scheme is depicted in Figure 4.34. The non-linearly amplified (NLA) QAM signals of three adjacent channels having carrier frequencies of f_1, f_2 and f_3 are received by the BS. Due to the power-efficient class-AB or class-B amplification

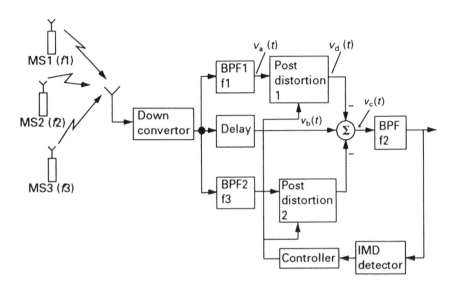

Figure 4.34: QAM-based Three-channel FDM Mobile Radio System using Postdistortion [33] ©IEEE, 1993, Quach et al

at the MSs, channels 1 and 3 spill their 3rd and 5th order intermodulation distortions into the adjacent channel 2. The postdistorter's coefficients are initially adjusted to cancel the typical average 3rd and 5th order IMD. Then their spectral spillage into channel 2 is measured by the IMD detector during channel 2's idle periods and the postdistorter coefficients are adaptively adjusted to minimise the IMD.

In this simple 3-channel scheme only two adjacent channels can spill IMD into channel 2's band. If, however, there are more channels and their 3rd or 5th order IMD falls into channel 2, the schematic of Figure 4.34 should be extended to reduce their spillage as well. The down-converted received signal is filtered by the band-pass filters BPF1 and BPF2 to pass only channel 1's signal to Postdistorter 1 and that of channel 3 to Postdistorter 2. The Delay block is provided to account for the processing delays of the BPFs and Postdistorters and to pass the received composite signal to the "distortion canceller" block, which is denoted by Σ. The postdistorted channel 1 and channel 3 signals are subtracted from the received composite signal and the "clean" channel 2 signal is band-pass filtered to remove any vestige of its OOB components.

Adaptive coefficient update can be introduced to counteract the slow IMD variations due to aging, temperature fluctuations, etc. The IMD Detector senses the OOB spillage of channel 1 and channel 3 into channel 2 during idle intervals of channel 2 and the Controller adaptively adjusts the postdistorter's coefficients to minimise the IMD.

4.5.3.2   Postdistorter Description

Similarly to the previously described pre-distorter, the postdistorter uses a memoryless, non-linear function to model the power amplifier's non-linearity. Using the postdistorter's input and output signal, $v_a(t)$ and $v_d(t)$, respectively, we have:

$$v_d(t) = v_a(t)F(|v_a(t)|^2),   \qquad (4.54)$$

where $F(|v_a(t)|^2)$ is the postdistorter's transfer function. Since we want to cancel the 3rd and 5th order IMDs, we assume that $v_d(t)$ is a 5th order function of the input signal $v_a(t)$. The postdistorter's transfer function $F(\ )$ is a second-order function of the envelope of $v_a(t)$, i.e., that of $x_a(t) = |v_a(t)|^2$, as given below:

$$
\begin{aligned}
F(|v_a(t)|^2) &= a_1 + a_3|v_a(t)|^2 + a_5(|v_a(t)|^2)^2 \\
&= a_1 + a_3 x_a(t) + a_5 x_a^2(t),   \qquad (4.55)
\end{aligned}
$$

where the coefficients a_1, a_3 and a_5 are complex. Then the postdistorter's output signal $v_d(t)$ will be a 5th order function of $v_a(t)$, as seen in Equation 4.56 below:

$$
\begin{aligned}
v_d(t) &= v_a(t)F(|v_a(t)|^2) \\
&= a_1 v_a(t) + a_3 v_a(t)|v_a(t)|^2 + a_5 v_a(t)|v_a(t)|^4.   \qquad (4.56)
\end{aligned}
$$

Again, similarly to the predistorter, the postdistorter's complex gain $F(\ )$ can be expressed as a function of the in-phase and quadrature-phase distortion functions as follows:

$$F[x_a(t)] = F_1[x_a(t)] + jF_2[x_a(t)].   \qquad (4.57)$$

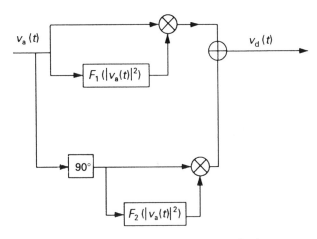

Figure 4.35: Postdistorter Block Diagram [33] ©IEEE, 1993, Quach et al

The inphase and quadrature phase components of the amplified signal $v_a(t)$ are multiplied by the corresponding $v_a(t)$-dependent nonlinear functions $F_1(|v_a(t)|^2)$ and $F_2(|v_a(t)|^2)$, respectively in order to form the complex signal $v_d(t)$ which is also reflected by Figure 4.35. The non-linearly class-AB or class-B amplified signal's expression is given by

$$v_a(t) = v_m(t)G[|v_m(t)|^2], \qquad (4.58)$$

where $v_m(t)$ is the modulated signal and $G[|v_m(t)|^2]$ is the non-linear class-AB power amplifier's complex gain, which is assumed to be a quadratic non-linear function of the envelope $x_m(t) = |v_m(t)|^2$. Then we have:

$$\begin{aligned} G[x_m(t)] &= g_1 + g_3 x_m(t) + g_5 x_m{}^2(t) \\ &= g_1 + g_3|v_m(t)|^2 + g_5|v_m(t)|^4. \end{aligned} \qquad (4.59)$$

Similarly to the predistorter we can define the complex system transfer function

$$\begin{aligned} K[|v_m(t)|^2] &= \frac{v_d(t)}{v_m(t)} \\ &= K_1[|v_m(t)|^2] + jK_2[|v_m(t)|^2] \\ &= k_1 + k_3 x_m(t) + k_5 x_m{}^2(t) \end{aligned}$$

$$= k_1 + k_3|v_m(t)|^2 + k_5|v_m(t)|^4.$$

$$(4.60)$$

Using Equations 4.56 and 4.58 we then get:

$$
\begin{aligned}
K[|v_m(t)|^2] &= \frac{v_a(t)F[|v_a(t)|^2]}{v_m(t)} \\
&= G[|v_m(t)|^2].F\left\{|v_m(t)G[|v_m(t)|^2]|^2\right\} \\
&= G[x_m(t)]F\{x_m(t).|G[x_m(t)]|^2\}, \quad (4.61)
\end{aligned}
$$

which has the reciprocal structure of the predistorter's complex transfer function given in Equation 4.47. Therefore the coefficients k_1, k_3 and k_5 of $K[|v_m(t)|^2]$ are obtained by interchanging a_i with g_i, $i = 1, 3, 5$ in Equation 4.52 yielding:

$$
\begin{aligned}
k_1 &= g_1 a_1 \\
k_3 &= g_3 a_1 + g_1 a_3 |g_1|^2 \\
k_5 &= g_5 a_1 + g_3 a_3 |g_1|^2 + g_1 a_5 |g_1|^4 + 2 g_1 a_3 Re\{g_1 g_3{}^*\},
\end{aligned}
$$

$$(4.62)$$

where * means the complex conjugate.

From Figure 4.34 we see that the IMD cancellation is carried out by subtracting the OOB IMD components of channel 1 and channel 3 from the delayed composite signal $v_b(t)$. Considering channel 1's IMD only, we obtain the "cleaned" signal $v_c(t)$ as follows:

$$v_c(t) = v_b(t) - v_d(t) = v_a(t) - v_d(t), \quad (4.63)$$

where we exploited that, apart from a delay component, $v_b(t) = v_a(t)$. Cancelling the IMD produced by channel 3 can be carried out in the same way, as specified by Equation 4.63. When substituting $v_a(t)$ from Equations 4.58 and $v_d(t) = K[|v_m(t)|^2].v_m(t)$ from Equation 4.60 into Equation 4.63 we have:

$$
\begin{aligned}
v_c(t) &= G[|v_m(t)|^2]v_m(t) - K[|v_m(t)|^2]v_m(t) \\
&= \{G[|v_m(t)|^2] - K[|v_m(t)|^2]\} v_m(t) \\
&= [(g_1 - k_1) + (g_3 - k_3)|v_m(t)|^2 + (g_5 - k_5)|v_m(t)|^4]v_m(t)
\end{aligned}
$$

$$(4.64)$$

Substituting the coefficients k_1, k_3 and k_5 from Equation 4.62 into Equation 4.64 the OOB spectral spillage into channel 2's band due to channel 1's IMD can be reduced by minimising the 3rd and 5th order coefficients of Equation 4.64, which are given below:

$$\begin{aligned}
(g_3 - k_3) &= g_3 - (g_3 a_1 + g_1 a_3 |g_1|^2) \\
(g_5 - k_5) &= g_5 - (g_5 a_1 + g_3 a_3 |g_1|^2 + g_1 a_5 |g_1|^4 + \\
&\quad 2g_1 a_3 Re\{g_1 g_3^*\})
\end{aligned}$$
(4.65)

Since the linear term $(g_1 - k_1)v_m(t)$ is due to channel 1's desired signal, it is outside of the bandwidth of BPF2, and therefore $(g_1 - k_1)$ can be set to any arbitrary value, it will be removed by BPF2. The remaining two terms, $(g_3 - k_3)$ and $(g_5 - k_5)$, must be minimised by appropriately choosing the post-distorter coefficients a_1, a_3 and a_5.

4.5.3.3 Postdistorter Coefficient Adaptation

Stapleton and Le Quach have shown [24] that the average OOB IMD power is a parabolic function of the postdistorter coefficients a_3 and a_5 and hence it has a global minimum, which can be located by optimisation algorithms. The initial setting of the postdistorter coefficients can be obtained by Least Squares Fitting (LSF) of the second order non-linear functions F_1 and F_2 to model the power amplifier's AM-AM an AM-PM characteristics, as described earlier in Section 4.5.2.3, in the context of the predistorter. This initial set-up can be significantly improved by optimisation methods, such as the Hook-Jeeve algorithm [25], as also proposed for the predistorter's optimisation in Section 4.5.2.3.

4.5.3.4 Postdistorter Performance

Stapleton and Le Quach [24] evaluated the adjacent channel's IMD rejection of a three-channel 16-QAM system with and without postdistortion by means of simulations. Their results are presented in Figure 4.36 for the following scenarios:

1. Without postdistortion.

2. With postdistortion using LSF coefficients.

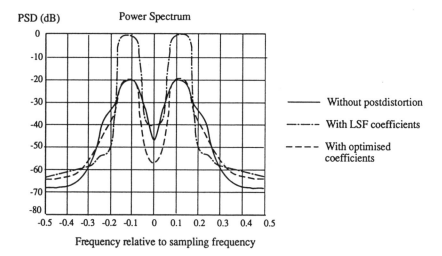

Figure 4.36: Power Spectra of a Postdistortion System with Optimal Coefficients, Channel 2 is Idle [24]©IEEE 1992, Stapleton et al

3. With Hook-Jeeves optimisation.

Observe the significant OOB IMD reduction in the idle channel 2 band from an average of about -40 dB to about -55 dB.

In summary, similarly to the predistorter, the postdistorter also offers significant out-of-band intermodulation distortion reduction, when using non-linear power amplifiers for QAM transmissions. Its performance and complexity is comparable to that of the predistorter, but it is incorporated into the BS, where its additional cost, complexity and power consumption is more readily justified than in the portable station.

Having considered a variety of QAM constellations, along with some pulse shaping and amplification techniques, we now focus our attention on differential versus non-differential QAM transmissions.

4.6 Non-differential coding for square QAM

When using a multi-level modulation scheme, it is necessary to map the binary bit stream to be transmitted onto the constellation in an optimal manner. Typically, each of the M constellation points is assigned an N bit code, where $M = 2^N$. The binary input stream is passed through an N bit serial-to-parallel convertor and the appropriate constellation point transmitted. The mapping of the data onto the constellation is generally not made in a haphazard fashion, but so as to minimise the number of bit errors given a symbol error. That is, if an incorrect symbol is received, composed of N bits, it is required that the number of bits in error be as small as possible. Since errors are most likely to be made to neighbouring symbol points this suggests that Gray coding should be employed, whereby the code for each constellation point only differs by one bit from any of its closest neighbours.

An example of an optimally coded 16-level QAM constellation is given in Figure 4.37, where two bits are Gray encoded onto the I axis and two onto the Q. Assuming that only one bit error occurs per symbol, which is the most likely form of error, we have that

$$P_{E^B} = \frac{1}{N} P_{E^S} \tag{4.66}$$

where P_{E^B} and P_{E^S} are the probability of bit error and of symbol error, respectively. With some constellations, it is not possible to have perfect Gray coding, (e.g. circular QAM with four points on the inner ring and eight on the outer [32]), and in this case the right hand side of the above equation must be multiplied by the Gray coding penalty, $g > 1$, to reflect this coding problem.

4.7 Differential coding for square QAM

A problem which arises in conjunction with most practical QAM constellations is that the receiver is unable to resolve a number of possible carrier lock positions without additional information from the transmitter. This problem was considered by Weber [32] and we follow his approach here. We define an L-fold rotationally symmetric constellation as a signal set for which the phasor constellation maps onto itself for a rotation of $\pm K \cdot (2\pi/L)$ radians where K and L are integers. Then, given $M = 2^N$ constellation points, the receiver cannot uniquely assign the N bits to each constellation point without resolving the L-fold ambiguity.

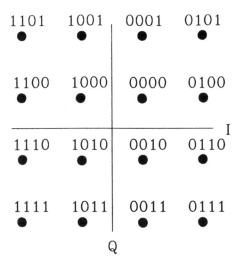

Figure 4.37: Perfect Gray coded 16-level QAM constellation

Weber suggested that a general algorithm for differentially encoding an arbitrary constellation, where $L = 2^I$, I integer, was to:

1) Divide the signal space into L equal pie-shaped sectors, and differentially Gray encode the identifiers of these sectors in a rotational manner. For example, in case of square 16-QAM the $L = 2^2 = 4$ pie-shaped sectors have a 90 degree angle, and are encoded by the identifiers 00, 01, 11, 10 sequentially when rotating around the constellation.

2) Gray encode the remaining $(N - I)$ bits within each sector. For our 16-QAM example $(N - I) = 2$ bits belonging to the same quarter of the constellation will be Gray-coded by assigning codes of 00 and 11 as well as 01 and 10 to opposite corners of a square. This will allow closest neighbours to differ only in one bit position.

This process has the advantage of differentially encoding as few of the bits as possible, which results in the best performance, by keeping error propagation to a minimum.

If it is assumed that the SNR is sufficiently high that errors are only made to neighbouring symbols then the penalty through using Gray coding can be readily computed. There are now two forms of errors, those within sectors and those between symbols in different sectors. For the former there will be no differential coding penalty, as differential coding has not been used within a sector. There may be a Gray coding penalty, depending on whether perfect Gray coding was possible. When a sector boundary is crossed, a minimum of two bit errors, one in each of two consecutive symbols due to the comparisons used in the differential decoding process, will result. Further errors may result if the sector identifier's Gray coding was such that it was not perfect across boundaries. This can be represented by a Gray coding penalty for boundary symbols. In order to derive a general formula representing this we form the following equation

$$P_{EB}(diff\ encoded) = F.P_{EB}(non\ diff) \qquad (4.67)$$

where F is the relative performance of the differentially coded system to the non-differentially coded system. For the non-differentially coded case the general relationship between bit and symbol errors is given by

$$P_{EB}(non\ diff) = \frac{g}{N}P_{ES} \qquad (4.68)$$

where g is the Gray coding penalty representing the average number of bits in error per symbol error, where only errors between adjacent symbols are considered. A similar expression for the differentially encoded non-ideal Gray coding case is

$$P_{EB}(diff\ encoded) = \frac{f}{N}P_{ES} \qquad (4.69)$$

where f is the differentially encoded Gray penalty. The penalty for differentially encoding a particular signal set is then given by

$$F = \frac{f}{g}. \qquad (4.70)$$

Weber suggests the following algorithm for finding f, which is demonstrated with reference to the square QAM constellation of Figure 4.38.

(a) Within a single sector draw lines between symbol point pairs separated by δ_{min} and let the total number of these lines by N_1.

(b) Write the Hamming distance i.e. the number of bits which differ between the two signal points, next to each line, and let the sum of all the Hamming distances within one sector be H_1.

(c) Draw lines between adjacent constellation points separated by δ_{min} and lying on opposite sides of the sector border, and let the number of these lines be N_2 and the sum of their Hamming distances be H_2.

(d) The differential coding penalty is then given by

$$f = \frac{H_1 + H_2 + 2N_2}{N_1 + N_2} \tag{4.71}$$

where the weighting factor of two of the third term in the numerator is due to error propagation in the differentially encoded bits. Note that $g = H_1/N_1$ is the Gray coding penalty within a sector, whereas H_2/N_2 is the Gray coding penalty across a sector.

In order to augment our exposition, an example showing the application of these steps to rectangular 16-level QAM is given in Figure 4.38. From the figure it can be seen that $N_1 = 4$ and $H_1 = 4$ whilst $N_2 = 2$ and $H_2 = 2$, implying that $g = 1$ and therefore there is no Gray coding penalty with this constellation. Because of this $F = f$ and we have that $F = (4+2+4)/(4+2) = 1.67$, or 2.22dB. For the general M-level square constellation it can be shown that [32]

$$\begin{aligned}
N_1 &= 2^{N-1} - 2^{N/2} \tag{4.72} \\
H_1 &= 2^{N-1} - 2^{N/2} \\
N_2 &= 2^{N/2-1} \\
H_2 &= \left(\frac{N}{2} - 1\right) 2^{(N/2-1)}
\end{aligned}$$

and since $g = 1$ we have that

$$F = 1 + \frac{N/2}{2^{n/2} - 1}. \tag{4.73}$$

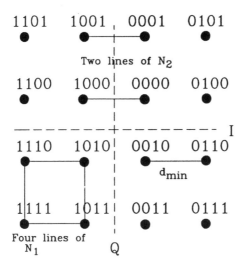

Figure 4.38: Calculating differential coding penalty with a square constellation

Because only two bits are ever required for differential coding of the four sectors, the coding penalty drops as the number of bits increases, from 2 (3dB) for N=2 (QPSK) to nearly 1 (0dB) for higher order systems.

A further problem arises when offset QAM (O-QAM) is employed as not only must the L-fold rotational ambiguity be resolved, but it is also necessary to determine which axis is delayed relative to the other. Weber proposed overcoming this ambiguity by encoding the I and Q channel transitions independently using separate differential coding systems so that now all bits are being differentially encoded. This will lead to a pattern of I bits and then Q bits, alternating. It will, therefore be of no importance which axis is staggered with relation to the other as they are now treated independently. This will increase the differential coding penalty to the full 3dB, and is an argument against using O-QAM as compared to QAM.

4.8   Summary

In this Chapter we have deepened our knowledge as regards to general QAM signal processing techniques. After a brief discourse on various QAM constellations for different channels we have analytically derived the transfer functions of the optimum transmitter and receiver filters. Both of these filters must retain a square root Nyquist shape in order to minimise the ISI and maximise the noise immunity. Various methods of generating QAM signals have been proposed and techniques of QAM detection, such as threshold detection, matched filtering and the correlation receiver have been reviewed. The Chapter was concluded by a short discussion on differential versus non-differential coding.

Equipped with these QAM techniques in the next Chapter we now consider the bit error rate versus channel SNR performance of 16-QAM and 64-QAM over AWGN channels.

Bibliography

[1] **J.G.Proakis**, "Digital Communications", McGraw Hill 1983.

[2] **J.G.Smith**, "Odd-bit quadrature amplitude shift keying", *IEEE Trans. Comms.*, Vol.COM-23, No.3, March 1975, pp385-389.

[3] **E.Malkamaki**, "Binary and multilevel offset QAM, spectrum efficient modulation schemes for personnal communications", *Proc.Globecom 1992*, pp325-328.

[4] **N.G.Kingsbury**, "Transmit and receive filters for QPSK signals to optimise the performance on linear and hard limited channels", *IEE Proc. Pt.F*, Vol.133, No.4, July 1986, pp345-355.

[5] **H. Nyquist**, "Certain Factors Affecting Telegraph Speed", *BSTJ.*, Apr. 1928, p617

[6] **R.W. Lucky, J. Salz and E.J. Weldon**, "Principles of Data Communication". McGraw-Hill, 1968

[7] **K.Feher**, "Digital communications - satellite/earth station engineering", Prentice Hall 1983.

[8] **K.Sam.Shanmugan**, "Digital and analogue communication systems", John Wiley, 1979.

[9] **K.Miyauchi, S.Seki and H.Ishio**, "New techniques for generating and detecting multilevel signal formats", *IEEE Trans. Comms.*, Vol.COM-24, No.2, Feb 1976, pp263-267.

[10] **D.H.Morais and K.Feher**, "NLA-QAM: A method of generating high power QAM signals through non-linear amplification", *IEEE Trans. Comms.*, Vol.COM-30, No.3, March 1982, pp517-522.

[11] **T.Hill and K.Feher**, "A performance study of NLA 64-state QAM" *IEEE Trans. Comms.* Vol.COM-31, No.6, June 1983, pp821-826.

[12] **B. Sklar**, "Digital Communications", *Prentice Hall*, 1988

[13] **M. Schwartz**, "Information Transmission, Modulation and Noise" *McGraw-Hill*, 1990

[14] **Y. C. Chow, A. R. Nix, J. P. McGeehan**, "Analysis of 16-APSK modulation in AWGN and Rayleigh fading channel", *Electronic Letters* Vol 28, pp 1608-1610, Nov 1992

[15] **K. Feher (Ed.)**, "Advanced Digital Communications", Prentice-Hall, 1987.

[16] **A.A.M. Saleh and D.C. Cox**, "Improving the Power-Added Efficiency of FET Amplifiers Operating with Varying Envelope Signals", *IEEE Tr. on Microwave Theory Tech.*, Vol. MTT-31, pp. 51-56, Jan. 1983.

[17] **D.P. Green**, "Characterisation and Compensation of Nonlinearities in Microwave Transmitters", *IEEE Tr. on Microwave Theory Tech.*, Vol. MTT-30, pp. 213-217, 1982.

[18] **F.J. Casadevall**, "The LINC Transmitter", *RF Design*, pp. 41-48, Febr. 1990.

[19] **Y. Akaiwa and Y. Nagata**, "Highly Efficient Digital Mobile Communications with a Linear Modulation Method", *IEEE JSAC*, vol. SAC-5, pp. 890-895, June 1987.

[20] **A. Bateman, D.M. Haines and R.J. Wilkinson**, "Linear Transceiver Architectures", *Proc. IEEE Veh. Tech. Conf.*, 1988, pp. 478-484

[21] **S.P. Stapleton and F.C. Costescu**, "An Adaptive Predistorter for a Power Amplifier Based on Adjacent Channel Emissions", *IEEE Tr. on Veh. Tech.*, Vol. VT-41. no. 1, pp. 49-56, Febr. 1992.

[22] **S.P.Stapleton, G.S.Kandola and K.Cavers**, "Simulation and analysis of an adaptive predistorter utilizing a complex spectral convolution", *IEEE VT*, Vol.41, No.4, Nov 1992, pp387-395.

[23] **A.S.Wright and W.G.Duntler**, "Experimental performance of an adaptive digital linearised power amplifier", *ibid*, pp395-400.

[24] **S.P. Stapleton and Le Quach**, "Reduction of Adjacent Channel Interference Using Postdistortion", *Proc. of 42nd IEEE Veh. Tech. Conf.*, Denver, Colorado, 10-13 May 1992, pp. 915-918

[25] **B.D. Bunday**, "Basic Optimisation Methods", London, Edward Arnold, 1984

[26] **J.Namiki**, "An Automatically Controlled Predistorter for Multilevel Quadrature Amplitude Modulation", *IEEE Tr. Comm.*, Vol. COM-31, pp. 707-712, May 1983.

[27] **T. Nojima and T. Konno**, "Cuber Predistortion Linearizer for Relay Equipment in the 800 MHz Band Land Mobile Telephone System", *IEEE Tr. on Veh. Tech.*, vol. VT-34, pp. 169-177, Nov. 1985.

[28] **M. Nannicini, P. Magni and F. Oggioni**, "Temperature Controlled Predistortion Circuits for 64 QAM Microwave Power Amplifiers", *IEEE Microwave Theory Tech. Dig.*, 1985, pp. 99-102

[29] **Y. Nagata**, "Linear Amplification Technique for Digital Mobile Communications", *Proc. IEEE Veh. Tech. Conf.*, San Francisco, CA. 1989, pp. 159-164

[30] **A.A.M. Saleh and J. Salz**, "Adaptive Linearization of Power amplifiers in Digital Radio Systems", *Bell Syst. Tech. J.*, Vol. 62. no. 4, pp. 1019-1033, Apr. 1983.

[31] **S.P.Stapleton and F.C.Costesu**, "An adaptive pre-distortion system", *Proc. IEEE VTC'92*, pp690-693.

[32] **W.J.Weber**, "Differential encoding for multiple amplitude and phase shift keying systems", *IEEE Trans. Comms.*, Vol.COM-26, No.3, March 1978, pp385-391.

[33] **L.D.Quach, S.P.Stapleton**, "A post-distortion receiver for mobile communications", *IEEE Tr. on VT.* Vol 42, No4, Nov. 1993, pp 604-616

Chapter 5

Square QAM

In this chapter we consider the transmission and demodulation of square QAM signals over Gaussian channels. The theory of QAM transmissions over Rayleigh fading channels is given in Chapter 10. In order to arrive at explicit BER versus SNR formulae, let us first review a few fundamental results of decision theory.

5.1 Decision Theory

The roots of decision theory stem from Bayes' theorem formulated as follows:

$$P(X/Y) \cdot P(Y) = P(Y/X) \cdot P(X) = P(X,Y), \qquad (5.1)$$

where the random variables X and Y have probabilities of $P(X)$ and $P(Y)$, their joint probability is $P(X,Y)$ and their conditional probabilities are given by $P(X/Y)$ and $P(Y/X)$.

In decision theory the above theorem is invoked in order to infer from the noisy analogue received sample y, what the most likely transmitted symbol was, assuming that the so-called *a-priory* probability $P(x)$ of the transmitted symbols $x_n, n = 1 \ldots M$ is known. Given that the received sample y is encountered at the receiver, the conditional probability $P(x_n/y)$ quantifies the chance that x_n has been transmitted:

$$P(x_n/y) = \frac{P(y/x_n) \cdot P(x_n)}{P(y)}, \qquad n = 1 \ldots N \qquad (5.2)$$

where $P(y/x_n)$ is the conditional probability of the continuous noise sample y, given that $x_n, n = 1 \ldots N$ was transmitted. The probability of encountering a specific y value will be the sum of all possible combinations of receiving y and $x_n, n = 1 \ldots N$ simultaneously, which is given by:

$$P(y) = \sum_{n=1}^{N} P(y/x_n) \cdot P(x_n) = \sum_{n=1}^{N} P(y, x_n). \qquad (5.3)$$

Let us now consider the case of binary phase shift keying (BPSK), where there are two legitimate transmitted wave forms, x_1 and x_2 which are contaminated by noise, as portrayed in Figure 5.1a. The conditional probability of receiving any particular analogue sample y given that x_1 or x_2 was transmitted is quantified by the Gaussian probability density functions (PDFs) seen in Figure 5.1a, which are described by:

$$P(y/x) = \frac{1}{\sigma\sqrt{2\pi}} e^{\frac{-(y-x)^2}{2\sigma^2}}, \qquad (5.4)$$

where $x = x_1$ or x_2 is the mean and σ^2 is the variance. Observe from the Figure that the shaded area represents the probability of receiving values larger than the threshold T_0, when x_1 was transmitted and this is equal to the probability of receiving a value below T_0, when x_2 was transmitted. As displayed in the Figure, when receiving a specific $y = y_0$ sample, there is an ambiguity, as to which symbol was transmitted. The corresponding conditional probabilities are given by $P(y_0/x_1)$, and $P(y_0/x_2)$ and their values are also marked on Figure 5.1a. Given the knowledge that x_1 was transmitted, we are more likely to receive y_0 than on condition that x_2 was transmitted. Hence, upon observing $y = y_0$ statistically speaking it is advisable to decide that x_1 was transmitted. Following similar logic, when receiving y_1 as seen in Figure 5.1a, it is logical to conclude that x_2 was transmitted.

Indeed, according to optimum decision theory [1], the optimum decision threshold above which x_2 is inferred is given by:

$$T_0 = \frac{x_1 + x_2}{2} \qquad (5.5)$$

and below this threshold x_1 is assumed to have been transmitted. If

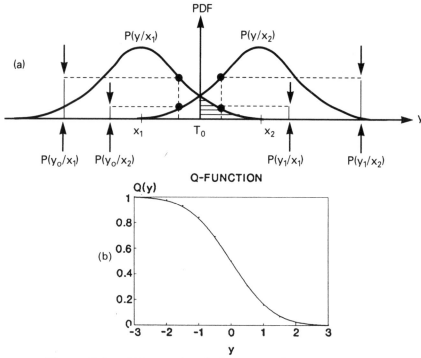

Figure 5.1: a/ Transmitted phasors and noisy received phasors for BPSK, b/ Gaussian Q-function

$x_1 = -x_2$ then $T_0 = 0$ is the optimum decision threshold minimising the bit error probability.

In order to compute the error probability in case of transmitting x_1, the PFD $P(y/x_1)$ of Equation 5.4 has to be integrated from x_1 to ∞, which gives the shaded area under the curve in Figure 5.1a. In other words, the probability of a zero-mean noise sample exceeding the magnitude of x_1 is sought, which is often referred to as *noise protection distance*, given by the so-called Gaussian Q-function:

$$Q(x_1) = \frac{1}{\sigma\sqrt{2\pi}} \int_{x_1}^{\infty} e^{\frac{-y^2}{2\sigma^2}} dy, \qquad (5.6)$$

where σ^2 is the noise variance. Notice that since $Q(x_1)$ is the probability of exceeding the value x_1, it is actually the complementary cumulative density function (CDF) of the Gaussian distribution.

Assuming that $x_1 = -x_2$, the probability that the noise can carry x_1 across $T_0 = 0$ is equal to that of x_2 being corrupted in the negative direction. Hence, assuming that $P(x_1) = P(x_2) = 0.5$, the overall error probability is given by:

$$\begin{aligned} P_e &= P(x_1) \cdot Q(x_1) + P(x_2) \cdot Q(x_2) \\ &= \frac{1}{2}Q(x_1) + \frac{1}{2}Q(x_1) = Q(x_1) \end{aligned} \tag{5.7}$$

The values of the Gaussian Q-function plotted in Figure 5.1b are tabulated in many text-books [1], along with values of the Gaussian PDF in case of zero-mean, unit-variance processes. For abscissa values of $y > 4$ the following approximation can be used:

$$Q(y) \approx \frac{1}{y\sqrt{2\pi}} e^{\frac{-y^2}{2}} \quad \text{for } y > 4. \tag{5.8}$$

Having provided a rudimentary introduction to decision theory, let us now focus our attention on the demodulation of 16-QAM signals in AWGN.

5.2 QAM modulation and transmission

In general the modulated signal can be represented by

$$s(t) = a(t)\cos[2\pi f_c t + \Theta(t)] = Re(a(t)e^{j[w_c t + \Theta(t)]}) \tag{5.9}$$

where the carrier $\cos(w_c t)$ is said to be amplitude modulated if its amplitude $a(t)$ is adjusted in accordance with the modulating signal, and is said to be phase modulated if $\Theta(t)$ is varied in accordance with the modulating signal. In QAM the amplitude of the baseband modulating signal is determined by $a(t)$ and the phase by $\Theta(t)$. The inphase component I is then given by

$$I = a(t)\cos\Theta(t) \tag{5.10}$$

and the quadrature component Q by

$$Q = a(t)\sin\Theta(t). \tag{5.11}$$

This signal is then corrupted by the channel. Here we will only consider AWGN. The received signal is then given by

$$r(t) = a(t)\cos[2\pi f_c t + \Theta(t)] + n(t) \tag{5.12}$$

where $n(t)$ represents the AWGN, which has both an inphase and quadrature component. It is this received signal which we will attempt to demodulate.

5.3   16-QAM Demodulation in AWGN

The demodulation of the received QAM signal is achieved by performing quadrature amplitude demodulations using the decision boundaries seen in Figure 3.3 for the I and Q components, as shown below for the bits i_1 and q_1:

$$\begin{array}{llll}
\text{if} & I, Q \geq 0 & \text{then} & i_1, q_1 = 0 \\
\text{if} & I, Q < 0 & \text{then} & i_1, q_1 = 1
\end{array} \tag{5.13}$$

The decision boundaries for the 3rd and 4th bits i_2 and q_2, respectively, are again shown in Figure 3.3, and thus:

$$\begin{array}{lllll}
\text{if} & & I, Q \geq 2d & \text{then} & i_2, q_2 = 1 \\
\text{if} & -2d \leq & I, Q < 2d & \text{then} & i_2, q_2 = 0 \\
\text{if} & -2d > & I, Q & \text{then} & i_2, q_2 = 1.
\end{array} \tag{5.14}$$

We will show that in the process of demodulation the positions of the bits in the QAM symbols associated with each point in the QAM constellation have an effect on the probability of them being in error. In the case of the two most significant bits (MSBs) of the four bit symbol i_1, q_1, i_2, q_2, i.e. i_1 and q_1, the distance from a demodulation decision boundary of each received phasor in the absence of noise is $3d$ for 50 % of the time, and d for 50 % of the time; if each phasor occurs with equal probability. The average protection distance for these bits is therefore $2d$ although the bit error probability for a protection distance of $2d$ would be dramatically different from that calculated. Indeed, the average protection distance is never encountered, we only use this term to aid our investigations. The two least significant bits (LSB), i.e. i_2 and q_2 are always at a distance of d from the decision boundary and consequently the average protection distance is d. We may consider our QAM system as a class one $(C1)$ and as a class two $(C2)$ subchannel, where bits transmitted via the $C1$ subchannel are received with a lower probability of error than those transmitted via the $C2$ subchannel.

Observe in the phasor diagram of Figure 3.3 that upon demodulation in the $C2$ subchannel, a bit error will occur if the noise exceeds d in one direction or $3d$ in the opposite direction, where the latter probability is insignificant. Hence the $C2$ bit error probability becomes

$$P_{2G} = Q\{\frac{d}{\sqrt{N_0/2}}\} = \frac{1}{\sqrt{2\pi}} \int_{\frac{d}{\sqrt{N_0/2}}}^{\infty} \exp(-x^2/2)dx \qquad (5.15)$$

where $N_0/2$ is the double-sided spectral density of the AWGN, $\sqrt{N_0/2}$ is the corresponding noise voltage, and the $Q\{\}$ function was given in Equation 5.6 and Figure 5.1. As the average symbol energy of the 16-level QAM constellation computed for the phasors in Figure 3.3 is

$$E_0 = 10d^2, \qquad (5.16)$$

then we have that

$$P_{2G} = Q\{\sqrt{\frac{E_0}{5N_0}}\}. \qquad (5.17)$$

For the $C1$ subchannel data the bits i_1, q_1 are at a protection distance of d from the decision boundaries for half the time, and their protection distance is $3d$ for the remaining half of the time. Therefore the probability of a bit error is

$$P_{1G} = \frac{1}{2}Q\{\frac{d}{\sqrt{N_0/2}}\} + \frac{1}{2}Q\{\frac{3d}{\sqrt{N_0/2}}\} = \frac{1}{2}[Q\{\sqrt{\frac{E_0}{5N_0}}\} + Q\{3\sqrt{\frac{E_0}{5N_0}}\}].$$
$$(5.18)$$

The probabilities P_{1G} and P_{2G} as a function of E_0/N_0 are given by Equation 5.17 and 5.18 and displayed in Figure 5.2. Also shown is the average probability P_{AV} of bit error for the 16-level QAM system as

$$P_{AV} = (P_{1G} + P_{2G})/2. \qquad (5.19)$$

Our simulation results gave practically identical curves to those in Figure 5.2, where the AWGN performance is seen to have only a small advantage in using the $C1$ subchannel over using the $C2$.

5.4 64-QAM Demodulation in AWGN

Each constellation point in 64-level QAM (64-QAM) systems is represented by a unique 6-bit symbol, which is Gray-coded to minimise the decoded error probability, as seen in Figure 5.3. The complex

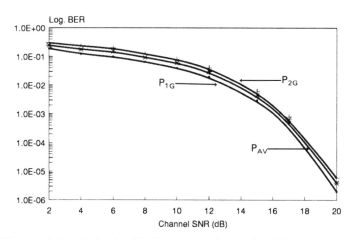

Figure 5.2: 16-QAM BER versus channel SNR curves over AWGN channel

phasors of the constellation are decomposed into the 8-level I and Q components. The amplitudes *7d, 5d, 3d, d, -d, -3d, -5d* and *-7d* of the I and Q *AM* signals are assigned the 3-bit Gray codes *011, 010, 000, 001, 101, 100, 110* and *111*, respectively. The three I and Q bits are denoted by i_1, i_2, i_3 and q_1, q_2, q_3, respectively. These bits are interleaved to give a 6-bit QAM symbol represented by i_1, q_1, i_2, q_2, i_3, q_3. The 64-level QAM phasors are transmitted over the channel, where they become corrupted. They are demodulated using the decision boundaries shown in Figure 5.3. Observe that the construction of the signal constellation is similar to that of a Karnough table, where in the left half plane of the coordinate axis i_1 is always logical 1 and in the bottom half plane q_1 is logical 1, etc. The bits i_1, q_1, i_2, q_2, i_3, q_3, i_4, q_4 are recovered according to

$$\begin{aligned} \text{if} \quad & I, Q \geq 0 \quad \text{then} \quad i_1, q_1 = 0 \\ \text{if} \quad & I, Q < 0 \quad \text{then} \quad i_1, q_1 = 1, \end{aligned} \tag{5.20}$$

for the most significant bits, and

$$\begin{aligned} \text{if} \quad & & I, Q \geq 4d \quad & \text{then} \quad i_2, q_2 = 1 \\ \text{if} \quad -4d \leq & I, Q < 4d \quad & \text{then} \quad i_2, q_2 = 0 \\ \text{if} \quad -4d > & I, Q & & \text{then} \quad i_2, q_2 = 1. \end{aligned} \tag{5.21}$$

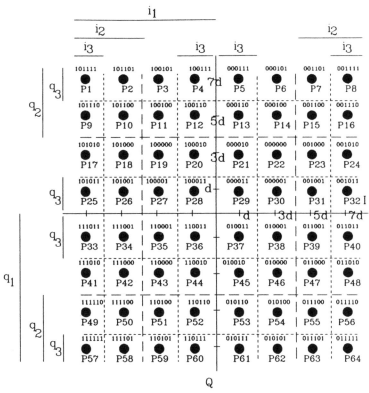

Figure 5.3: Square 64-QAM phasor constellation

- - - - - Class II sub-channel decision boundaries

------------- Class III sub-channel decision boundaries

for the next most significant bits, while finally for the least significant bits

$$
\begin{array}{llllll}
\text{if} & & I, Q & \geq & 6d & \text{then} & i_3, q_3 = 1 \\
\text{if} & 2d \leq & I, Q & < & 6d & \text{then} & i_3, q_3 = 0 \\
\text{if} & -2d \leq & I, Q & < & 2d & \text{then} & i_3, q_3 = 1 \quad (5.22) \\
\text{if} & -6d \leq & I, Q & < & -2d & \text{then} & i_3, q_3 = 0 \\
\text{if} & -6d > & I, Q & & & \text{then} & i_3, q_3 = 1.
\end{array}
$$

Similarly to 16-QAM the position of the bits in the 6-bit QAM symbol has an effect on their error probabilities. In case of the i_1, q_1 bits, for example, the phasor can be at a distance d, *3d*, *5d* or *7d* from the decision boundary represented by the coordinate axis. Therefore their "average protection distance" is $16d/4 = 4d$. Note again that this average protection distance is never encountered and due to the non-linear nature of the $Q\{\}$ function the actual BER will be quite different from that of a $4d$ average distance PSK constellation. Figure 5.3 reveals that this average protection distance for the i_2, q_2 bits is $2d$, while for the i_3, q_3 bits it is d. We may view the bits (i_1, q_1), (i_2, q_2) and (i_3, q_3) as three subchannels each having different integrities. These channels will be referred to as $C1$, $C2$ and $C3$, respectively.

We assume that an independent random data sequence is conveyed to each of the $C1$, $C2$ and $C3$ subchannels, and that perfect coherent detection is carried out at the receiver using Equations 5.20 to 5.22. Let us determine the BER performance of the I component, as the Q component being in quadrature will support data that is subjected to the same BER.

Let us consider first the $C3$ subchannel (i_3, q_3) with its decision boundaries of *-6d*, *-2d*, *2d* and *6d*. Each phasor has a different error probability, depending on its position in the constellation of Figure 5.3. The bit i_3 of phasor P_5 (a logical 1) will, for example, be corrupted, if a noise sample with larger amplitude than d is added to it when the decoded phasor is P_6. This probability is represented by the first term of Equation 5.23. However, when P_5 is carried by a noise vector having larger than $5d$ amplitude over the $C3$ decision boundary at $6d$, the decision becomes error-free again, although the decoded phasor is erroneously considered to be P_8. This is quantified by the third term in Equation 5.23, where the negative sign takes account of the favourable influence of this event on the BER. In the negative direction there is no corruption until the noise amplitude exceeds $-3d$ (phasor P_3) in the negative direction, which has the same probability as exceeding $3d$ in the positive direction, and hence contributes the second term to Equation 5.23. For noise vectors having amplitudes between $-3d$ and $-7d$ there are erroneous decisions. However, once the $-6d$ decision boundary is exceeded, i.e., the negative noise value is larger than $-7d$, the received sample falls into the error-free domain again, although the decoded phasor is P_1 which is reflected by the fourth term of Equation 5.23. The i_3 bit-error probability of the P_5 phasor is then given by the following summation of Q-functions:

$$P_{e5} = Q[\frac{d}{\sqrt{N_0/2}}] + Q[\frac{3d}{\sqrt{N_0/2}}] - Q[\frac{5d}{\sqrt{N_0/2}}] - Q[\frac{7d}{\sqrt{N_0/2}}], \quad (5.23)$$

where $N_0/2$ denotes the double-sided Gaussian noise spectral density and $\sqrt{N_0/2}$ is the corresponding noise voltage. After averaging the powers of the individual phasors $P_1 \ldots P_{64}$ the average symbol energy for $64 - QAM$ is found to be $E = 42d^2$. Substituting $d = \sqrt{E/42}$ into Equation 5.23, and introducing the average SNR $\gamma = E/N_0$, we get:

$$P_{e5} = Q[\sqrt{\frac{\gamma}{21}}] + Q[3\sqrt{\frac{\gamma}{21}}] - Q[5\sqrt{\frac{\gamma}{21}}] - Q[7\sqrt{\frac{\gamma}{21}}]. \quad (5.24)$$

For the phasor P_8 the situation is different, as its $C3$ bit i_3 is not corrupted by positive noise samples of arbitrary large amplitudes. For negative noise levels it cycles in and out of error as the noise increases past -d, -5d, -9d and -13d, as seen in Figure 5.3. Therefore the associated error probability is given by

$$P_{e8} = Q[\sqrt{\frac{\gamma}{21}}] + Q[9\sqrt{\frac{\gamma}{21}}] - Q[5\sqrt{\frac{\gamma}{21}}] - Q[13\sqrt{\frac{\gamma}{21}}]. \quad (5.25)$$

Following a similar argument the error probability P_{e6} of the i_3 bit of phasor P_6 is

$$P_{e6} = Q[\sqrt{\frac{\gamma}{21}}] + Q[3\sqrt{\frac{\gamma}{21}}] - Q[5\sqrt{\frac{\gamma}{21}}] + Q[9\sqrt{\frac{\gamma}{21}}], \quad (5.26)$$

while

$$P_{e7} = Q[\sqrt{\frac{\gamma}{21}}] + Q[3\sqrt{\frac{\gamma}{21}}] - Q[7\sqrt{\frac{\gamma}{21}}] + Q[11\sqrt{\frac{\gamma}{21}}]. \qquad (5.27)$$

The error probabilities P_{e1}, P_{e2}, P_{e3}, P_{e4} are equivalent to those given by P_{e8}, P_{e7}, P_{e6}, P_{e5}, respectively, and the same holds for all corresponding phasors in the columns of the phasor diagram of Figure 5.3. Furthermore, the q_3 bit error probability is identical to that of i_3, if independent random sequences are transmitted. Averaging the $C3$ bit error probabilities yields:

$$P_{C3}(\gamma) = Q[\sqrt{\frac{\gamma}{21}}] + \frac{3}{4}Q[3\sqrt{\frac{\gamma}{21}}] - \frac{3}{4}Q[5\sqrt{\frac{\gamma}{21}}] - \frac{1}{2}Q[7\sqrt{\frac{\gamma}{21}}] \quad (5.28)$$
$$+ \frac{1}{2}Q[9\sqrt{\frac{\gamma}{21}}] + \frac{1}{4}Q[11\sqrt{\frac{\gamma}{21}}] - \frac{1}{4}Q[13\sqrt{\frac{\gamma}{21}}].$$

The last three terms in Equation 5.28 represent extremely unlikely events as the Gaussian noise sample must exceed the $9d$ protection distance of the best protected $C1$ bit. Consequently we neglect these terms.

Applying similar arguments to those used in the formulation of $P_{C3}(\gamma)$, we have the bit error probabilities for $C2$ and $C1$ as

$$P_{C2}(\gamma) = \frac{1}{2}Q[\sqrt{\frac{\gamma}{21}}] + \frac{1}{2}Q[\sqrt{\frac{3\gamma}{21}}] + \frac{1}{4}Q[\sqrt{\frac{5\gamma}{21}}] + \frac{1}{4}Q[\sqrt{\frac{7\gamma}{21}}], \quad (5.29)$$

and

$$P_{C1}(\gamma) = \frac{1}{4}Q[\sqrt{\frac{\gamma}{21}}] + \frac{1}{4}Q[\sqrt{\frac{3\gamma}{21}}] + \frac{1}{4}Q[\sqrt{\frac{5\gamma}{21}}] + \frac{1}{4}Q[\sqrt{\frac{7\gamma}{21}}]. \quad (5.30)$$

The P_{C1}, P_{C2} and P_{C3} error probability curves evaluated using Equations 5.28-5.30 are displayed in Figure 5.4. Our simulation results differed by less than a dB from these curves. Observe from the figure the consistent BER advantage obtained using the $C1$ subchannel. All subchannels have $BERs < 10^{-3}$ for SNR values in excess of 23 dB. They are therefore suitable for example for digitised speech transmission. Notice that for $SNRs$ above 23 dB there is only a modest BER advantage in using the $C1$ subchannel.

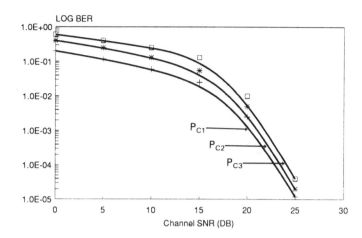

Figure 5.4: Square 64-QAM BER versus channel SNR curves over AWGN channel

As we have seen, both 64-QAM and 16-QAM possess subchannels with different BERs. The subchannel integrities are consistently different and these differences can be used advantageously when transmitting speech and video signals. The most sensitive speech or image bits can be transmitted via the lower BER subchannel, while the more robust source coded bits can be sent over the higher BER subchannel. In certain applications this property is very advantageous, because it might remove the need for complex forward error correction codecs with unequal error protection [2]-[5].

5.5 Summary

In this chapter we have examined the theoretical performance of square QAM transmissions over Gaussian channels. Theoretical calculations showed the presence of different classes of bits with different performance within the constellation, and we will see in Chapter 10 how the relative performance of these bits diverges even further when the constellation is transmitted over mobile radio channels.

In the next chapter we consider some of the practical difficulties of receiving modulated signals by examining clock and carrier recovery

techniques. These are needed to recover the symbol timing and the
carrier phase, respectively.

Bibliography

[1] **B.Sklar**, "Digital communications", *Prentice Hall*, 1988

[2] **L. Hanzo, R. Steele and P.M. Fortune**, "A Subband Coding, BCH Coding and 16-QAM System for Mobile Radio Speech Communications", *IEEE Trans. on Veh. Techn.*, Nov. 1990, Vol 39, No 4, pp 327-340

[3] **L. Hanzo, R. Salami, R. Steele and P.M. Fortune**, "Transmission of Digitally Encoded Speech at 1.2 KBd for PCN", *IEE Proceedings, Part I*, Vol. 139, No.4., Aug 1992, pp 437-447

[4] **R. Stedman, H. Gharavi, L. Hanzo and R. Steele**, "16-QAM Transmission of Sub-band Coded Images via Microcellular Mobile Channels", *IEEE Tr. on Circuits and Systems for Video Technology*, Vol.3, No.1, Feb 1993, pp15-27.

[5] **P.M.Fortune, L.Hanzo and R.Steele**, "On the computation of 16-QAM and 64-QAM performance in Rayleigh fading channels", *IEICE Trans. Comms.*, Vol.E75-B, No.6, June 1992, pp466-475.

Chapter 6

Clock and Carrier Recovery Systems for QAM

6.1 Introduction

Both clock and carrier recovery systems attempt to derive information about timing from the received signal, often in a similar manner. Whilst carrier recovery is only necessary in a coherent demodulation system, clock recovery is required in all schemes, and accurate clock recovery is essential for reliable data transmission. Confusion often exists between clock and carrier recovery. Clock recovery attempts to synchronise the receiver clock with the baseband symbol rate transmitter clock, whereas carrier recovery endeavours to align the receiver local oscillator with the transmitted carrier frequency.

It is not our intention here to give a detailed recount of all clock and carrier recovery schemes, such background information can be found in References [1]-[4]. Instead we describe the particular clock and carrier recovery schemes which have proved suitable for QAM over Gaussian channels. In many cases these are either the same, or modified versions of timing recovery systems which have been used for binary modulation, and in these instances we describe how these schemes have been adapted for QAM. We consider the issue of timing recovery systems for mobile radio transmissions in Chapter 12.

6.2 Clock Recovery

There exists a plethora of different clock recovery techniques. However, many apparently different clock recovery techniques can be shown to be equivalent, and this is not surprising as they must all make use of the properties of the received waveform. Basic clock recovery systems which can be used successfully in conjunction with QAM include times-two, early-late, zero crossing and synchroniser clock recovery systems [1].

We now consider each of these clock recovery systems. We have evaluated the performance of all these systems using computer simulation and found that they all offer similar performance in a Gaussian environment.

6.2.1 Times-two clock recovery

The most fundamental of all clock recovery schemes is the times-two, or squaring system [1]. Typical BPSK data signals often contain sections of repetitive strings of -1,+1,-1,+1,... which after bandlimiting and pulse-shaping has a waveform similar to that shown on the left hand side of Figure 6.1. Observe that this signal has periodic sections having a frequency of half the signalling clock rate. Therefore, if the received demodulated signal is squared, or passed through a non-linear rectifier, then it will possess a periodic frequency domain component at the symbol rate. A bandpass filter tuned close to the symbol rate will extract this periodic signal, allowing derivation of the required timing information. This is shown diagrammatically at baseband for both a binary and a multilevel modulation scheme in Figure 6.1. The times-two clock recovery works best for binary modulation schemes where the -1,+1,-1,+1... sections are frequent and hence the energy of the clock frequency component is high, but not so well for multilevel ones. The reason for this is that the multilevel scheme has a reduced component at the symbol frequency due to the increased possibility of non-zero crossing transitions such as +3,+1,-1.... A schematic of a simple baseband times-two clock recovery system is shown in Figure 6.2 where the clock pulse regenerator could be implemented with a saturating amplifier, leading to

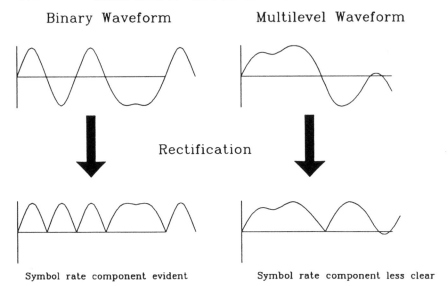

Figure 6.1: Effect of squaring waveforms

a rectangular pulse shape.

6.2.2 Early-late clock recovery

Another well known form of clock recovery is early-late clock recovery [5], which is portrayed in Figure 6.3. Whilst times-two clock recovery exploits the whole of the incoming waveform, early-late clock recovery works on the peaks in the received waveform. The basic assumptions made by the early-late method are that the peaks in the incoming waveform are at the correct sampling points and that these peaks are symmetrical. This is often true, but for some modulation schemes, such as partial response raised cosine arrangements [6], neither of these assumptions is valid. It may still be possible to use early-late clock recovery with these modulation schemes but the timing jitter will be increased.

The early-late scheme of Figure 6.3 firstly squares the incoming signal in order to render all peaks positive, and then takes two samples of the received waveform, both equi-spaced around the predicted sampling instant. If the predicted sampling instant is aligned with the correct sample point, and the assumptions made above are correct, then the sample taken just prior to the sample point - the early

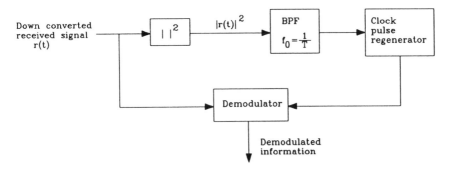

Figure 6.2: Times-two clock recovery schematic

sample - will be identical to the sample taken just after the sampling instant - the late sample. If the early sample is larger than the late sample, this indicates that the recovered clock is sampling too late, and if the early sample is smaller than the late sample this indicates that the recovered clock is sampling too early. It is common practice to low-pass filter (LPF) the difference of each pair of samples to reduce the effect of random noise on the system. This filtered difference signal adjusts the frequency of a voltage controlled oscillator (VCO) in order to delay or advance the arrival of the next clock impulse, as required by the early and late samples.

The early-late clock recovery works well in conjunction with binary modulation schemes which have peaks in most of the symbol periods, but as with times-two clock recovery, less satisfactorily with multilevel schemes because there are fewer distinctive peaks.

6.2.3 Zero crossing clock recovery

The zero-crossing clock recovery principle is similar to early-late clock recovery, in that it looks for a specific feature in the received waveform. This works on the premise that with symmetrical signalling pulses, the received waveform will pass through zero exactly

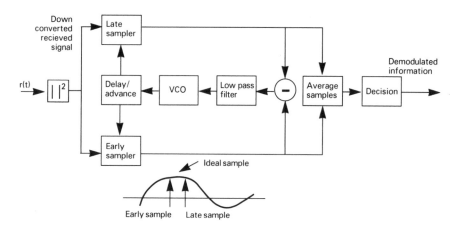

Figure 6.3: Early-late clock recovery schematic

midway between the sampling points. The receiver detects a change in the polarity of the received signal, and if this does not occur midway between predicted sampling points, it speeds up or slows down its reconstructed clock appropriately. Again, the zero crossing clock recovery is a scheme which works well for binary modulation, but the assumption that the waveform will pass through zero midway between sampling instances is not always valid with multilevel schemes. For example, if the received waveform moves between amplitudes of +1 and -3 in a smooth manner, it will pass through zero before the middle of the sample period.

There are two solutions to allow the use of zero crossing with multilevel modulation. The first is to ignore this problem, as on average the crossing will be in the middle of the symbol period, and to low pass filter or integrate the observed zero crossing point in order to produce this average. This increases the timing jitter compared to binary modulation schemes. The second is only to observe the zero crossings when we expect them to fall midway between sampling instants [8]. If we detect a transition between two symbols of equal magnitude but opposite polarity then we can expect the zero crossing associated with this transition to be in the middle of a symbol period and can use this to update the timing. If only these transitions are used for timing updates then, because of the accuracy of the zero crossing detection, less averaging needs to be performed to remove any noise and so the filtering requirements are reduced, leading to a lower jitter in the recovered clock.

In the case of binary modulation, a similar schematic to that of Figure 6.3 is applicable to zero crossing clock recovery. However, in the case of multi-level modulation a control logic block must be included in order to enable or disable sampling adjustments, depending on whether zero crossings fall midway between sampling instances.

6.2.4 Synchroniser

A completely different clock recovery system is the so-called synchroniser. This is the scheme used by the pan-European mobile radio system known as GSM. In this system the transmitter periodically sends a sounding sequence. The receiver searches for this sequence by performing an auto-correlation at a rate significantly faster than the symbol rate (typically four times). The oversampling point at which the maximum correlation occurs is deemed to be the correct sampling point, and is assumed to remain correct until the next sounding sequence is received. This scheme is simple, but requires a sounding sequence to be periodically inserted into the data stream, increasing the bandwidth requirements. It also requires that the transmitter and receiver clocks do not drift significantly over a synchronisation block, which may place constraints on the circuitry that can be employed. This synchronisation scheme has the advantage that it performs equally well regardless of the modulation scheme. The simplified block diagram of such a scheme is shown in Figure 6.4.

6.3 Carrier Recovery

Carrier recovery has received more attention than clock recovery [9, 10] but is not always required as non-coherent detection can often be applied, whereas all modulation schemes require accurate clock recovery. Carrier recovery is always required for square QAM con-

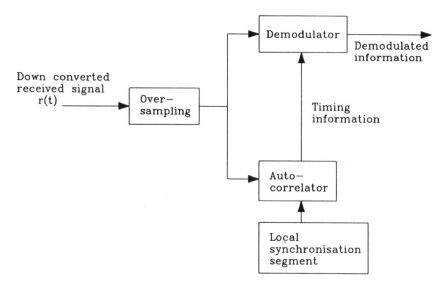

Figure 6.4: Synchroniser clock recovery schematic

stellations, even when differential coding is employed. For an explanation of differential coding see Chapter 4. This is because the square constellation consists of discrete information encoded on the I and Q axes separately. In order to decode this information it is essential to be able to separate the effects of the I and Q modulation and this can only be performed if a coherent source exists within the receiver.

The effect of coherent detection suffering from inaccurate carrier recovery in the case of a non-differential square 16-QAM system is shown in Figure 6.5, and that on a differential system is shown in Figure 6.6. With the non-differential system a constellation point with a magnitude of (3,1) on the I and Q axes, respectively, is shown to be transformed to another one with magnitude of approximately (2.2,2.2) due to the channel induced carrier phase rotation. When demodulated with reference to the original co-ordinate system drawn in dashed lines this could easily be decoded as an incorrect symbol. For the differential case shown in Figure 6.6 let us suppose that the information to be transmitted requires that the constellation point be moved positively by one quadrant and positively by 90 degrees within that quadrant. At the receiver when demodulating using the original un-rotated co-ordinates shown in dashed lines we will perceive the correct quadrant move but the received point is on the boundary of the decision bars, and only a small amount of noise would be require to move it into any of the four decision areas within the quadrant, giving a high probability of error.

Circular QAM constellations do not need carrier recovery if differential encoding is used. This is because, with these constellations the information is encoded onto the phase and amplitude of the signal, corresponding to a polar rather than rectangular encoding, and so only phase and amplitude differences are required which can be obtained even when the receiver's carrier reference is at a different frequency from the transmitter reference. In Gaussian channels, the performance of a non-coherent system using full differential encoding will be 3dB worse than a coherent system with *perfect* carrier recovery. This is because, with the differential coding, if one symbol is outside the appropriate decision boundary it will cause two errors, one when it is compared to the previous symbol, and another when the next symbol is compared with it. In a non-differential system only one error will be experienced.

A common problem for most carrier recovery schemes is an inability to resolve phase ambiguities encountered in the case of rotationally symmetric, or near-symmetric constellations. So for constellations such as QPSK, phase lock can be established at all multiples of 90 degrees, but without additional transmitted information it is not possible to resolve the angle at which phase lock has been established. This problem can be overcome by sending a sounding sequence known to the receiver, or through the use of differential coding. The decision as to whether to employ coherent non-differential, coherent differential, or non-coherent differential modulation depends on the particular environment and the QAM constellation chosen. If the channel changes only very slowly, which would be the case for a Gaussian channel with a high SNR, then coherent non-differential transmission is to be preferred, with a training sequence in order to resolve the false locking problem. If the square constellation is employed in channels whose phase change can be relatively rapid then coherent differential modulation will prevent

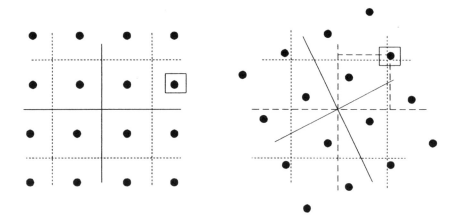

Figure 6.5: Coherent detection suffering from inaccurate carrier recovery in the case of non-differential QAM

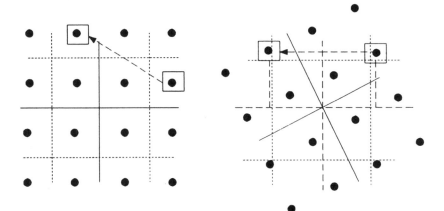

Figure 6.6: Coherent detection suffering from inaccurate carrier recovery in the case of differential QAM

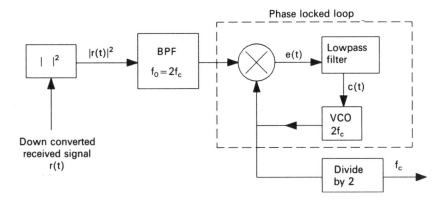

Figure 6.7: Times-two carrier recovery schematic

error bursts caused by the possible false locking. If acceptable carrier recovery performance cannot be achieved then non-coherent differential modulation coupled with a circular **QAM** constellation is preferable.

After this introduction we now describe some of the more common carrier recovery systems and examine techniques which have been proposed for QAM systems.

6.3.1 Times-n carrier recovery

As with clock recovery, a common form of carrier recovery for binary schemes is the times-two or the squared carrier recovery. In this scheme the incoming carrier wave is squared leading to a periodic component at the carrier frequency which can be isolated using a filter and phase locked loop. Times-two carrier recovery can be implemented using the schematic of Figure 6.7 [7]. Assuming BPSK modulation and noiseless communications for the sake of simplicity, the received signal is given by

$$r(t) = a(t).\cos(w_c t + \psi), \tag{6.1}$$

where $a(t) = \pm 1$ represents the modulating signal, and ψ the phase of the carrier. After squaring the received signal we get

$$r^2(t) = a^2(t)\cos^2(w_c t + \psi) \qquad (6.2)$$
$$= \frac{1}{2}[1 + \cos[2(w_c t + \psi)]].$$

Upon removing the DC component and bandpass filtering, the remaining signal $\cos[2(w_c t + \psi)]$ can be used to drive a phase locked loop (PLL) constituted by a lowpass filter, a multiplier and a voltage controlled oscillator.

Assuming that the VCO oscillates at $2w_c$ and has an initial phase of $\hat{\psi}$, its output signal of $\sin[2(w_c t + \hat{\psi})]$ is multiplied by $\cos[2(w_c t + \psi)]$ in order to generate the signal

$$e(t) = \cos[2(w_c t + \psi)].\sin[2(w_c t + \hat{\psi})] \qquad (6.3)$$
$$= \frac{1}{2}\sin[4w_c t + 2(\psi + \hat{\psi})] + \frac{1}{2}\sin[2(\hat{\psi} - \psi)].$$

The first term of the above equation is removed by the lowpass loop filter, while the second term of

$$c(t) = \frac{1}{2}\sin[2(\hat{\psi} - \psi)] \approx \Delta\psi \ if \ \Delta\psi \ll 1 \qquad (6.4)$$

is used to drive the VCO. Finally, the output from the VCO is divided by two.

Unfortunately, according to Franks [1] the squaring approach does not work with quadrature modulation. This is because when a quadrature signal with equal power on average in each quadrature branch is squared the signal power in each of the branches tends to cancel leaving a low signal level on which to perform carrier recovery. However, this can be overcome through the use of a fourth-power device which can generate a significant component at four times the carrier frequency. This can then be divided by four to provide carrier recovery. Passing the complex received signal through a fourth-power device has the effect of raising the magnitude of the received phasor to the fourth power and multiplying the phase angle by four. Times-four carrier recovery was investigated by Rustako et al [11].

Rustako notes that decision directed carrier recovery (see Section 6.3.2) suffers when the occasional receiver outage destroys the accuracy of the data detections. This causes a loss of carrier recovery and considerable time may be required to re-acquire the carrier. Furthermore, when adaptive equalisers are used, which update their tap coefficients using a decision directed algorithm, then the equaliser and carrier recovery system can interact in unwanted manner. He notes that times-four carrier recovery does not depend on data decisions or interact with the equaliser. Higher powers than four increase carrier jitter due to the increased effects of the data pattern.

A schematic diagram of their proposed carrier recovery circuit is shown in Figure 6.8. The received RF signal is down-converted by mixing with the local oscillator LO. Selectivity and automatic gain control are achieved at the IF stage. The input is raised to the fourth power and input to the PLL. The function of the PLL is to extract the line component at four times the carrier frequency, and to filter out the random component due to the data. Observe that in Figure 6.8 the PLL has an identical structure to that of Figure 6.7, except that it is tuned to f_c rather than $4f_c$, and hence it delivers the required output frequency. The carrier frequency f_c must then be multiplied by four as shown in the $\times 4$ block. This could be achieved by raising the signal to the fourth power. Rustako noted that the times-four function could be performed by a frequency-doubler which by virtue of its design also produces frequencies at a fourth power. With suitable filtering such a device could be readily used. In his paper, Rustako gives a thorough mathematical derivation of the theory of times-four carrier recovery. Rustako then went on to construct a times-four carrier recovery and test it using a fading channel simulator. From his experiment Rustako noted that using this form of carrier recovery synchronisation can be maintained even when severe fading causes high error rates. The drawback is that in order to keep pattern-related phase jitter under control, the PLL noise bandwidth must be made small. This will slow down acquisition when loss of carrier does occur. Therefore, times-four carrier recovery will be most suitable in situations where fades are benign and hence loss of lock is not a frequent event.

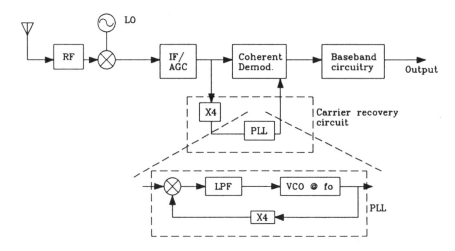

Figure 6.8: Times-four carrier recovery block diagram

6.3.2   Decision directed carrier recovery

A carrier recovery scheme which is completely different from all the
carrier and clock recovery systems discussed so far is decision directed carrier recovery. In fixed link QAM systems this has proved to
be one of the most popular carrier recovery schemes. In this scheme,
a decision is made as to which was the most likely constellation point
transmitted given the received symbol. This is normally the constellation point closest to the received symbol. It is then assumed that
the phase difference between the received symbol and the constellation point is due to carrier recovery drift, and the receiver carrier recovery is updated accordingly. Decision directed carrier recovery has
the advantage that it can work with all constellations, however, they
typically exhibit a BER threshold. If the prevailing channel BER is
less than this threshold then such methods operate extremely well
as they effectively remove additive noise from the input phasor. If
the BER is higher than this threshold then cumulative catastrophic
failure can result whereby the constellation point selected in the receiver is the wrong one. The update signal to the carrier recovery
system is therefore erroneous, driving the carrier phase further away
from the correct value and further increasing the chance of error,

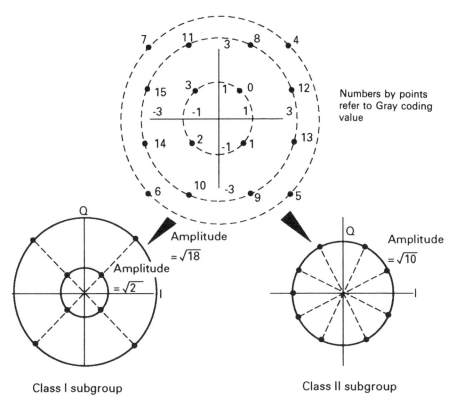

Figure 6.9: 16-level QAM subgroups

etc. Whether decision directed carrier recovery will be suitable for a specific application will depend on this BER threshold, which itself is dependent on the number of modulation levels used.

Whilst simple in principle, decision directed carrier recovery can often require a moderately complex implementation such as that proposed by Horikawa *et al* [12] who produced an elegant arrangement for decision directed carrier recovery combined with QAM. The basic premise of the circuit is that the quality of carrier recovery will be acceptable if only half of the input signals are used for carrier recovery update.

The 16 QAM phasors can be divided into 2 sub-groups called class I and class II phasors. (Note these are not related to the class 1 (C1) and class 2 (C2) subchannels derived in Chapter 5.) This is shown in Figure 6.9. Class I consists of the 8 phasors lying on the angles

$$\theta_I = \pi/2 \times (n + 1/2) \quad n = 0, 1, 2, 3 \tag{6.5}$$

and class II consists of all the remaining phasors, namely

$$\theta_{II} \approx \pi/2 \times (n \pm 1/5) \quad n = 0, 1, 2, 3, \tag{6.6}$$

where the subscripts refer to class I and class II respectively, and $(\pi/2) \cdot (1/5) = (\pi/10) = 18° \approx \tan^{-1}(1/3)$ from the geometry of the figure. In the square 16-QAM constellation shown in Figure 6.9 the class I phasors have $|I| = |Q|$, where $|x|$ means magnitude of x and I and Q refer to the received voltage on the real and imaginary axes, respectively. The class II signals have $|I| = 3|Q|$ or $|Q| = 3|I|$. The normalised amplitudes for class I phasors are $\sqrt{18}$ and $\sqrt{2}$, and for the class II phasors $\sqrt{10}$.

Horikawa's circuit operates only on class I phasors. It does so by comparing the values of the incoming I and Q signals and if they satisfy the relationship

$$|I|/m < |Q| < n \times |I|, \tag{6.7}$$

where m and n are typically 2 then the circuit concludes that a class I phasor has been sent. For a class I signal received with perfect carrier recovery over a perfect channel we would have $|I| = |Q|$. By subtracting $|I|$ from $|Q|$ we have a signal whose polarity indicates the direction of carrier drift. Determining the quadrant of transmission allows deduction of the required signal to be applied to the VCO. This computation can be carried out by a simple algorithm using the following quantities:

$$
\begin{aligned}
a &= pol(I) \, XOR \, pol(Q) \tag{6.8}\\
b &= pol(I + Q)\\
c &= pol(I - Q)\\
d &= (a \, XOR \, b) \, XOR \, c
\end{aligned}
$$

where $pol(x)$ is a function which returns "0" if x is negative and "1" if x is positive. The value of d is then used to drive the VCO so that if $d = 1$ the VCO runs slower and if $d = 0$ the VCO runs faster.

For example, say a phasor at 135 degrees had been sent but because of an increase in the receiver carrier frequency this had been received with a phase advance at 140 degrees. This would give $I =$ -1.08 and $Q = 0.91$. So $a = (0 \ XOR \ 1) = 1$, $b = pol(-0.17) = 0$, $c = pol(-1.99) = 0$ and $d = [(1 \ XOR \ 0) \ XOR \ 0] = 1$. Thus the VCO would be instructed to run slower as required. Examples taken from any quadrant can be seen to function correctly.

The circuit is shown in Figure 6.10. The input phasor is split into real and imaginary components using the receiver's recovered clock. The quadrature components are low pass filtered (LPF) to remove the unwanted frequency components of the mixing operation. As mentioned, the decision as to whether a class I signal has been received is based on evaluating whether $|I|/2 < |Q| < 2 \cdot |I|$. Both quadrature components are full wave rectified and input to a comparator which determines whether the signal level is within the limits expected for a class I signal. The XORed output from both comparators are fed into the control input (c) of an enabling gating arrangement which allows the updating of the VCO if the I and Q amplitudes are within a ratio of two. The central part of the circuit performs the algorithm described above by computing the parameters a, b, c, d in Equation 6.8, with the loop filter and VCO acting as a phase locked loop (PLL).

This circuit suffers from possible false locking as 90 degree rotations of the constellation will not change the parameters $a \ldots d$. This must be resolved through the use of a training sequence or some other ambiguity resolving technique.

6.3.2.1 Frequency and phase detection systems

Within amplitude modulation schemes where the phase shift imposed by the modulating signal on the carrier remains constant it is possible to use phase locked loop (PLL) systems. In PLLs phase detectors (PDs) are deployed in order to detect the phase difference between the recovered carrier and the internal reference frequency of the receiver which is used to update the internal reference frequency appropriately. Such a system is referred to as a phase locked loop, which is described in detail in Reference [13].

Such simple systems cannot be used in conjunction with phase or quadrature modulation schemes due to the variation in the car-

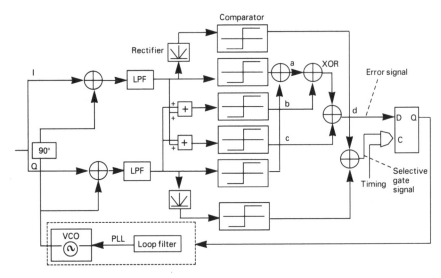

Figure 6.10: Implementation of a decision directed carrier recovery system for 16-level square QAM [14] ©IEEE, 1988, Sari et al

rier phase imposed by the encoded information. These modulation induced carrier phase variations can either be ignored with the assumption that the average of this phase deviation will be zero, or attempts can be made to remove the phase variation using decision directed methods such as those described in the previous subsection.

Further problems associated with PLL methods for point-to-point microwave links are discussed by Sari and Moridi [14]. Sari notes that the high number of modulation levels used in point-to-point links requires a low phase jitter, which demands narrow phase locked loop bandwidths. However, the frequency uncertainty of the RF oscillators used in the up and down conversion process was often greater than the affordable phase locked loop bandwidth. Possible solutions to this problem include:

1) Switching of the loop filter. Here a large filter bandwidth is used during the initial phase acquisition process and then a narrow bandwidth is invoked once lock has been achieved. In its most simple form such a system would include two loop filters, and a switch operated by the carrier recovery circuit once the error signal was sufficiently

small. The problem with this method is that some means of detecting lock, i.e. a lock detector is required in order to activate and deactivate the switch optimally.

2) The use of non-linear elements in the loop filter. Due to this the error signal is no longer proportional to the phase error. The non-linear function is chosen to increase sensitivity (i.e. the phase error seen by the PLL) near lock, and reduce sensitivity further away from lock. Taking the square root or logarithm of the phase error would achieve the desired effect. The chosen non-linear element is placed between the PD and loop filter. Appropriate non-linear devices can often be difficult to construct.

3) Frequency sweeping. This is a common technique within digital microwave systems whereby the receiver's frequency is slowly changed until lock is achieved using a narrow bandwidth detector. Such a detector should then be able to maintain accurate lock if the channel is relatively benign. In practice the IF oscillator frequency is swept over the uncertainty interval by adding a periodic signal to the filtered PD output. Once phase lock has been achieved frequency sweeping is halted. This process has the disadvantage of taking some time due to theoretical constraints as regards to the speed at which the sweep can take place.

4) Frequency detectors (FDs). These are devices which produce a signal proportional to the frequency difference between the received signal and local reference carriers. Hence they can readily determine the frequency offset between the received signal and the local reference but as the frequency error does not depend on the phase they cannot be used for phase tracking. They are therefore often used in parallel with PDs, the FD being used during initial acquisition. When the FDs give a near-zero output then a switch is operated such that the FDs are deactivated and the PDs are activated. Sari notes that such a system requires a substantial amount of circuitry.

In his paper, Sari describes an architecture for a new implement-

ation of a combined phase and frequency detector which he refers to
as a PFD. A diagram showing the architecture of such a system is
given in Figure 6.11. The top PD will be converted into an FD by
appropriately manipulating its output. The down-converted received
signal is input to a pair of sinusoidal phase detectors (PD) operating
in quadrature with each other so that their outputs are $sin\phi(t)$ and
$cos\phi(t)$, where $\phi(t)$ is the phase error, as shown in Figure 6.12. Note
that the required stable lock points for a rectangular QAM constellation are at $n \cdot (\pi/2), n = 1, 2, 3, 4,$ and these points can be identified
as those at the zero crossings of $sin\phi$ in Figure 6.12, where $cos\phi$ is
simultaneously positive. During steady state, the phase error $\phi(t)$
fluctuates around a stable lock point where $sin\phi \ll 1$, and only the
upper PD and the VCO are being used in a normal PLL configuration. However, during the initial acquisition phase the phase error
$\phi(t)$ significantly deviates from zero, and changes at a rate proportional to the frequency offset between the received signal and VCO
reference according to $\phi(t) = \Delta wt + \phi(0)$. Clearly, the PD output
is a sinusoid with a frequency equal to the difference Δw between
the received signal and VCO reference, and therefore has a zero DC
content delivering no information about the polarity of the frequency
error. In contrast, an FD would provide a DC signal proportional to
the frequency offset Δw.

The circuit of Figure 6.11 overcomes this problem by the use of
a track and hold device. The device tracks the upper PD when it
is in phase lock and so its output is in the range $k\pi/2 \pm \theta$ where
$k = 1, 2, 3, 4$ is an integer representing phase lock in four different
quadrants, and θ is the maximum allowed phase deviation. In order
to track the phase error the circuitry also requires that the output
from the lower quadrant PD is positive which pinpoints the stable
locking domains. Should, however, the phase error $|\phi(t) - n\pi/2|$ be
outside the range $\pm\theta$, the circuitry operates in a hold mode and the
track and hold device retains the last valid level. The control signal
$sin\phi$ originating from the upper PD determines whether the phase
error $\phi(t)$ is within a predetermined interval $\pm\theta$ and $cos\phi$ originating
from the lower PD allows recognition of the stable lock points as seen
in Figure 6.12. The operation of the device is now explained with

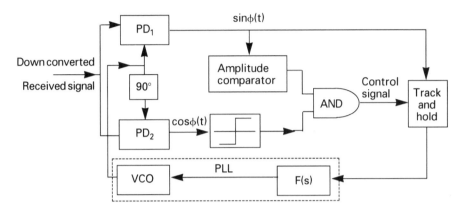

Figure 6.11: PFD block diagram

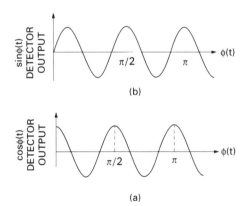

Figure 6.12: Inphase and quadrature phase PD output signal [14] ©IEEE, 1988, Sari et al

reference to Figure 6.13.

The operation of the PFD of the circuit of Figure 6.11 for positive and negative frequency offsets is shown in Figures 6.13(a) and (b), respectively. In these figures which show the situation during initial phase acquisition (i.e. lock has not been acquired) the dashed line represents the error signal from the upper PD and the solid line represents the output of the track and hold device (and thus the input to the VCO). With a positive frequency offset as shown in Figure 6.13(a) the upper PD tracks the offset until it falls outside the range θ. At this point the amplitude comparator detects that the PD output has moved outside the allowed range and switches the track and hold device to hold mode. It is maintained in this configuration until the output from the upper PD falls back within the allowed range. Note that the continuous line does not fall back to the dashed line as the latter passes through the axis moving downwards. This is because at this point the track and hold device is maintained in the hold position by the output of the lower PD which precedes that of the upper by 90° as demonstrated in Figure 6.12. When $\cos\phi$ is negative, so the upper branch is moving from +90° to −90°, the track and hold device is maintained at hold. As can be seen, in the positive case portrayed in Figure 6.13(a), the control signal to the VCO is predominantly positive ensuring that there is sufficient information to allow acquisition. This condition is detected by the comparator at the output of the lower PD. Once lock is acquired, the system will automatically revert to a tracking role as the upper PD output falls within its allowed range. A similar effect can be seen for a negative frequency offset as shown in Figure 6.13(b). The parameter θ should be chosen to maximise the DC at the detector output. For a sinusoidal PD this means that θ should be approximately 16°.

In the case of QAM, according to Sari, the phase error associated with each incoming symbol is assessed, and the error angle becomes the PD's output. This is then passed to the track and hold block which performs its function as before. However, with 16-level square QAM, when the receiver's local oscillator is unsynchronised with that of the transmitter, three circles are apparent, as shown in Figure 6.14. On the inner and outer circles there are four equi-spaced

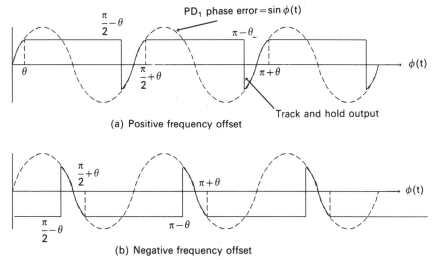

(a) Positive frequency offset

(b) Negative frequency offset

Figure 6.13: PFD waveforms for positive and negative frequency offsets

points forming a QPSK signal set. On the middle ring there are 8, non-regularly spaced points which can lead to phase ambiguity when used in a circuit of the form proposed by Sari as there will now be 8 possible lock positions, but only in four of these can data be correctly demodulated. To overcome this problem, Sari, like Horikawa, proposed to invoke only the Class I QAM signals, using a windowing system in order to determine whether a symbol is suitable for carrier recovery. A block diagram of such a system is shown in Figure 6.15.

In this figure the input signal is quadrature down-converted, low-pass filtered (LPF) and analogue-to-digital converted (ADC). It is then input to a practical version of the PFD shown in Figure 6.11. In this scheme the track and hold function is performed by a D-type flip-flop which will only pass the input to the output when clocked. The flip-flop is normally clocked regularly by the clock recovery system (not shown) but can be inhibited by the control logic device. This latter device determines whether the incoming signal is within one of the windows shown as square boxes on the QAM constellation in Figure 6.14. If the signal is within these boxes then the PD signal is used for carrier recovery purposes, otherwise the input to the loop filter is maintained at the previous level.

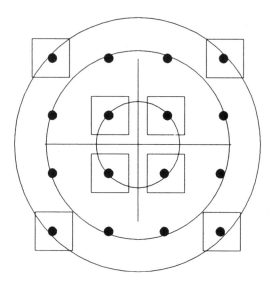

Figure 6.14: Circles and windows within a 16-level square QAM constellation

Sari claimed a substantially reduced acquisition time for his system compared to a discrete FD and PD system and a reduced complexity architecture.

6.4 Summary

In this chapter we have considered clock and carrier recovery techniques for fixed link QAM systems. Clock recovery techniques used in this environment have tended to be similar or identical to those used for other modulation schemes, with zero crossing techniques often finding favour. That clock recovery has not been a particular problem for QAM is evidenced by a paucity of publications on the topic.

A considerably more problematic issue has been that of carrier recovery schemes for QAM. Many of the existing schemes proved unsuitable because of the phase related content of the encoded information and also because a more accurate lock was required due to the higher number of levels used compared to binary modulation. The carrier recovery techniques employed essentially were either times-N

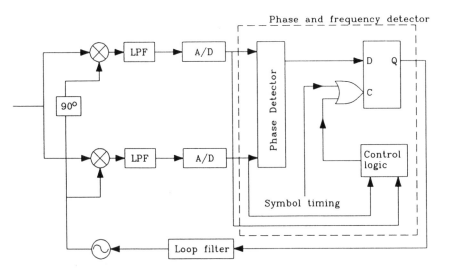

Figure 6.15: General block diagram of a PFD system

or decision directed. Decision directed methods generally were more suitable where the BER was low so that few decisions were in error, and where there were no problems caused by a decision feedback equaliser interacting with a decision directed carrier recovery system in such a way that system performance was impaired.

Of the decision directed carrier recovery schemes, the one proposed by Sari and Moridi addressed the issue of both frequency and phase acquisition whereas that of Horikawa looked at practical implementation of the discrete time phase detector required. Both decided to use only the Class I QAM symbols for carrier recovery, although for different reasons, Sari to prevent possible false locking errors and Horikawa to simplify the decoding circuitry required.

In the next chapter we consider another important component building block for modems, particularly those which attempt high bit rate transmission. In this case the channel introduces a particular form of interference between symbols, and we examine some equalisers which can be employed to overcome this.

Bibliography

[1] **L.E.Franks**, "Carrier and bit synchronisation in data communications A tutorial review", *IEEE Trans. Comms.*, Vol.COM-28, No.8, Aug 1980, pp1107-1121.

[2] **B.Sklar**, "Digital communications", *Prentice Hall*, 1988.

[3] **R.E.Ziemer and R.L.Peterson**, "Digital communications and spread-spectrum systems", *MacMillan Publishing Co.*, 1985.

[4] **L.E.Franks**, "Synchronisation subsystems: Analysis and design" in K.Feher (Ed.) "Digital communications, satellite/earth station engineering", *Prentice Hall*, Chater 7, 1981.

[5] **A.B.Carlson**, "Communications systems", *McGraw Hill*, 1986.

[6] **N.G.Kingsbury**, "Transmit and receive filters for QPSK signals to optimise the performance on linear and bandlimited channels", *IEE Proc Pt. F*, Vol.133, No.4, July 1986, pp345-355.

[7] **J.G.Proakis**, "Digital communications", *McGraw Hill*, 1989.

[8] **I.J.Wassell**, "Digital mobile radio communication" Ph.D. Thesis, *University of Southampton*, 1991.

[9] **R.L.Cupo. and R.D.Gitlin**, "Adaptive carrier recovery systems for digital data communications receivers", *IEEE J-SAC*, Vol.7, No.9, Dec 1989, pp1328-1339.

[10] **W.C.Lindsey and M.K.Simon**, "Carrier synchronisation and detection of polyphase signals", *IEEE Trans. Comms.*, June 1972, pp441-454.

[11] **A.J.Rustako, L.J.Greenstein, R.S.Roman and A.A.M.Saleh**, "Using times-four carrier recovery in M-QAM digital radio receivers", *IEEE J-SAC*, Vol.SAC-5, No.3, April 1987, pp524-533.

[12] **I.Horikawa,T.Murase and Y.Saito**, "Design and performance of a 200Mbit/s 16 QAM digital radio system", *IEEE Trans. Comms.*, Vol.COM-27, No.12, Dec 1979, pp1953-1958.

[13] **J.Smith**, "Modern communications circuits", McGraw Hill, 1986.

[14] **H.Sari and S.Moridi**, "New phase and frequency detectors for carrier recovery in PSK and QAM systems", *IEEE Trans. Comms.*, Vol.36, No.9, Sept 1988, pp1035-1043.

Chapter 7

Basic Equaliser Techniques

7.1 Introduction

In Chapter 4 we considered the transmission of information via band-limited channels. It was shown that all band-limited channels have impulse responses of infinite duration which may result in inter-symbol interference (ISI). However, if the Nyquist criterion is met then the impulse response has zeros at adjacent signalling instants and a unity main tap. Therefore, no ISI is introduced.

In contrast to the approach pursued in Chapter 4, where it was assumed that the channel is distortion-free and hence has a constant frequency domain transfer function and linear phase within the pass-band, here we consider the more realistic scenario of transmission media having linear distortions. If we characterise the channel by its baseband impulse response $g(t)$, then the baseband received signal $y(t)$ is given by the following convolution:

$$y(t) = x(t) * g(t).$$

A typical continuous channel impulse response is depicted in Figure 7.1. Note that it is no longer symmetric, its zero-crossings are no longer uniformly spaced and this channel introduces linear distortions, which can be seen in the eye pattern.

The aim of channel equalization is to remove the distortions introduced by the channel. This can be carried out either in frequency

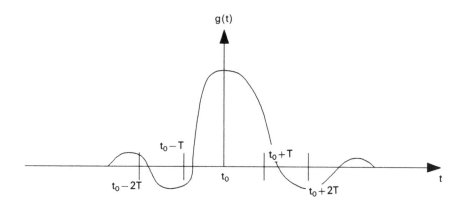

Figure 7.1: Typical Channel Impulse Response

domain by filtering the received signal through the inverse filter of the channel, or in the time domain by convolving it with the appropriate equaliser impulse response.

Linear distortions are introduced, for example, by wideband radio channels described in Chapter 2, when there are a multitude of radio paths between the transmitter and the receiver, and the delay on some of these paths is significantly greater than on others. In extreme cases the longer paths can result from reflections off mountains, more often they occur due to reflections off nearby buildings and sometimes from vehicles such as buses. Wideband channels can be characterised by their impulse response. This is the signal that would be received were an impulse (i.e., a pulse of extremely short duration) transmitted. The impulse response is composed of the superposition of all the paths arriving at the receiver, each path suffering a certain attenuation and delay. Text books often show example impulse responses as exponentially decaying curves falling off steeply at first and then becoming more gently undulating. This is because the responses that are significantly delayed are often highly attenuated due to the extra distance which they have travelled.

Historically, wideband channels have been rare in QAM implementations. The only areas where significant multipath fading has been encountered are on high transmission rate (typically $> 140 \text{Mbits/s}$) point–to–point radio links. These are characterised by slowly varying impulse responses extending over a few symbol periods only. Furthermore, the high transmission rate has implied relatively simple equalisers if they are to be implemented with existing circuitry. Two equalisers which are frequently used are the linear and decision feedback equaliser, while the Viterbi equaliser has rarely been used for QAM mainly due to its high complexity. For that reason we do not describe the Viterbi equaliser here, but refer the reader to Proakis [1]. In the following two sections we consider linear and decision feedback equalisers. In the final section we consider aspects of equalisers specific to QAM, and consider some actual implementations. For more in-depth treatment of equalization the interested reader is referred to References [2]–[7].

7.2 Linear Equalisers

7.2.1 Zero-Forcing Equalisers

The basic structure of a linear equaliser (LE) system is given in Figure 7.2. It is a linear transversal filter with an impulse response of

$$c(t)_{t=jT} = c(jT) = \sum_{j=-N}^{N} c(j)z^{-jT}, \qquad (7.1)$$

where $c(t)$ is represented by its T-spaced samples. Equalization is performed by convolving the T-spaced samples of the received signal, $y(t) = y_k$, with $c(t)$. In practice it is performed by passing y_k through a delay chain and the equalised output I_k is derived by a multiplication using taps with variable coefficients $c(j)$. Thus

$$I_k = \sum_{j=-N}^{N} c(j)y(k-j), \qquad (7.2)$$

where there are $(2N+1)$ taps.

In order to satisfy the Nyquist criterion, the equaliser taps can be chosen to drive the T-spaced samples of the combined impulse

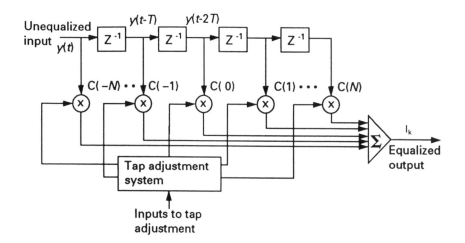

Figure 7.2: General Linear Equaliser System

response of the concatenated channel and equaliser towards zero, allowing only for the main tap to be non-zero. Due to its operating principle this scheme is referred to as a zero-forcing equaliser. Naturally, zero-forcing is only possible over the length of the transversal filter's memory. Nevertheless, as the filter-length tends to infinity, the ISI at the equaliser's output tends to zero for all values of jT, $j = 1, 2, \ldots \infty$. The fundamental limitation of the zero-forcing equaliser is due to the fact that the channel transfer function's inverse filter $C(f)$ constituted by the equaliser when cascaded with the channel transfer function $G(f)$ enhances the channel noise in those frequency intervals, where $G(f)$ has a high attenuation. This is because the flat noise spectrum $N(f)$ is boosted along with the signal, where the channel inflicted a high attenuation, which becomes particularly adverse for transmissions over frequency-selective fading radio channels.

There are numerous ways of deriving the coefficients $c(j)$. If the channel impulse response can be considered time invariant as a leased telephone line, then the coefficients are constant. In most cases, however, the channel impulse response is time variant and so the tap coefficients need to be variable. A large class of linear equalisers adjust these coefficients by comparing the equalized output with the nearest constellation point and adjusting the coefficients so as to reduce the error. A form of recursive least squares algorithm is normally used in making these adjustments. This is adequate for slowly varying channels with low BERs. If the BER exceeds a certain threshold then catastrophic failure will occur due to the wrong symbol being decoded and hence the wrong adjustment being applied to the tap coefficients. These mal-adjusted coefficients further distort the signal increasing the probability of error, and so on until complete failure ensues.

Robustness can be increased by the periodic use of a training sequence to ensure that the coefficient values are close to optimum. The data to be transmitted is divided into blocks, and at the start of each block a known sequence is transmitted. This method can be further subdivided into convergence training and channel sounding, depending on the known sequence transmitted and the processing at the receiver. In the former, any known sequence can be sent. Because the receiver knows this sequence there can be no decoding errors during this period and so the coefficients can be driven towards the optimal value with little risk of catastrophic failure. During normal data transmission the coefficients can either be left unchanged, or updated according to a more cautious update rule compared to that used during the training period.

Another way that the transmission of a known sequence can be used is to periodically sound the channel and then set the coefficients accordingly, eliminating the need for complicated convergence algorithms. The channel may be sounded by sending a maximal length pseudo random binary sequence (PRBS) having a flat, almost "white" spectrum as the known sequence, and correlating the received sequence against a replica of itself held in the receiver. This correlation process is invoked for each of the symbol intervals over which the expected delay spread of the incoming signal occurs. Maximal length PRBSs have the property that the peak amplitude of the autocorrelation function with zero delay is equal to the length of the code, but for any offset delay the autocorrelation function is equal to -1. The autocorrelation is performed with the XOR function giv-

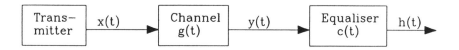

Figure 7.3: System Model with Equaliser

ing a result of either 1 or -1 (rather than 1 or 0). This method is used for example in the CCITT V.27, V.29, V.32 and V.33 standard high-speed data modems proposed for telephone lines having linear distortions. These schemes will be described in Chapter 9. Once we have sounded the channel and its impulse response is known we can calculate the tap coefficients for the LE.

The optimal coefficients for an infinite length LE are the T-spaced samples of the inverse filter. Again, if the baseband equivalent transmitted signal is $x(t)$, and the baseband impulse response of the channel is $g(t)$, then the baseband equivalent input to our receiver is

$$y(t) = g(t) * x(t) \qquad (7.3)$$

where * symbolises convolution. An equaliser at the receiver having an impulse response $c(t)$ results in an equalized output

$$h(t) = c(t) * y(t) = c(t) * g(t) * x(t) \qquad (7.4)$$

which, to be equal to the input $x(t)$, requires

$$c(t) * g(t) = \delta(t) \qquad (7.5)$$

where $\delta(t)$ is the unit pulse sequence [1,0,0,..]. This system is shown in Figure 7.3. Applying the z-domain transfer function to Equation 7.5 gives the z-transform of the filter required to equalize the channel having transfer function $G(z)$ as:

$$C(z) = \frac{1}{G(z)}. \qquad (7.6)$$

In practice the channel response is of finite length and we represent it by

$$G(z) = g(0) + g(1)z^{-1} + \ldots + g(n)z^{-n} \qquad (7.7)$$

where $g(0)$, $g(1) \ldots g(n)$ are the coefficients of the finite impulse response (FIR) filter modelling $G(z)$. Its inverse filter has a z-transform computed as follows:

$$\begin{aligned} C(z) &= \frac{1}{g(0) + g(1)z^{-1} + \ldots + g(n)z^{-n}} \\ C(z) &= c(0) + c(1)z^{-1} + c(2)z^{-2} + \ldots \end{aligned} \qquad (7.8)$$

where $c(0), c(1) \ldots$ form an infinite length sequence of equaliser coefficients. If the ISI is mild then this sequence will decay sharply and the equaliser coefficients, i.e. $c(n)$, are insignificant for large n. Then we can set the coefficients, $c(n)$, of the LE by the long division of $1/G(z)$, which requires little computational effort and can easily be implemented in real time. Thus, if our channel filter has a response of

$$G(z) = g(0) + g(1)z^{-1} + \ldots + g(n)z^{-n} \qquad (7.9)$$

where $g(n)$ is a complex number then the complex equaliser coefficients are given by

$$\begin{aligned} c(0) &= \frac{1}{g(0)} \\ c(1) &= \frac{[-c(0) \times g(1)]}{g(0)} \\ c(2) &= \frac{[(-c(0) \times g(2)) + (-c(1) \times g(1))]}{g(0)} \end{aligned} \qquad (7.10)$$

and generally

$$c(n) = \frac{\sum_{i=0}^{n-1}(-c(i) \times g(n-i))}{g(0)}. \qquad (7.11)$$

If there is no single dominant tap in the impulse response then the coefficients of the LE may fail to decay for a reasonable value of n. In this case the coefficients calculated by this long division method are no longer the optimal coefficients for the finite length equaliser. Although optimal values for the coefficients of the finite length linear equaliser can be found by more complex processes [1] the linear equaliser is no longer suitable.

7.2.2   Least Mean-Squared Equalisers

Least mean-squared (LMS) equalisers are considered superior to zero forcing (ZF) equalisers, because they can minimise the joint effects of ISI and noise at the equaliser's output over their memory length. In our analysis, however, we assume a high signal-to-noise ratio and neglect the effect of noise for the sake of simplicity. We also note that LMS equalisers in general can tolerate higher ISI and have faster convergence than ZF equalisers.

Lucky et al [2] define the mean squared distortion (MSD) as

$$MSD = \frac{1}{h^2(0)} \sum_{\substack{n=-\infty \\ n \neq 0}}^{\infty} h^2(n), \qquad (7.12)$$

which is simply the normalised sum of the square of symbol period spaced system response samples at the equaliser's output. Recall from Equation 7.4 that $h(n)$ is the convolution of the received signal $y(n)$ and the equaliser's impulse response, giving:

$$h(n) = y(n) * c(n) = \sum_{j=-N}^{N} c(j)y(n-j), \qquad (7.13)$$

and hence

$$h(0) = \sum_{j=-N}^{N} c(j)y(-j). \qquad (7.14)$$

Minimising the effects of ISI requires minimising the mean squared error (mse) term of:

$$\epsilon = \sum_{\substack{n=-\infty \\ n \neq 0}}^{\infty} h^2(n) = \left(\sum_{n=-\infty}^{\infty} h^2(n) \right) - h^2(0), \qquad (7.15)$$

which due to Equation 7.13 and Equation 7.14 is a quadratic function of the equaliser coefficients $c(j)$ and hence it has a minimum. Then from Equation 7.15 we get:

$$\frac{\partial \epsilon}{\partial c(j)} = \left(\sum_{k=-\infty}^{\infty} 2h(n)\frac{\partial h(n)}{\partial c(j)} \right) - 2h(0)\frac{\partial h(0)}{\partial c(j)} = 0, \qquad (7.16)$$

and exploiting Equations 7.13 and 7.14 yields:

$$\sum_{n=-\infty}^{\infty} h(n)y(n-j) = h(0)y(-j), \quad j = -N \ldots N. \tag{7.17}$$

The main tap value $h(0)$ does not play any role in minimising the *mse* of the system response's ISI contributions. Hence for the sake of simplicity we set the main tap to $h(0) = 1$ and fulfil this condition by appropriately scaling all equaliser taps by a constant at a later stage.

Substituting Equation 7.13 into Equation 7.17 gives:

$$\sum_{n=-\infty}^{\infty} \sum_{k=-N}^{N} c(k)y(n-k)y(n-j) = y(-j). \tag{7.18}$$

After exchanging the order of summations we arrive at:

$$\sum_{k=-N}^{N} c(k) \sum_{n=-\infty}^{\infty} y(n-k)y(n-j) = y(-j), \tag{7.19}$$

where

$$b(j,k) = \sum_{n=-\infty}^{\infty} y(n-k)y(n-j) \tag{7.20}$$

is recognised as the correlation coefficients of the received signal $y(n)$. Therefore Equation 7.19 simplifies to:

$$\sum_{k=-N}^{N} c(k)b(j,k) = y(-j) \quad j = -N \ldots N. \tag{7.21}$$

This is a set of $(2N+1)$ simultaneous, linear equations, from which the $(2N+1)$ equaliser coefficients $c(k)$, $k = -N \ldots N$, minimising the *mse* term of Equation 7.12 can be determined. Subsequently all coefficients must be scaled by a constant in order to arrive at $h(0) = 1$, which does not affect the shape of the equaliser transfer function. In a more convenient matrix form Equation 7.21 is expressed as:

$$B \cdot c = y \tag{7.22}$$

where B is a $[2N+1] \times [2N+1]$ dimensional matrix of correlations, while c and y are $[2N+1]$ dimensional column vectors. Assuming a stationary received signal $y(n)$, its correlation coefficients will not be dependent on the actual values of the indices (j, k), only their differences, hence Equation 7.22 can be written as follows:

$$
\begin{bmatrix}
b(0) & b(1) & \cdots & b(2N) \\
b(1) & b(0) & \cdots & b(2N-1) \\
b(2) & b(1) & \cdots & b(2N-2) \\
\vdots & \vdots & & \vdots \\
b(2N) & b(2N-1) & \cdots & b(0)
\end{bmatrix}
\begin{bmatrix}
c(-N) \\
c(-N+1) \\
c(-N+2) \\
\vdots \\
c(N)
\end{bmatrix}
=
\begin{bmatrix}
y(N) \\
y(N-1) \\
y(N-2) \\
\vdots \\
y(-N)
\end{bmatrix}.
$$
(7.23)

Observe that the correlation matrix in Equation 7.23 is not only symmetric but all the elements along the main diagonals are identical, hence it has a so-called Töplitz structure. This set of equations is often referred to as the Wiener–Hopf equations in the literature of LMS spectral estimation.

An important consequence of Equation 7.21 can be inferred as follows [2]. The ideal system response has a unity value at $n = 0$, i.e., $h(0) = 1$ and $h(n) = 0$ otherwise. Any deviation from these desired values is actually the error sample $e(n)$ associated with sampling instant n, therefore

$$
\begin{aligned}
e(0) &= h(0) - 1 \text{ for } n = 0 \\
e(n) &= h(n) \quad \text{for } n \neq 0.
\end{aligned}
$$
(7.24)

From Equation 7.17 we infer that

$$
\sum_{\substack{n=-\infty \\ n \neq 0}}^{\infty} h(n)y(n-j) + h(0)y(-j) = h(0)y(-j),
$$
(7.25)

and hence

$$
\sum_{\substack{n=-\infty \\ n \neq 0}}^{\infty} h(n)y(n-j) = \sum_{\substack{n=-\infty \\ n \neq 0}}^{\infty} e(n)y(n-j) = 0 \quad j = -N \dots N.
$$
(7.26)

Equation 7.26 implies that the optimum equaliser setting will result in an error sequence $e(n)$ which is uncorrelated with the equaliser's input signal $y(n)$ within its range of $[-N \dots N]$.

Similar sets of simultaneous equations are frequently encountered in various spectral estimation problems and a plethora of computationally efficient recursive algorithms are available for their solution.

For example, when computing the optimum predictor coefficients
in linear predictive speech coding, a similar set of equations must
be solved, which is often carried out using the Levinson–Durbin algorithm [3]. Another example is that of designing an optimum auto-
regressive filter in the decoding of Bose–Chaudhuri–Hocquenghem
block codes, which generates the required sequence of syndromes
and facilitates the computation of the error locations. In this application the Berlekamp–Massey algorithm is normally employed [3].
The specific solution to be used will depend on the final formulation of Equation 7.21 as regards to the computation of $b(j, k)$ in
Equation 7.20. Namely, the error minimisation in Equation 7.15 extends over $[-\infty \ldots \infty]$, but in practical terms it must be set to zero
outside a finite interval length. Depending on how this windowing
is carried out, different solutions arise, because the matrix B containing the elements $b(j, k)$ will have different properties. Efficient
solutions avoid straight matrix inversion, because their complexity
is usually proportional to N^3. Instead, recursive solutions exploiting
the symmetry of B or the Toplitz structure are generally favoured
due to their lower complexity, which is typically proportional to N^2.

The solution of Equation 7.22 in terms of matrix inversion is given
in the form

$$c^{\text{opt}} = B^{-1}y \qquad (7.27)$$

but as mentioned, iterative solutions are preferable.

A frequently used straightforward iterative procedure is the **steepest descent or gradient algorithm**, where an arbitrary initial
coefficient vector c_0 is assumed. As seen from Equation 7.13 and
Equation 7.15, the mse is a quadratic function of the equaliser coefficients comprised by c, and hence exhibits a minimum. The initial c_0
equaliser setting corresponds to an arbitrary momentary mse ϵ_0 on a
$(2N+1)$–dimensional paraboloid surface. The $(2N+1)$–dimensional
gradient vector g_0 of the mse at this instant is given by:

$$g_0 = \frac{\partial \epsilon}{\partial c_0}. \qquad (7.28)$$

With the $(2N + 1)$ gradient components $g_{-N} \ldots g_N$ known, every
equaliser coefficient is modified by a step-value $d_0(n)$, $n = -N \ldots N$,

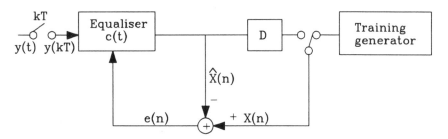

Figure 7.4: Adaptive Equaliser Schematic

proportional to its magnitude in the direction opposite to its gradient. For example, if the point c_0 was at a location of negative gradient on the $(2N+1)$–dimensional paraboloid in terms of all $(2N+1)$ components, all components must be increased by the common stepsize d and vice-versa, giving the relationship

$$c_{k+1}(n) = c_k(n) - d \cdot g_k(n), \quad n = -N \ldots N. \qquad (7.29)$$

Observe that the convergence speed and accuracy of the algorithm depends on the choice of the stepsize $d_k(n)$ that was fixed to d in our approach. In Section 7.4 we will show that faster convergence can be achieved using a technique referred to as Kalman filtering [1]. In general, the larger the stepsize, the faster the initial convergence and the larger the residual convergence error. The minimum *mse* cannot be attained with this algorithm, but due to its simplicity the method is quite popular.

7.2.3 Decision-Directed Adaptive Equalisers

The simplified schematic of a decision-directed automatic adaptive equaliser is portrayed in Figure 7.4, where the term decision directed implies that after a training period the equaliser is required to update its coefficients on the basis of the signal at the output of the receiver's decision device D, which is not always an error-free signal. Initially a training sequence known to both the transmitter and the receiver is sent, allowing the equaliser to derive the error signal $e(n) = x(n) - $

$\hat{x}(n)$ from the transmitted signal $x(n)$ and the equalized received signal $\hat{x}(n)$. Observe that in this formulation $e(n)$ can now contain both ISI and noise. Then the *mse* term of

$$\epsilon = \sum_{n=-\infty}^{\infty} e^2(n) \qquad (7.30)$$

can be used to adjust the equaliser's coefficients. After the training segment has elapsed, the transmitted signal $x(n)$ becomes unknown. However, assuming that no transmission errors have occurred, the output signal of the decision device D in Figure 7.4 is the exact replica of the transmitted signal $x(n)$. Therefore flipping the switch in Figure 7.4 to the output of the decision device D allows decision-directed equalization to continue unhindered. Using this approach the error signal is given by:

$$e(n) = x(n) - \sum_{k=-N}^{N} c(k)y(n-k). \qquad (7.31)$$

Then the *mse* is yielded as:

$$\epsilon = \sum_{n=-\infty}^{\infty} \left[x(n) - \sum_{k=-N}^{N} c(k)y(n-k) \right]^2 \qquad (7.32)$$

which we want to minimise as a function of the equaliser coefficients $c(k)$. Upon setting the partial derivatives to zero we arrive at:

$$\frac{\partial \epsilon}{\partial c(i)} = -2 \sum_{n=-\infty}^{\infty} \left\{ \left[x(n) - \sum_{k=-N}^{N} c(k)y(n-k) \right] y(n-i) \right\} = 0. \qquad (7.33)$$

After rearranging Equation 7.33 we get:

$$\sum_{n=-\infty}^{\infty} x(n)y(n-i) = \sum_{n=-\infty}^{\infty} \sum_{k=-N}^{N} c(k)y(n-k)y(n-i) \qquad (7.34)$$

which on exchanging the order of summations yields:

$$\sum_{n=-\infty}^{\infty} x(n)y(n-i) = \sum_{k=-N}^{N} c(k) \sum_{n=-\infty}^{\infty} y(n-k)y(n-i). \qquad (7.35)$$

In Equation 7.32 it was implicitly assumed that the error is minimised over the interval $-\infty < n < \infty$, which cannot be implemented
in practice. Depending on how the input data undergoing spectral
estimation is windowed to a finite interval two frequently used methods arise, the so called autocorrelation method and the covariance
method [3]. Pursuing the former we implicitly suppose that the data
outside the equaliser's range $[-N \ldots N]$ is set to zero. Then recog-
nising that in Equation 7.35 for a stationary received signal $y(n)$

$$r(i,k) = r(|i - k|) = \sum_{n=-N}^{N} y(n - k)y(n - i) \qquad (7.36)$$

is the autocorrelation of the received samples, while

$$\psi(-i) = \sum_{n=-N}^{N} x(n)y(n - i) \qquad (7.37)$$

is the cross-correlation of the received samples with the transmitted
samples, which in the case of error free decisions are known to the
receiver, allows us to express Equation 7.35 as follows:

$$\sum_{k=-N}^{N} c(k)r(|i - k|) = \psi(-i), \quad i = -N \ldots N. \qquad (7.38)$$

Similarly to Equation 7.21, Equation 7.38 also represents a set of
$(2N + 1)$ simultaneous equations, from which the equaliser coefficients $c(k)$ can be determined. The sole difference arises at the right
hand side of Equation 7.38, where now we have the cross-correlation
between the received samples $y(n)$ and the transmitted samples $x(n)$
that are assumed to be locally known. This implies either that the received signal $y(n)$ is an error-free replica of $x(n)$ or that an equaliser
training pattern is transmitted, which is known to both the transmitter and the receiver. The solution of Equation 7.38 ensues similarly
to that of Equation 7.21, i.e. either by Gauss-Jordan elimination or
by some recursive method.

For the success of the equaliser training process it is vital to establish initial synchronisation before the training segment is received in
order to ensure that the error signal $e(n)$ is derived from the appropriately synchronised received and locally stored training patterns.

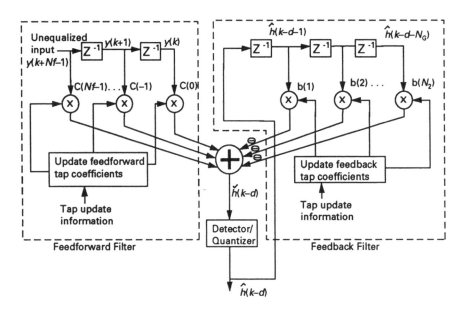

Figure 7.5: General Decision Feedback Equaliser Structure

If the bit error rate (BER) is low, the decision-directed equaliser is capable of tracking slowly varying channel characteristics, such as slow drift in telephone lines, etc. High BERs, however, result in catastrophic error precipitation. In order to attain fast initial convergence, usually a larger step-size is used during the training process, which is reduced to a smaller one during decision-directed operation to maintain a low tracking error.

7.3 Decision Feedback Equalisers

The structure of a general decision feedback equaliser (DFE) is shown in Figure 7.5. The equaliser is composed of a feedforward and feedback section. The feedforward section is identical to the linear equaliser but the feedback section differs in its input. Instead of using the received input signal, a decision is made as to the transmitted symbol, and this value is passed into the feedback section. This leads to a number of advantages. The data passed into the feedback section is the output signal of the detector and hence no longer contains any noise, thus increasing the accuracy of the interference cancellation. The structure of the feedback system implies that the length of the feedback register needs only be as long as the delay spread of the received signal. This is in contrast to the linear equaliser where the equaliser length is governed by the effective length of the infinite impulse response inverse filter, and can easily be an order of magnitude greater than the delay spread.

From Figure 7.5 following Cheung's approach [6] we infer the equalized signal at the detector's input as:

$$\check{h}(k-d) = \sum_{m=0}^{N_f - 1} c(m)y(k+m) - \sum_{p=1}^{N_b} b(p)\hat{h}(k-d-p), \qquad (7.39)$$

which has been delayed by d sampling intervals. The error signal $e(k-d)$ between the transmitted signal $x(k-d)$ and the equalized signal $\check{h}(k-d)$ can be expressed by the help of Equation 7.39 as follows:

$$
\begin{aligned}
e(k-d) \;&=\; x(k-d) - \check{h}(k-d) \qquad\qquad\qquad\qquad\quad (7.40) \\
&=\; x(k-d) - \sum_{m=0}^{N_f - 1} c(m)y(k+m) + \sum_{p=1}^{N_b} b(p).\hat{h}(k-d-p)
\end{aligned}
$$

Using the minimum *mse* criterion requires the minimisation of the expected value

$$\epsilon = E\{|e(k-d)|^2\}. \qquad (7.41)$$

As we have seen in the previous section, this is achieved by that equaliser setting, which renders the error signal $e(k-d)$ uncorrelated with the equaliser's input signal. As regards to the forward filter this requires

$$E\{e(k-d) \cdot y^*(k+m)\} = 0 \quad m = 0\ldots(N_f - 1) \qquad (7.42)$$

and for the backward filter:

$$E\{e(k-d) \cdot \hat{h}^*(k-d-q)\} = 0 \quad q = 1\ldots N_b \qquad (7.43)$$

where the superscript * represents conjugate complex computation. Supposing that no decision errors have been encountered, we have

$$\hat{h}(k - d) = x(k - d) \tag{7.44}$$

i.e., the detector's output signal is an identical replica of the transmitted signal. Upon substituting Equation 7.40 into Equation 7.43 we arrive at:

$$E\{\left[x(k - d) - \sum_{m=0}^{N_f-1} c(m)y(k + m) + \sum_{p=1}^{N_b} b(p)\hat{h}(k - d - p)\right] \tag{7.45}$$
$$\cdot\hat{h}^*(k - d - q)\} = 0 \quad q = 1\ldots N_b$$

and taking into account Equation 7.44 yields:

$$E\{\left[x(k - d) - \sum_{m=0}^{N_f-1} c(m)y(k + m) + \sum_{p=1}^{N_b} b(p)x(k - d - p)\right] \tag{7.46}$$
$$\cdot x^*(k - d - q)\} = 0 \quad q = 1\ldots N_b.$$

For the random uncorrelated transmitted signal samples we have:

$$E\{x(k - d - p) \cdot x^*(k - d - q)\} = \begin{cases} 1 & \text{for } p = q \\ 0 & \text{otherwise} \end{cases} . \tag{7.47}$$

The received signal $y(k)$ is the convolution of the L_c samples long channel impulse response $g(k)$ and the transmitted signal $x(k)$ contaminated by the additive noise $n(k)$, as shown below:

$$y(k) = \sum_{i=0}^{L_c-1} g(i) \cdot x(k - i) + n(k). \tag{7.48}$$

Taking Equation 7.47 and 7.48 into account, Equation 7.46 can be written as:

$$\sum_{m=0}^{N_f-1} c(m) \sum_{i=0}^{L_c-1} E\{[g(i)x(k + m - i) + n(k + m)] \cdot x^*(k - d - q)\}$$
$$= \sum_{p=1}^{N_b} b(p)E\{x(k - d - p) \cdot x^*(k - d - q)\} \quad q = 1\ldots N_b$$

$$\tag{7.49}$$

Exploiting the orthogonality of the additive noise $n(k+m)$ and transmitted signal $x(k - d - q)$ we have:

$$E\{n(k+m) \cdot x^*(k - d - q)\} = E\{n^*(k + m)x(k - d - p)\} = 0 \quad (7.50)$$

and therefore Equation 7.50 simplifies to:

$$\sum_{m=0}^{N_f-1} c(m)g(m + d + q) = b(q) \quad q = 1 \dots N_b. \quad\quad (7.51)$$

Explicitly, Equation 7.51 is a set of N_b simultaneous equations delivering the feed-back filter's coefficients $b(q)$, $q = 1 \dots N_b$ as a function of the feed-forward filter coefficients $c(m)$, $m = 0 \dots (N_f - 1)$, and that of the channel impulse response $g(m + d + q)$. The feed-forward coefficients can be determined using Equation 7.21, while the channel impulse response is derived by means of channels sounding methods.

7.4 Fast Converging Equalisers

As we have seen in Section 7.2.2, the stochastic gradient method is a low-complexity equaliser coefficient adjustment technique, which exhibits slow convergence properties. Considerably faster convergence can be attained using a computationally more demanding recursive coefficient adjustment technique, which is referred to as Kalman filtering [8].

Kalman filtering is a fast converging spectral estimation algorithm for the solution of Wiener–Hopf type normal equations and it has been well documented in references on adaptive filtering and channel equalization [1, 4, 5], . In our deliberations we follow the approach of Proakis [1] and Haykin [5].

7.4.1 Least Squares Method

The minimum mean squared estimation method used in Section 7.2.2 and 7.2.3 was based on a statistical ensemble average minimisation of the square of the error signal, which led to the standard Wiener–Hopf equations given in Equation 7.21 or Equation 7.38. The set of simultaneous equations was then solved by matrix inversion, recursive solutions or by the computationally simple steepest descent

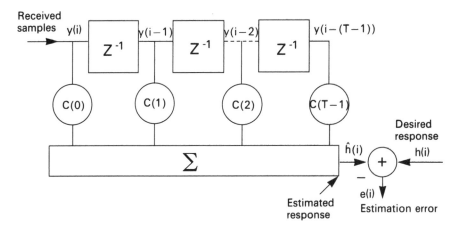

Figure 7.6: LS equaliser structure

algorithm, which yielded slow convergence due to applying a common step-size d, as seen in Equation 7.29.

In contrast, the least squares (LS) method's optimisation criterion is expressed in terms of a time-average, rather than ensemble average. The LS estimation problem is then formulated as estimating the required equaliser output sequence $h(i)$ by $\hat{h}(i)$ from its input sequence $y(i)$ by the help of the equaliser coefficients $c(t)$, using a linear relationship similar to that in Equation 7.31,

$$h(i) = \sum_{t=0}^{T-1} c(t)y(i-t) + e(i) \qquad (7.52)$$

where the index t is used to emphasize the notion of time-dependence and $e(i)$ represents the random estimation error. This scheme is depicted in Figure 7.6. In other words, Equation 7.52 states that the required equaliser output sample $h(i)$ can be estimated from the previous T received samples by a linear combination, where the random estimation error $e(i)$ has zero mean and a variance of σ^2. This formulation of the estimation problem is identical to the linear regression model often used in source encoding theory.

Our approach is now to find the equaliser coefficients $c(t)$, which minimise the cost function defined as the sum of error squares over a finite interval. The estimation error is expressed from Equation 7.52

as follows:

$$e(i) = h(i) - \hat{h}(i)$$

$$= h(i) - \sum_{t=0}^{T-1} c(t)y(i - t). \tag{7.53}$$

Then the optimisation cost function ϵ depends on the equaliser coefficients $c(t)$, $t = 0 \ldots T - 1$ and can be expressed as:

$$\epsilon = \sum_i |e(i)|^2$$

$$= \sum_i |h(i) - \sum_{t=0}^{T-1} c(t)y(i - t)|^2, \tag{7.54}$$

where the interval over which minimisation is carried out depends on the data windowing method invoked. Observing that our cost function ϵ to be minimised in Equation 7.54 is similar to that of Equation 7.32 in Section 7.2.3 and setting the range over which optimisation is carried out in accordance with the covariance method to $i = 1 \ldots I$, the equaliser coefficients can be computed.

Setting the partial derivatives of Equation 7.54 with respect to the equaliser coefficients $c(t)$, $t = 0 \ldots T - 1$ to zero gives a similar set of equations to Equation 7.38, which is shown below:

$$\sum_{t=0}^{T-1} c(t)\Phi(t, k) = \psi(-k), \ \ k = 0 \ldots (T - 1) \tag{7.55}$$

Here

$$\psi(-k) = \sum_{i=1}^{I} h(i)y(i - k), \ \ k = 0 \ldots (T - 1) \tag{7.56}$$

is the time-averaged cross-correlation between the equaliser's input signal $y(i)$ and its desired output signal $h(i)$, $c(t)$ represents the equaliser coefficients, while

$$\phi(t, k) = \sum_{i=1}^{I} y(i - k)y(i - t), \ \ 0 \le t, \ k \le T - 1 \tag{7.57}$$

is the time-averaged correlation of $y(i)$. In matrix form we have:

$$\Phi \cdot c = \Psi \tag{7.58}$$

or explicitly:

$$
\begin{pmatrix}
\phi(0,0) & \phi(1,0) & \phi(2,0) & \cdots & \phi(T-1,0) \\
\phi(0,1) & \phi(1,1) & \phi(2,1) & \cdots & \phi(T-1,1) \\
\phi(0,2) & \phi(1,2) & \phi(2,2) & \cdots & \phi(T-1,2) \\
\vdots & \vdots & \vdots & & \vdots \\
\phi(0,T-1) & \phi(1,T-1) & \phi(2,T-1) & \cdots & \phi(T-1,T-1)
\end{pmatrix}
$$

$$
\begin{bmatrix}
c(0) \\
c(1) \\
c(2) \\
\vdots \\
c(T-1)
\end{bmatrix}
=
\begin{bmatrix}
\psi(0) \\
\psi(-1) \\
\psi(-2) \\
\vdots \\
\psi(-T+1)
\end{bmatrix} .
$$

$$(7.59)$$

The elements of ϕ can be computed from Equation 7.57 as follows:

$$
\phi(0,0) = y(1)y(1) + \ldots + y(I)y(I) \tag{7.60}
$$

$$
= \sum_{i=1}^{I} y(i)y(i)
$$

$$
\phi(0,1) = y(0)y(1) + \ldots + y(I-1)y(I)
$$

$$
= \sum_{i=1}^{I} y(i-1)y(i)
$$

$$
\vdots
$$

$$
\phi(0,T-1) = y(2-T)y(1) + \ldots + y(I-T+1)y(I)y(I)
$$

$$
= \sum_{i=1}^{I} y(i-T+1)y(i)
$$

$$
\phi(1,0) = y(1)y(0) + \ldots + y(I)y(I-1)
$$

$$
= \sum_{i=1}^{I} y(i)y(i-1)
$$

$$
\phi(1,1) = y(0)y(0) + \ldots + y(I-1)y(I-1)
$$

$$
= \sum_{i=1}^{I} y(i-1)y(i-1)
$$

$$
\vdots
$$

$$
\phi(1,T-1) = y(2-T)y(0) + \ldots + y(I-T+1)y(I-1)
$$

$$
= \sum_{i=1}^{I} y(i-T+1)y(i-1)
$$

$$\vdots$$

$$
\begin{aligned}
\phi(T-1,0) &= y(1)y(2-T) + \ldots + y(I)y(I-T+1) \\
&= \sum_{i=1}^{I} y(i)y(i-T+1)
\end{aligned}
$$

$$\vdots$$

$$
\begin{aligned}
\phi(T-1,T-1) &= y(2-T)y(2-T) + \ldots + y(I-T+1)y(I-T+1) \\
&= \sum_{i=1}^{I} y(i-T+1)y(i-T+1)
\end{aligned}
$$

The diagonal elements of the matrix Φ are now not identical, so it does not have a Töplitz structure. The equaliser coefficients optimised for the interval $i = 1 \ldots I$ can be found from Equation 7.58 by simply inverting the matrix Φ or using more efficient recursive algorithms. Having presented the fundamental principles of LS estimation, in the next subsection we present a recursive LS (RLS) algorithm for equaliser coefficient adjustment.

7.4.2   Recursive Least Squares Method [5]

7.4.2.1   Cost-Function Weighting

The principle of the RLS algorithm is that given the current LS equaliser coefficient set, it is possible to update this set, when new equaliser input samples arrive. The RLS algorithm converges quickly, but has a high complexity, as we will see. The cost function, ϵ, of RLS estimation usually contains an exponentially decaying multiplicative weighting factor β^{n-i} in order to reduce the effect of "old" error terms and emphasize more recent ones, as seen below:

$$\epsilon = \sum_{i=1}^{n} \beta^{n-i} |e(i)|^2, \tag{7.61}$$

where the error term $e(i)$ was given in Equation 7.53. The factor β is typically close to, but less than unity, and the number of error terms n in the cost function above is variable. This is because in the RLS method the computations commence from a known initial state determined for example by the LS method described in the previous subsection, and new received samples are then used to update previous estimates. For the observation interval n the equaliser coefficients $c(t), t = 0 \ldots (T - 1)$ remain unchanged.

For our further deliberations it is useful to introduce the vector of equaliser input samples, which can be complex valued:

$$y(i) = [y(i), y(i - 1), y(i - 2) \ldots y(i - (T - 1))]^T, \qquad (7.62)$$

where the superscript T means transposition. Then we can express the correlation matrix $\Phi(n)$ for the observation interval n as follows:

$$\Phi(n) = E\left\{y(i) \cdot y^{*T}(i)\right\} = \sum_{i=1}^{n} y(i) \cdot y^{*T}(i) =$$

$$\begin{bmatrix} \sum_{i=1}^{n} y(i)y^*(i) & \cdots & \sum_{i=1}^{n} y(i)y^*(i - T + 1) \\ \sum_{i=1}^{n} y(i-1)y^*(i) & \cdots & \sum_{i=1}^{n} y(i-1)y^*(i - T + 1) \\ \vdots & & \vdots \\ \sum_{i=1}^{n} y(i-T+1)y^*(i) & \cdots & \sum_{i=1}^{n} y(i-T+1)y^*(i - T + 1) \end{bmatrix}.$$

$$(7.63)$$

Observe that apart from the upper summation limit n this matrix has the same elements as in the previous subsection.

The key-equation in Equation 7.55 or 7.58 is now defined in terms of the modified correlation matrix incorporating the exponential scaling factor β^{n-i} as seen below:

$$\Phi(n) = \sum_{i=1}^{n} \beta^{n-i} y(i) \cdot y^{*T}(i), \qquad (7.64)$$

while the cross-correlation $\Psi(n)$ takes the form of:

$$\Psi(n) = \sum_{i=1}^{n} \beta^{n-i} y(i) \cdot h^*(i). \qquad (7.65)$$

7.4.2.2 Recursive Correlation Update

Since we intend to derive a recursive update formula for $\Phi(n)$ based on its previous value, we separate the last term from the summation in Equation 7.64 yielding:

$$\Phi(n) = \beta \left[\sum_{i=1}^{n-1} \beta^{n-i-1} y(i) \cdot y^{*T}(i) \right] + y(n)y^{*T}(n), \qquad (7.66)$$

where the square bracketed term can be recognised as $\Phi(n-1)$. Hence Equation 7.66 can be simplified to the required recursive relationship given below:

$$\Phi(n) = \beta\Phi(n-1) + y(n)y^{*T}(n), \tag{7.67}$$

where the matrix given by the outer product $y(n)y^{*T}(n)$ constitutes the correction term in the update process. Analogously, the update formula for $\Psi(n)$ accrues as follows:

$$\Psi(n) = \beta\Psi(n-1) + y(n)h^{*}(n). \tag{7.68}$$

Again, similarly to the LS method, the normal equations given by Equation 7.58 have to be solved either by matrix inversion, or preferably by computationally more efficient recursive methods for $n = 1, 2 \ldots \infty$. According to Haykin [5] this can be achieved using Woodbury's identity [7], which is also known as the matrix inversion lemma, if the matrix $\Phi(n)$ is non-singular, i.e., it has a non-zero determinant and hence it is invertible.

7.4.2.3 The Ricatti Equation of RLS Estimation

Upon exploiting Woodbury's identity the following recursive formula accrues for the inverted matrix Φ^{-1} [5]:

$$\Phi^{-1}(n) = \beta^{-1}\Phi^{-1}(n-1) - \frac{\beta^{-2}\Phi^{-1}(n-1)y(n)y^{*T}(n)\Phi^{-1}(n-1)}{1 + \beta^{-1}y^{*T}(n)\Phi^{-1}(n-1)y(n)} \tag{7.69}$$

This is already an explicit recursive expression for updating $\Phi^{-1}(n-1)$, when new received signal samples $y(n)$ become available, which can be further streamlined using the following shorthand:

$$k(n) = \frac{\beta^{-1}\Phi^{-1}(n-1)y(n)}{1 + \beta^{-1}y^{*T}(n)\Phi^{-1}(n-1)y(n)}, \tag{7.70}$$

where $k(n)$ is a $T \times 1$ vector, since the numerator is a $T \times 1$ vector, while the denominator is a scalar. Then we have:

$$\Phi^{-1}(n) = \beta^{-1}\Phi^{-1}(n-1) - \beta^{-1}k(n)y^{*T}(n)\Phi^{-1}(n-1), \tag{7.71}$$

which is the so-called Ricatti equation of RLS estimation [5]. The vector expression $k(n)$ in Equation 7.70 can further be simplified by multiplying both sides of it with the denominator, giving:

$$k(n) + \beta^{-1}k(n)y^{*T}(n)\Phi^{-1}(n-1)y(n) = \beta^{-1}\Phi^{-1}(n-1)y(n)$$

which leads to:

$$\begin{aligned}
k(n) &= \beta^{-1}\Phi^{-1}(n)y(n) - \beta^{-1}k(n)y^{*T}(n)\Phi^{-1}(n-1)y(n) \\
&= \left[\beta^{-1}\Phi^{-1}(n) - \beta^{-1}k(n)y^{*T}(n)\Phi^{-1}(n-1)\right]y(n).
\end{aligned}$$
$$(7.72)$$

Closer scrutiny of Equation 7.71 reveals that the square bracketed term of Equation 7.72 is equal to $\Phi^{-1}(n)$, hence Equation 7.72 simplifies to:

$$k(n) = \Phi^{-1}(n)y(n), \qquad (7.73)$$

which defines the vector $k(n)$ as a transformed version of the received signal vector $y(n)$, where the transformation is carried out by rotating $y(n)$ with the aid of the inverse of the correlation matrix.

7.4.2.4 Recursive Equaliser Coefficient Update

Based on the normal equations in Equation 7.58 and the recursive update formula in Equation 7.68 the estimated equaliser coefficients can be expressed by means of $\Phi^{-1}(n)$ as follows:

$$\begin{aligned}
\hat{c}(n) &= \Phi^{-1}(n)\Psi(n) \\
&= \beta\Phi^{-1}(n)\Psi(n-1) + \Phi^{-1}(n)y(n)h^{*}(n). \qquad (7.74)
\end{aligned}$$

Substituting $\Phi^{-1}(n)$ in the first term of Equation 7.74 by Equation 7.71 leads to:

$$\begin{aligned}
\hat{c}(n) &= \Phi^{-1}(n-1)\Psi(n-1) - k(n)y^{*T}(n)\Phi^{-1}(n-1)\Psi(n-1) \\
&\quad + \Phi^{-1}(n)y(n)h^{*}(n). \qquad (7.75)
\end{aligned}$$

Upon substituting the vector

$$\Phi^{-1}(n-1)\Psi(n-1) = \hat{c}(n-1) \qquad (7.76)$$

into Equation 7.75 we arrive at:

$$\hat{c}(n) = \hat{c}(n-1) - k(n)y^{*T}(n)\hat{c}(n-1) + \Phi^{-1}(n)y(n)h^{*}(n). \quad (7.77)$$

Exploiting Equation 7.73 simplifies Equation 7.77 even further to:

$$\begin{aligned}
\hat{c}(n) &= \hat{c}(n-1) - k(n)y^{*T}(n)\hat{c}(n-1) + k(n)h^{*}(n) \\
&= \hat{c}(n-1) + k(n)\left[h^{*}(n) - y^{*T}(n)\hat{c}(n-1)\right] \\
&= \hat{c}(n-1) + k(n)i(n) \quad\quad\quad\quad\quad\quad (7.78)
\end{aligned}$$

where

$$i(n) = h^{*}(n) - y^{*T}(n)\hat{c}(n-1) \quad (7.79)$$

represents an estimation error term given by the difference of the desired equaliser output $h^{*}(n)$ and its estimate $y^{*T}(n)\hat{c}(n-1)$. In this light the estimation error term of Equation 7.79 is weighted in Equation 7.78 by the gain vector $k(n)$ in order to update the equaliser coefficient set $\hat{c}(n-1)$ to arrive at the RLS estimate $\hat{c}(n)$. Since the estimate $y^{*T}(n)\hat{c}(n-1)$ of $h^{*}(n)$ is based on the previous RLS estimate $\hat{c}(n-1)$, the estimation error term $i(n)$ in Equation 7.79 is an *a priori* estimation error, as opposed to the *a posteriori* estimation error of

$$e(n) = h(n) - \hat{c}^{*T}(n)y(n). \quad (7.80)$$

In other words, $i(n)$ is the estimation error, which would arise without updating the equaliser coefficients from $\hat{c}(n-1)$ to $\hat{c}(n)$. Due to updating the error reduces to $e(n)$, which was our cost function given in Equation 7.53 in the RLS estimation procedure.

In summary, the RLS equaliser coefficient estimation algorithm is specified by Equations 7.70, 7.79, 7.78 and 7.71, which are repeated for convenience:

$$k(n) = \frac{\beta^{-1}\Phi^{-1}(n-1)y(n)}{1 + \beta^{-1}y^{*T}(n)\Phi^{-1}(n-1)y(n)}$$

$$i(n) = h^{*}(n) - y^{*T}(n)\hat{c}(n-1)$$

$$\hat{c}(n) = \hat{c}(n-1) + k(n)i(n)$$

$$\Phi^{-1}(n) = \beta^{-1}\Phi^{-1}(n-1) - \beta^{-1}k(n)y^{*T}(n)\Phi^{-1}(n-1).$$

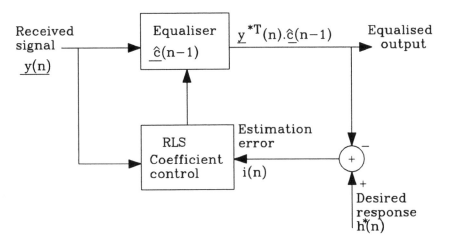

Figure 7.7: Kalman Filtering Block Diagram [5]©Prentice Hall, 1984, Haykin

Observe that Equation 7.79 describes how the received signal $y(n)$ is equalized by the coefficient set $\hat{c}(n-1)$, giving an equalized output of $\hat{c}(n-1) \cdot y^{*T}(n)$, as seen in Figure 7.7. The estimation error $i(n)$ is computed according to Equation 7.79 and it is weighted by the so-called Kalman–gain factor $k(n)$ in the computation of the new set of equaliser coefficients, as portrayed by Equation 7.78. Before the recursion enters a new iteration cycle, the inverse of the correlation matrix $\Phi(n)$ is updated in harmony with Equation 7.71 and used to compute the next value of $k(n)$ according to Equation 7.70. The sequence of operations is best illustrated by Haykin's signal flow diagram [5] seen in Figure 7.8.

The fast convergence of the RLS Kalman algorithm is particularly important for example in data transmission modems for telephone links, where the length of the equaliser training pattern is limited. If adequate equalization is not established within the training window a new training procedure is initiated, which might be prolonged indefinitely. The Kalman algorithm can also be used in time division multiple access (TDMA) mobile radio systems, where the channel is sounded in every TDMA burst in order to acquire an accurate

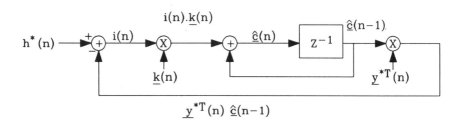

Figure 7.8: Kalman Filtering Signal Flow Diagram [5]
©Prentice Hall, 1984, Haykin

estimate of the non-stationary channel impulse response [6]. In this
scenario the Kalman algorithm is fed with the locally stored original
and received sounding sequence in order to derive the estimate of
the channel impulse response, which can be used for example in a
DFE. Cheung [6] followed this approach in a TDMA mobile scenario, evaluating the channel estimation error for various SNR values
and tabulated the computational complexity associated with various
steps of the algorithm. The convergence rates of the steepest descent
or stochastic gradient and the Kalman algorithm can be characterised by the typical *mse* versus iteration index curves [1], as seen in
Figure 7.9 where an 11-tap equaliser was used.

7.5   Adaptive Equalisers for QAM

The equalisers discussed so far are suitable in their original form for
baseband pulse amplitude modulated (PAM) schemes. If the channel
SNR allows the deployment of QAM, higher bit rates can be achieved
within the same bandwidth using QAM modems [4], [9].

Figure 7.10 shows the schematic diagram of a QAM system with

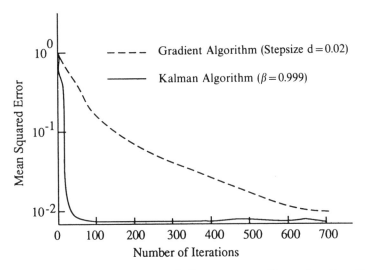

Figure 7.9: Comparison of Convergence Rate for the Kalman and Gradient Algorithm [1]©McGraw Hill, 1989, Proakis

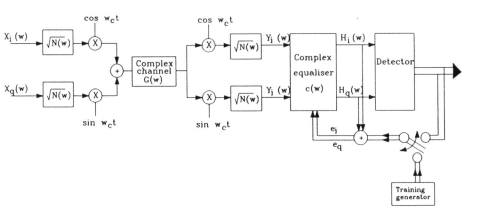

Figure 7.10: QAM System with Complex Adaptive Baseband Equaliser

the square-root Nyquist filters $\sqrt{N(\omega)}$ and an adaptive, complex baseband equaliser $C(\omega)$. In Chapter 2 on communications channels we have shown the equivalence of passband and baseband channels. The passband modulated signal can be portrayed as follows:

$$\begin{aligned} x(t) &= A(t)\cos(\omega_c t + \phi(t)) \\ &= x_i(t)\cos(\omega_c t) - x_q(t)\sin(\omega_c t) \end{aligned} \tag{7.81}$$

where the baseband in-phase and quadrature-phase components are given by:

$$\begin{aligned} x_i(t) &= A(t)\cos[\phi(t)] \\ x_q(t) &= A(t)\sin[\phi(t)] \end{aligned} \tag{7.82}$$

Exciting the complex lowpass equivalent communication channel represented by its impulse response $g(t)$ with the complex baseband equivalent signal

$$x(t) = x_i(t) + jx_q(t) \tag{7.83}$$

the complex baseband system response becomes:

$$\begin{aligned} y(t) &= x(t) * g(t) \\ &= y_i(t) + jy_q(t) \\ &= [x_i(t) + jx_q(t)] * [g_i(t) + jg_q(t)] \\ &= [x_i(t) * g_i(t) - x_q(t) * g_q(t)] + j[x_i(t) * g_q(t) + g_i(t) * x_q(t)] \end{aligned} \tag{7.84}$$

where the quadrature components of the channel output $y(t)$ are given by:

$$\begin{aligned} y_i(t) &= x_i(t) * g_i(t) - x_q(t) * g_q(t) \\ y_q(t) &= x_i(t) * g_q(t) + g_i(t) * x_q(t). \end{aligned} \tag{7.85}$$

Using the above complex baseband representation the system model seen in Figure 7.3 is redrawn in terms of complex QAM signals in Figure 7.11. As seen in the figure, the real in-phase equaliser paths $c_i(t)$ cancel the ISI in both of the received components $y_i(t)$ and $y_q(t)$, while the cross-coupling equaliser paths with impulse responses $c_q(t)$ combat the cross-interference between $y_i(t)$ and $y_q(t)$ caused by channel asymmetries, or clock- and carrier-recovery imperfections. The price paid for the higher spectral efficiency of the QAM modem is its quadruple equalization complexity.

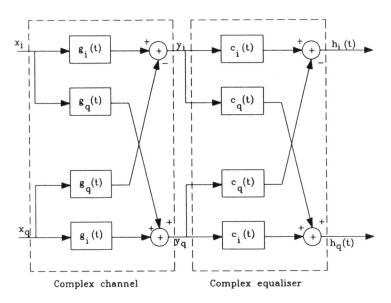

Figure 7.11: Complex Baseband Channel and Equaliser Schematic

7.6 Viterbi Equalisers for Partial Response Modulation

7.6.1 Partial Response Modulation

Although the full treatment of partial response (PR) modulation techniques and that of their equalisation is beyond the scope of this book, for the sake of completeness we briefly highlight the principles of maximum likelihood sequence estimation (MLSE) used for the detection and equalisation of PR systems. The most frequently used MLSE scheme is the Viterbi Algorithm (VA), which can also be invoked for the maximum likelihood detection of trellis coded modulation (TCM) that will be the subject of the next Chapter. For a full treatment of partial response modulation, Viterbi decoding and Viterbi equalisation the reader is referred to Chapters 4 and 6 of reference [3].

The class of constant envelope, continous phase modulation (CPM) schemes is widely used over fading mobile radio channels due to their robustness against signal fading and interference, while maintaining good spectral efficiency. Many of their attractive properties are attributable to the fact that the transmitted signal has a constant envelope, which facilitates the employment of highly power efficient class C amplifiers. In contrast, in QAM systems linearised class AB amplifiers must be used, as we highlighted in Chapter 4. The immunity of CPM to fading is also a consequence of the constant signal envelope, since only the phase changes carry information.

The simplest such constant envelope CPM arrangement is minimum shift keying (MSK), where the modulated signal's phase is constrained to change linearly between adjacent signaling instants over the duration of one signaling interval. Hence MSK is a so-called full-response system. However, the derivative of the phase trajectory has discontinuities at the sampling instants due to its step-wise linear nature, indicating that further spectral efficiency gains are possible, when introducing smoother phase changes.

It is plausible that the slower and smoother the phase changes engendered by the modulating signal, the narrower the modulated signal's spectrum and the better the spectral efficiency. Spreading phase changes with maximally flat zero initial and final slopes over several modulation intervals yields a so-called partial response system. Although this PR scheme introduces inter symbol interference (ISI), this can be removed using appropriately designed channel equalisers, which can cope with the additional deliberately introduced controlled ISI (CISI). An attractive representative of this PR CPM family is called Gaussian Minimum Shift Keying (GMSK), where the phase changes are spread typically over two to four signaling intervals using a Gaussian filter [3].

The schematic of the GMSK modulator is portrayed in Figure 7.13. The impulse response $g(t)$ of the Gaussian filter is given by [10]:

$$g(t) = \frac{1}{2T} \left[Q \left(2\pi B_b \frac{t - T/2}{\sqrt{\ell n 2}} \right) - Q \left(2\pi B_b \frac{t + T/2}{\sqrt{\ell n 2}} \right) \right] \qquad (7.86)$$

for

$$0 \leq B_b T \leq \infty$$

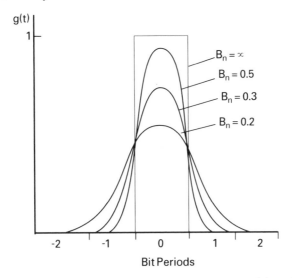

Figure 7.12: Gaussian impulse response $g(t)$ of GMSK for various normalised bandwidths B_N [3] ©Pentech Press, 1992, Steele

where $Q(t)$ is the Q-function

$$Q(t) = \int_{t}^{\infty} \frac{1}{\sqrt{2\pi}} \exp(-\tau^2/2) d\tau \qquad (7.87)$$

B_b is the 3 dB-down bandwidth of the Gaussian phase shaping filter, T is the signaling interval duration and

$$B_N = B_b T \qquad (7.88)$$

is the normalised bandwidth.

The Gaussian impulse response $g(t)$ is shown in Figure 7.12 for different normalised bandwidths B_N.

Observe in Figure 7.13 that the Gaussian filter is preceeded by an integrator, which converts the data-induced input frequency changes to phase changes $\phi(t, \alpha_n)$. Taking the sin and cos of this phase yields the base-band equavalent in-phase and quadrature-phase modulating signals, which modulate two quadrature carriers. Finally, the orthogonal quadrature components are added and transmitted in the same frequency band.

7.6.2 Viterbi Equalisation

A set of standardised dispersive wide-band mobile radio channels used in the Pan-European mobile radio system, known as GSM has

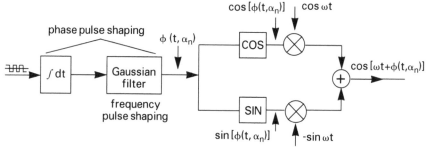

Figure 7.13: GMSK modulator schematic diagram

been introduced in Chapter 2, in Figure 2.21. Since dispersive wide-band channels can be described by impulse responses extending over a number of signaling intervals, their un-controlled ISI must be counteracted by the channel equaliser. Clearly, the equaliser now has to have a longer memory in order to be able to remove the superimposed effects of the channel impulse response plus the CISI introduced by the PR GMSK scheme.

If, however, the transmitted signal's bandwidth is narrow compared to the channel's coherence bandwidth (B_c), all transmitted frequency components encounter nearly identical propagation delays, i.e., the so-called narrow band condition is met and the signal is subjected to non-frequency-selective or flat envelope fading. In this case the channel's impulse response is an ideal Dirac delta, implying no channel induced ISI and the equaliser has to remove solely the CISI.

Both during and after the definition of the GSM standards a number of Viterbi Equaliser (VE) implementations have been proposed in the literature, which have different complexities and performances [11], [12], [13], [14], [16]. A simple general VE block diagram is shown in Figure 7.14.

In conventional time division multiple access (TDMA) mobile systems, such as the GSM system, communications is maintained using transmission bursts, incorporating a so-called midamble sequence in the centre of the burst. This periodically transmitted Dirac delta-like sequence has a sharply decaying auto-correlation sequence, which facilitates for the system to measure the channel's impulse response and hence assists in the equalisation process. Furthermore, since the midamble is typically a 16-bit unique word, its detection using

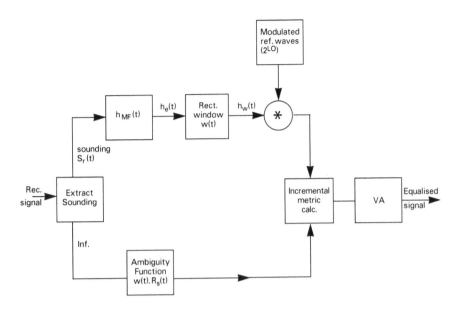

Figure 7.14: MLSE block diagram

autocorrelation facilitates frame synchronisation. This synchroniser concept was briefly introduced already in Subsection 6.2.4.

Explicitly, the modulated TDMA burst with the channel sounding sequence $s(t)$ in its centre is convolved with the channel's impulse response $h_c(t)$ and corrupted by noise. Neglecting the noise for simplicity, the received sounding sequence becomes:

$$s_r(t) = s(t) * h_c(t). \qquad (7.89)$$

Then the received sounding sequence $s_r(t)$ is matched filtered (MF) using the causal impulse response h_{MF}. (For further notes on matched filtering the reader is referred to Subsection 4.4.2.) In order to derive the estimate $h_e(t)$ of the channel's impulse response we can then use the following convolution:

$$h_e(t) = s_r(t) * h_{MF}(t) = s(t) * h_c(t) * h_{MF}(t) = R_s(t) * h_c(t), \quad (7.90)$$

where $R_s(t)$ is the sounding sequence's autocorrelation function. If $R_s(t)$ is a highly peaked Dirac impulse-like function, then its convolution with $h_c(t)$ becomes $h_e(t) \approx h_c(t)$. With $s(t)$ in the middle of the TDMA burst, the estimated channel impulse response $h_c(t)$ can be considered quasi-stationary for the burst duration, and can be used to equalise the useful information bits at both sides of it. However, the time-variant channel typically precipitates higher bit error rates towards the burst edges, where the impulse response estimate becomes less accurate due to the channel's quasi-stationarity.

Since the complexity of the VE increases exponentially with the number of signaling intervals over which the received signal can be spread due to ISI and CISI, the estimated channel response $h_c(t)$ has to be windowed to a computationally affordable length using the rectangular function $w(t)$. However, it has to retain a sufficiently long memory to compensate for the typical channel impulse responses encountered. Specifically, in addition to the duration L_{CISI} of the controlled ISI, also the channel's delay-spread L_c has to be considered in calculating the required observation interval $L_o = L_{CISI} + L_c$ of the 2^{L_o-1}-state VE.

In order to augment our exposition, we invoke the GSM system's example. When using a bit interval of 3.69 μs corresponding to the GSM TDMA burst rate of about 270 kbits/s and a maximum channel impulse response duration of around 15–20 μs, as seen in Figure 2.21, a VE with a memory of 4-6 bit intervals is a good compromise. Note that $h_c(t)$ might have an excessively long decay time and hence for practical reasons it is retained over that particular 4-6 bit interval of its total time domain support length, where it is exhibiting the highest energy. In general, L_o consecutive transmitted bits give rise to 2^{L_o} possible transmitted sequences, which are first input to a local modulator to generate the modulated waveforms, and then convolved with the windowed estimated channel response $h_w(t)$ in order to derive the legitimate reference waveforms for metric calculation, as portrayed in Figure 7.14.

Recall that the condition $h_e(t) = h_c(t)$ is met, ie. the estimated impulse response is identical to the true channel impulse response only, if $R_s(t)$ is the Dirac delta function. This condition cannot be met when finite-length sounding sequences are used. The true channel response $h_c(t)$ could only be computed by deconvolution from Equation 7.90 upon neglecting the rectangular window $w(t)$, which does not give a unique decomposition. Alternatively, the received signal can be convolved for the sake of metric calculation with the known windowed autocorrelation function $w(t) \cdot R_s(t)$ often referred to as ambiguity function, as seen in the lower branch of Figure 7.14 after extracting the sounding sequence from the received TDMA burst. Clearly, this way the received signal is 'predistorted' using the ambiguity function, identically to the estimated impulse response in Equation 7.90. This filtered signal is then compared to all possible locally generated reference signals and the incremental metrics m_i, $i = 0 \ldots (2^{L_o-1})$ are computed. Lastly, the incremental metrics are utilised by the Viterbi algorithm (VA) in order to determine the maximum likelihood transmitted sequence, as explained in references [3], [16]. Suffice to note here that the maximum likelihood transmitted sequence is identified on the basis of the metrics by finding the specific reference sequence that has the lowest deviation from the currently processed received sequence. The same procedure can be used in order to infer the maximum likelihood transmitted trellis coded sequence in the next Chapter.

7.7 Summary

This chapter has briefly dealt with the issue of equalisers for QAM transmissions, and has given a brief summary of conventional equalization techniques. For advanced QAM equalization strategies the reader is referred to Chapter 14 where equalisers for QAM transmissions over dispersive mobile radio channels are considered.

In the next chapter we consider a transmission technique whereby the design of the constellation used in the modulation scheme and the error correction coding used to improve the channel error rate are combined into one system. Such a system can be shown to have distinct advantages and is known as trellis code modulation.

Bibliography

[1] **J.G. Proakis**, "Digital Communications", McGraw-Hill, 1983

[2] **R.W. Lucky, J. Salz and E.J. Weldon**, "Principles of Data Communication", McGraw-Hill, 1968

[3] **R. Steele (Ed.)**, "Mobile Radio Communications", Pentech Press, 1992

[4] **K. Feher**, "Advanced Digital Communications: Systems and Signal Processing Techniques", Prentice Hall, 1987

[5] **S. Haykin**, "Adaptive Filter Theory", Prentice Hall, 1991

[6] **J.C.S. Cheung**, "Adaptive Equalisers for Wideband Time Division Multiple Access Mobile Radio", *Ph.D. Thesis*, Dept. of Electr. and Comp. Sc., Univ. of Southampton, 1991

[7] **M. Woodbury**, "Inverting Modified Matrices", *Mem.Rep. 42, Statistical Research Group*, Princeton University, Princeton, N.J., U.S.A.

[8] **B. Picinbono**, "Adaptive Signal Processing for Detection and Communication in Communication Systems and Random Process Theory", *J.K. Skwirzinsky (Ed.), Sijthof and Noordhoff*, Alphen aan den Rijn, The Netherlands, 1978

[9] **M. Shafi and D.J. Moore**, "Further Results on Adaptive Equalizer Improvements for 16 QAM and 64 QAM Digital Radio", *IEEE Trans. Comms., vol. COM-34, no.1*, pp. 59-66, Jan. 1986

[10] **K.Murota** and **K.Hirade**: "GMSK modulation for digital mobile radio telephony," *IEEE Trans. Commun.*, Vol. 29, pp.1044-1050, Jul 1981.

[11] **L.B. Lopes.** "GSM radio link simulation". *IEE Colloquium, University research in Mobile Radio*, pp. 5/1-5/4, 1990.

[12] **J.C.S. Cheung, R. Steele.** "Modified Viterbi equaliser for mobile radio channels having large multi-path delay". *Electronics Letters, vol.25, no.19*, pp. 1309-1311, 14 Sept., 1989

[13] **N.S. Hoult, C.A. Dace, A.P. Cheer.** "Implementation of an equaliser for the GSM system". *Proc. of the 5th Int. Conf. on Radio Receivers Associated Systems, Cambridge, U.K.*, 24-26 July, 1990.

[14] **R.D'Avella, L. Moreno, M. Sant'Agostino.** "An adaptive MLSE receiver for TDMA digital mobile radio". *IEEE Journal on Selected Areas in Communications, vol.7, no.1*, pp. 122-129, January 1989.

[15] **J.C.S. Cheung.** "Receiver techniques for wideband time division multiple access mobile radio systems". *PhD Mini-Thesis, Univ. of Southampton*, 1990.

[16] **J.B. Anderson, T. Aulin, C.E. Sundberg.** *Digital phase modulation*, Plenum Press, 1986.

Chapter 8

Trellis Coded Modulation

8.1 Introduction

Historically, modulation and forward error correction (FEC) have been treated as distinct subjects, where FEC is typically invoked in order to lower the BER of the modem. However, in his visionary paper of 1974 Massey [1] surmised that treating modulation and FEC as an integrated entity would allow significant coding gains to be achieved over power and bandlimited transmission media. The first practical coded modulation scheme was proposed by Imai and Hirakawa [2], shortly followed by Ungerboeck's more frequently referenced papers [3, 4] , where the term trellis coded modulation (TCM) is introduced.

During the 1980s TCM has reached a state of maturity and has been incorporated into the CCITT V. Series multi-level modems designed for Gaussian telephone channels (see Chapter 9). With the emergence of widespread digital communications via hostile fading mobile radio channels, researchers turned their attention towards adapting TCM principles for these applications which led to the invention of block coded modulation (BCM) [5]. The importance of coded modulation is evidenced in the large number of conferences [5], special issues [6], and books [7] devoted to this subject.

The motivation for TCM is based on the disadvantages of the conventional approach of using separate modulation and coding blocks. In power limited applications, such as satellite channels, FEC codes can be invoked in order to improve power efficiency at the cost of expanding the bandwidth required. In a bandwidth limited scenario, more bits/symbol can be transmitted but at the cost of increased power requirements. In trellis coded modulation the advantages of higher level modulation are combined with those of FEC, where modulation/encoding and demodulation/FEC decoding form an integral operation.

TCM and BCM were initially deployed over telephone channels. The telephone channel has historically been the scene of the earliest applications of many efficient modulation systems. This is because this ubiquitous medium constitutes a benign channel, being relatively time invariant with a high SNR, normally modelled as 28dB. However, the channel is severely bandlimited between some 300-3000Hz. Calculations of channel capacity [8] showed that uncoded modulation techniques were not realising the full potential of the channel, as also suggested by Figure 2.4. For example, if one-dimensional pulse amplitude modulation (PAM) is transmitted with m bits per dimension using one of the 2^m equally likely levels, normally $\pm 1, \pm 3, \pm 5, \ldots \pm (2^m - 1)$, then the average energy of each coordinate is given by

$$S_m = (4^m - 1)/3 \tag{8.1}$$

and it then follows that

$$S_{m+1} = 4S_m + 1. \tag{8.2}$$

Therefore, it takes approximately 4 times as much energy (6dB) to send a further 1 bit/dimension, or 2 bits/symbol. The maximum possible information transmission rate over a noisy channel was determined by Shannon [9] by defining the so-called channel capacity C as

$$C = \frac{1}{2}\log_2(1 + S/N) \; bits/dimension, \tag{8.3}$$

where S is the signal energy, N is the noise energy, and so S/N is the SNR. When $S/N \gg 1$ it takes approximately 4 times as much energy to increase the capacity by 1 bit/dimension. Therefore, the ratio of bits/dimension to channel capacity which is a good measure of how efficiently the channel is being exploited, approaches 1 as S

becomes large. How this high efficiency is achieved is not stated by Shannon, but adding more modulation levels until the maximum channel capacity is reached would initially seem the best approach. Unfortunately, high-level modulation schemes are prone to error and hence joint modulation and coding might contribute better towards approaching the predicted maximum channel efficiency.

However, many authors [1, 10] regard a parameter R_0, defined below, as a better estimate of the maximum rate that is practically achievable where [11]

$$R_0 = \frac{1}{2} \log_2(1 + S/2N) \ bits/dimension. \qquad (8.4)$$

According to Equation 8.4 it therefore takes 3dB more power to signal at a certain number of bits/dimension. The practical potential saving using coding is therefore probably about 3dB/dimension, or 6dB for two-dimensional QAM.

This gain was not achievable using standard coding techniques. It was this which led workers to investigate alternative coding techniques which would actually realise this coding gain.

8.2 TCM Fundamentals

Whilst considerable work has been performed on channel coding (for more details see References [12]- [16]), here we consider a different approach where coding implies the introduction of interdependancies between sequences of signal points such that not all sequences are possible. The surprising consequence of this is that the minimum distance d_0 between two uncoded sequences in 2-dimensional space is increased to d_{min} in an expanded N-dimensional space when coding is used. Use of maximum likelihood sequence detection at the receiver yields a coding gain of a factor of d_{min}^2/d_0^2 in energy efficiency, less the amount of extra energy needed for the transmission of the additional redundant coding bits. Conventional channel coding cannot realise this gain. Instead it is necessary to use a principle described by Ungerboeck [4] as "mapping by set partition" .

The basis of set partitioning is shown in Figure 8.1 and described below. The original constellation shown in Figure 8.1(a) which is

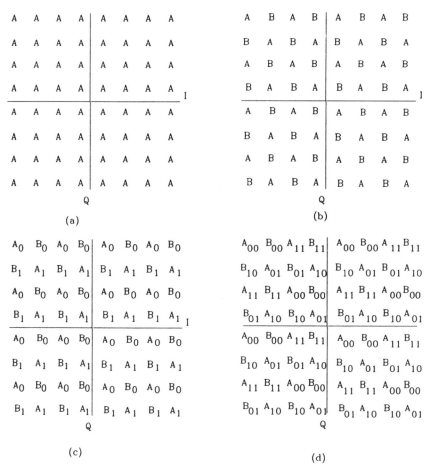

Figure 8.1: Mapping by set partition

64-level square QAM in this example can be initially divided into two subsets (Figure 8.1(b)) by assigning alternate points A and B to each subset. This has the result that the minimum squared distance between points within a subset is twice that between points in the original constellation given by d_0^2. Observe that the points in each subset now lie on a rectangular grid rotated by 45 degrees with respect to the original grid. This procedure can be repeated to yield 4, 8, 16... subsets with similar properties and intra-subset squared distances of 4, 8, 16... times d_0^2. This is illustrated in Figure 8.1 for 2 subsets (A,B) of 32 points, 4 subsets (A_0, A_1, B_0, B_1) of 16 points and 8 subsets (A_{00},...A_{11}, B_{00},...B_{11}) of 8 points. A relatively simple coding technique can then be employed. Some of the incoming six data bits of a modulation symbol are encoded in a channel coder resulting in a larger number of bits due to the coding process. The additional protection bits are used to select which subset the phasor representing the original input bits will be assigned to. The remaining uncoded bits select the specific constellation point to be transmitted within the subset selected. The coding can be either block or convolutional, although convolutional coding has consistently proved both more effective and simpler to implement for Gaussian channels, and so we concentrate our efforts on convolutionally coded TCM.

8.3 8-PSK TCM

It is not our intention here to describe TCM in detail as Ungerboeck has written an excellent tutorial paper [4] which fully describes TCM, and which this section is based upon. Ungerboeck suggested that for an AWGN channel, significant gains could be achieved by expanding the symbol set size and using the extra bit(s) accommodated by a higher level modulation scheme for channel coding, as explained above. In its most common form this is known as Trellis Coded Modulation (TCM).

TCM schemes employ redundant non-binary modulation in combination with a finite state FEC encoder which governs the selection of the modulation signals to generate coded signal sequences. Essentially the expansion of the original symbol set gives more bits per symbol than required by the data rate, and these extra bit(s) are used by a convolutional encoder which restricts the possible state transitions. In the receiver, the noisy signals are decoded by a soft-decision maximum-likelihood sequence decoder. This takes the incoming data stream and attempts to fit it onto each of the legitimate phasor sequences allowed by the constraints imposed by the encoder. The best fit sequence having the minimum Euclidean distance from the received sequence is used as the most likely estimate of the transmitted sequence.

Simple 4-state TCM schemes, where 4-state refers to the number of possible states that the encoder can be in, can improve the robust-

ness of digital transmission against additive noise by 3dB compared
to conventional uncoded modulation. With more complex TCM systems the coding gain can reach 6dB. As opposed to traditional error correction schemes, these gains are obtained without bandwidth
expansion, or reduction of the effective information rate. This is because the FEC encoder's parity bits are absorbed by expanding the
signal constellation in order to transmit a higher number of bits per
symbol. The term "trellis" is used because these schemes can be described by a state transition diagram similar to the trellis diagrams
of binary convolutional codes [16]. The difference is that in the TCM
scheme the trellis branches are labelled with redundant non-binary
modulation phasors rather than with binary code symbols.

We now illustrate the principle of TCM using the example of a
four-state trellis code for 8-PSK modulation, as this relatively simple
case helps understanding of the principles involved. We will then go
on to consider coding schemes suitable for QAM.

The partitioned signal set proposed by Ungerboeck [4] is shown
in Figure 8.2 where the binary phasor identifiers are now not Gray
encoded. Observe in the figure that the Euclidean distance amongst
constellation points is increased at every partitioning step. The underlined last two bits, bit 1 and bit 2, are used to identify one of the
four partitioned sets, while bit 0 finally pinpoints a specific phasor
in each partitioned set.

Signal sets and state transition diagrams for (a) uncoded 4-PSK
modulation and (b) coded 8-PSK modulation with four trellis states
are given in Figure 8.3 while the corresponding four state encoder
modulator structure is shown in Figure 8.4. Observe that after differential encoding bit 0 is fed direct to the 8-PSK signal mapper, whilst
bit 1 is half rate convolutionally encoded by a two-stage four-state
linear circuit. The convolutional encoder adds the parity bit, bit 2,
to the sequence, and these two protected bits are used to identify
which constellation subset the bits will be assigned to, whilst the
more widely spaced constellation points will be selected according to
the unprotected bit 0.

The trellis diagram for 4-PSK is a trivial one-state trellis which
serves to indicate uncoded 4-PSK from the viewpoint of TCM. Every

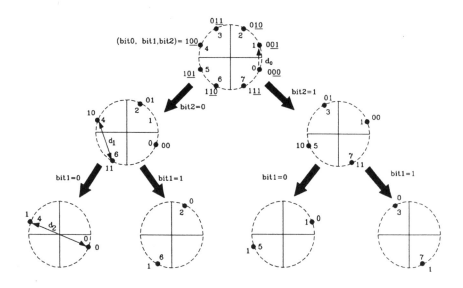

Figure 8.2: 8-PSK set partitioning

connected path through the trellis represents an allowed signal sequence. In both systems, starting from any state, four transitions can occur, as required to encode two bits/symbol. The four parallel transitions in the one state trellis diagram of Figure 8.3(a) do not restrict the sequence of 4-PSK symbols that can be transmitted, i.e. there is no symbol coding and therefore all trellis paths are legitimate. Hence the optimum detector can only make nearest signal decisions for each individual symbol received. The smallest distance between the 4-PSK signals is $\sqrt{2}$, denoted as d_0, and this is termed the free distance of uncoded 4-PSK. Each 4-PSK symbol has two nearest neighbours at this distance. Each phasor is represented by a two bit symbol and transitions from any state to any other are legitimate.

The situation for 8-PSK TCM is a little less simplistic. The trellis diagram of Figure 8.3(b) is constituted by four states according to the four possible states of the shift register of Figure 8.4 which we represent by the four vertically stacked bold nodes. Following the

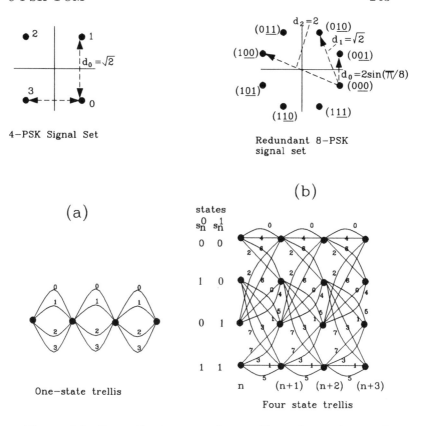

Figure 8.3: Constellation and trellis for 4 and 8-PSK [4]©IEEE, 1982, Ungerboeck

elapse of a signal period a new two-bit input symbol arrives and the convolutional encoder's shift register is clocked. This event is characterised by a transition in the trellis from state S_n to state S_{n+1}, tracking one of the four possible paths corresponding to the four possible input symbols.

In the four-state trellis of Figure 8.3(b) for the coded 8-PSK scheme, the transitions occur in pairs and the states corresponding to the bold nodes are represented by the shift register states S_n^0 and S_n^1 in Figure 8.4. Due to the limitations imposed by the convolutional encoder of Figure 8.4 only a limited set of state transitions associated with certain phasor sequences are possible. These limitations allow us to detect and reject illegitimate decoded sequences. For example, when the shift register of Figure 8.4 is in state $(0,0)$, only trans-

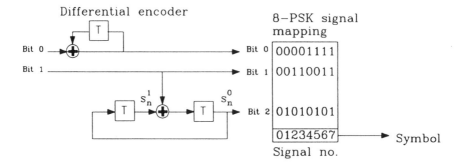

Figure 8.4: Encoder for the four state 8-PSK trellis [4]©IEEE, 1982, Ungerboeck

itions to phasor points (0,2,4,6) are legitimate whilst those to phasor points (1,3,5,7) are illegitimate. Observe in the 8-PSK constellation of Figure 8.3 that the underlined bit 1 and bit 2 identify four twin-phasor subsets whose phasors are opposite to each other and hence have a high intra-subset separation. The unprotected bit 0 is then invoked to select the required phasor point within the subset. Since the redundant bit 2 is also one of the shift register state bits, namely S_n^0, assuming initial states of $(S_n^0,S_n^1) = (0,0)$ or $(0,1)$ only phasors (0,2,4,6) can emerge as also seen in Figure 8.3(b). Similarly, if we have $(S_n^0,S_n^1) = (1,0)$ or $(1,1)$ then the branches emerging from these lower two states of the trellis in Figure 8.3(b) can only be associated with phasors (1,3,5,7).

There are other possible codes, for example four distinct transitions from each state to all possible successor states, but the one selected here proved to be the most effective [4]. Within the 8-PSK constellation we have the following distances: $d_0 = 2\sin(\pi/8)$, $d_1 = \sqrt{2}$ and $d_2 = 2$. The 8-PSK signals are assigned to the transitions in the four state trellis in accordance with the following rules a) Parallel transitions are associated with phasors having a maximum distance of (d_2) between them, which is characteristic of phasor points in the subsets $(0,4)$, $(1,5)$, $(2,6)$ and $(3,7)$. Since these parallel transitions belong to the same subset and are controlled by the un-protected bit 0, symbols associated with them should be as far apart as possible.

b) All four state transitions originating from, or merging into any one state are labelled with phasors having a distance of at least $d_1 = \sqrt{2}$ between them. These are the phasors belonging to subsets $(0,2,4,6)$ or $(1,3,5,7)$.

c) All 8-PSK signals are used in the trellis diagram with equal frequency.

Observe that the assignment of bits to the 8-PSK constellation of Figure 8.3 does not obey Gray coding, adjacent phasors can have arbitrary Hamming distances between them. However, the bit map-ping and encoding process employed is designed to exploit the high Euclidean distances between sets of points in the constellation. The underlined bit 1 and bit 2 representing the convolutional codec's out-put are identical for all parallel branches of the trellis. For example, the branches labelled with phasors 0 and 4 between states $(0,0)$ and $(0,0)$ are associated with bit 1=0 and bit 2=0, while the uncoded bit 0 can be either "0" or "1". However, due to appropriate code design this unprotected bit has a maximum protection distance of $d_2 = 2$, requiring the corruption of phasor 0 into phasor 4 in order to inflict a single bit 0 error.

The effect of channel errors exhibits itself at the decoder by diver-ging from the trellis path in the encoder. Let us consider the example of Figure 8.5, where the encoder traversed through the phasors 0-0-0 from state $(0,0)$, but due to channel errors the decoder's path was different from this, with the phasor sequence 2-1-2 being en-countered. The so-called free distance of a TCM scheme can be computed as the lower one of two distances. Namely, the Euclidean distances between parallel branches in the trellis associated with the uncoded bit(s) which is $d_2 = 2$ in our example, as well as the dis-tances between diverging and remerging trellis paths. The lower one of these two distances characterises the error behaviour of the un-

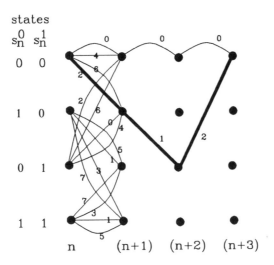

Figure 8.5: Diverging trellis paths for the computation of d_{free}

derlying TCM scheme, since the error event associated with it will be the one most frequently encountered. If the received phasors are at a Euclidean distance larger than half of the code's free distance from the transmitted phasor, an erroneous decision will be made. It is essential to ensure that by appropriate code design the number of decoded bit errors is minimised in the most likely error events, and this is akin to Gray coding a non-trellis coded constellation.

The Euclidean distance between parallel branches is $d_2 = 2$ in our example. The distance between the diverging phasor sequences of 0-0-0 and 2-1-2 portrayed in Figure 8.5 is inferred from Figure 8.3 as d_1-d_0-d_1. By inspecting the trellis in Figure 8.3 we infer that this diverging path is the shortest one that can be found, all other diverging paths have higher free distances from the error-free 0-0-0 path. Furthermore, this is the only path having this minimum free distance. The free distance of this TCM sequence is given by

$$d_{free} = min\{d_2; \sqrt{d_1^2 + d_0^2 + d_1^2}\} \quad (8.5)$$
$$= min\{2; \sqrt{2 + (2.\sin\frac{\pi}{8})^2 + 2}\}.$$

Clearly, the free distance of this TCM scheme is given by the Euc-

lidean distance between parallel trellis branches associated with the
uncoded bit 0, i.e.

$$d_{free} = 2. \tag{8.6}$$

The free distance of the uncoded 4-PSK constellation of Figure 8.3
was $\sqrt{2}$ and hence the use of TCM has given a coding gain of $g = 2^2/(\sqrt{2})^2 = 2$, which corresponds to 3dB. There is only one nearest
neighbour phasor at $d_{free} = 2$, corresponding to the π-rotated phasor
in Figure 8.3. Consequently the phasor arrangement can be rotated
by π whilst retaining all of its properties, but other rotations are not
admissible.

The number of erroneous decoded bits induced by the diverging
path 2-1-2 is seen from the phasor constellation of Figure 8.3 to be
1-1-1, yielding a total of three bit errors. The more likely event of
a bit 0 error which is associated with a Euclidean distance $d_2 = 2$
yields only a single bit error.

The soft decision decoding is accomplished in two steps. The first
step is known as subset decoding, where within each phasor subset
assigned to parallel transitions, i.e. the uncoded bits, the phasor
closest to the received channel output in terms of Euclidean distance
is determined. In the second step the Viterbi algorithm is used to find
a signal path through the trellis with the minimum sum of squared
Euclidean distances from the sequence of noisy channel outputs received. Only the signals already selected by the subset decoding are
considered. For a description of the Viterbi algorithm the reader is
referred to References [12]-[16].

8.4 16-QAM TCM

For the case of, say, 16-level QAM, TCM causes an expansion of
the constellation to a minimum of 32 levels. We then have five bits
per symbol while previously we had four, and the extra bit is used
for FEC encoding. We partition the constellation into eight groups,
known as D-groups, numbered from 0 to 7, each consisting of four
points as portrayed in Figure 8.6. The partitioning is performed in
such a way that the four uncoded constellation points representing
two uncoded bits of any of the eight coded groups are widely spaced

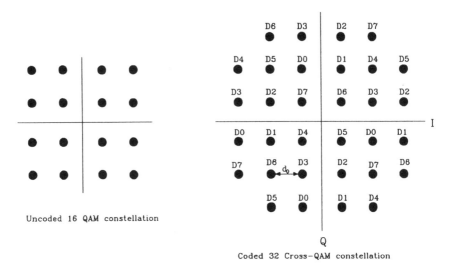

Uncoded 16 QAM constellation

Coded 32 Cross—QAM constellation

Figure 8.6: Set partitioning of a 32-level QAM constellation

across the constellation, thus decreasing the probability that one of these uncoded four points will be mistakenly decoded for any of the other three points within that subset. Such an error would not be corrected as these bits are unprotected. This procedure is adopted for each of the eight sets of four bits. This has the effect that originally neighbouring constellation points reside within different D-groups. An error to a neighbouring point will therefore result in an incorrect D-group being detected. However, due to the FEC coding employed with these groups, this error may be corrected.

Essentially, of the five bits which now constitute a symbol, two bits have a low error probability, and three bits a higher one. The three bits, though, are protected by a 2/3 rate FEC code which has the effect of decreasing the error probability of the two protected bits to near that of the uncoded two bits. It should be noted that no two points of the same D group are in close proximity. Of the incoming data, two bits are directly mapped onto one of the four states in each D-group, and the other two bits are passed to the convolutional encoder which generates a third parity bit. This is shown in Figure 8.7. These three bits are mapped onto one of the eight D-groups.

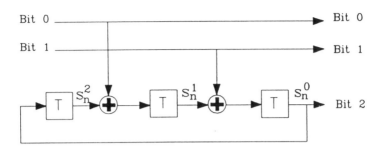

8-state TCM encoder

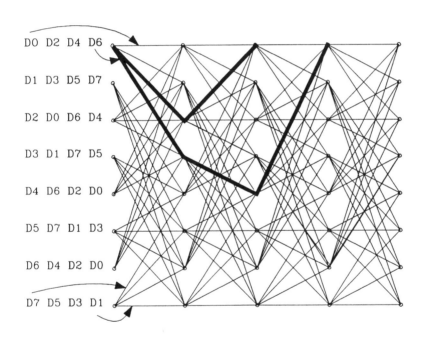

Trellis for 8 state encoder

Figure 8.7: 16-QAM TCM encoder and trellis [4]©IEEE, 1982, Ungerboeck

For this constellation the minimum distance between any two points is d_0. Between phasor points of the subsets forming the first division, i.e. between any point in the set (D0, D2, D4, D6) and any point in the set (D1, D3, D5, D7) the minimum distance will be $\sqrt{2}d_0$ as can be inferred from the geometry of Figure 8.6. Between the points of the subsets forming the next division, i.e. between any point in the set (D0, D4) and any point in the sets (D1, D5), (D2, D6) or (D3, D7), the minimum distance will be $\sqrt{4}d_0$. Finally, between any two points of any subset in the final partition the minimum distance will be $\sqrt{8}d_0$.

Since the convolutional encoder of Figure 8.7 now has three state bits (S_n^0, S_n^1, S_n^2), the trellis representing this TCM scheme has eight states. The redundant bit, bit 2, is also called S_n^0. In the eight state trellis shown, four transitions diverge from and merge into each state. The overall signal set of Figure 8.6 is denoted by A0, which contains 2^{m+1} levels, where $m = 4$ is the original number of bits/symbol required to be sent per modulation interval. Each of the subsets, or D groups, then contains $2^{m-2} = 4$ phasor points. The transitions in the trellis therefore represent $2^{m-2} = 4$ parallel transitions. The assignment of signal subsets to transitions satisfies the same rules as the coded PSK, appropriately adapted to the cross-constellation.

The four transitions to or from the same state are always assigned either the set (D0, D2, D4, D6) or (D1, D3, D5, D7) according to the value of the redundant bit 2. Since each D-group hosts four phasors this allows sixteen legitimate phasors to be transmitted from each node. By consulting Figure 8.6 it can be seen that the intra-subset distances are always larger than the minimum distances between points of different D-groups. The order of assignment of the even or odd transition sets (D0, D2, D4, D6) or (D1, D3, D5, D7) against each of the states in Figure 8.7 can be found by examining the action of the encoder in Figure 8.7. For example, in state (0,0,1), the next to top state on the trellis diagram, an input pair of (bit 1,bit 0)=(0,0) changes the encoder to (1,0,0) and leads to an output of (0,0,0) thus moving from state 1 to 4, the latter being the fifth from top on the trellis diagram. The input pair of (0,0) corresponds to the lowest path number, in this case D1.

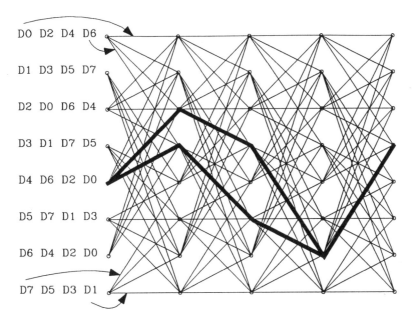

DO D2 D4 D6

D1 D3 D5 D7

D2 D0 D6 D4

D3 D1 D7 D5

D4 D6 D2 D0

D5 D7 D1 D3

D6 D4 D2 D0

D7 D5 D3 D1

Figure 8.8: 16-QAM TCM path differing by the minimum distance

When the decoder's path diverges from the encoder's path at any state in Figure 8.7 this can happen only within either even or odd indexed groups, i.e. from any path associated with (D0, D2, D4, D6) to any other within this set, or from any path in (D1, D3, D5, D7) to any other within this set. This guarantees a squared phasor distance of at least $2d_0^2$ when sequences diverge plus the same amount when they immediately remerge. If paths re-merge after two transitions then the squared phasor distance must be at least $4d_0^2$ when they diverge and $2d_0^2$ when they reconverge, making a total distance of $6d_0^2$. This is shown by the uppermost of the bold sequences in Figure 8.7 which is erroneously decoded when 0-0-0 was transmitted. In the first symbol period a D4 phasor is erroneously decoded when a D0 was transmitted. These points can be seen from Figure 8.6 to be separated by a squared distance of $4d_0^2$. In the second symbol period a D0 subset is erroneously decoded as a D2, with a squared distance between them of $2d_o^2$.

For longer divergent sequences, such as the lowermost bold sequence of Figure 8.7 at least one intermediate transition must contribute an additional squared signal distance d_0^2. This means that the minimum differing path length involves a divergence within a 4 member subgroup giving $2d_0^2$, a transition giving d_0^2 and a reconvergence giving $2d_0^2$, totalling $5d_0^2$. This is smaller than the $8d_0^2$ squared intra-subset distance. The minimum distance is therefore $\sqrt{5}d_0$. Observe that although this lower bold divergent path has remerged one signalling interval later than the upper one, it had a lower minimum distance from the transmitted path.

Two further differing code paths with this distance are shown in Figure 8.8, where the upper bold path indicates the tranmitted sequence, while the lower one indicates the erroneous received one. The divergence at the first node is caused by a D2 transition being erroneously decoded as a D0 transition with a squared Euclidean distance of $2d_0^2$ as can be seen from Figure 8.6. At the next node D4 is erroneously decoded as D1 with a squared Euclidean distance of d_0^2, and at the final node before remerging D7 is erroneously decoded as D1 encountering a squared Euclidean distance of $2d_0^2$. Therefore, the total squared Euclidean distance by which these two sequences differ is $5d_0^2$.

The coding gain for this scheme is given by

$$G_c = 10 \log_{10} \left[\frac{d_{free,coded}^2}{d_{free,uncoded}^2} \frac{E_{uncoded}}{E_{coded}} \right] \qquad (8.7)$$

where $E_{uncoded}$ and E_{coded} are the average signal energy for the uncoded 16-level constellation and coded 32-level constellation, respectively. The increase in terms of squared distance is a factor of 5, and upon adapting Equation 8.1 for the 16-QAM/32-TCM case the increase in signal energy will always be approximately 2. Hence the coding gain $G_c = 10 \log_{10}(5/2) \approx 4$dB.

Ungerboeck surmises [4] that in general it is possible to gain 3dB when using a two-stage shift register associated with four trellis states, 4dB with 8 states, 5dB with 16 states and up to 6dB with 128 or more states. In his paper he publishes code tables giving optimal codes for a number of different modulation schemes and number of encoder states.

8.5 Performance of TCM Under Phase Rotation

Unfortunately, TCM codes are usually not invariant to all phase rotations under which the signal set is invariant. In Figures 8.3(b) and 8.2 we have seen that the 8-PSK TCM constellation was rotationally invariant to a rotation of π, but not for the other multiples of $\pi/4$ over which the constellation itself retains rotational symmetry. Oeder [17] has found 8-PSK TCM constellations having rotational symmetry for $(n.\pi)/4$ rotations but these schemes require more than four states to achieve a coding gain of 3dB. Similarly, Wei [18] found that a code could be made invariant to 90 degree rotations by introducing a non-linear device into the convolutional coder. This system is actually used in the CCITT standard V.32 modem and will be discussed in Chapter 9. This code suffers the penalty of 0.8dB lower coding gain than linear convolutional codes. The system designer must determine whether such a penalty is worthwhile for overcoming false locking problems.

The TCM scheme of Figure 8.3 requires coherent demodulation if low error rates are to be achieved. Where loss of phase synchronisation is unlikely this is not problematic, as by inspection of the metrics in the Viterbi decoder it is possible to determine that an incorrect phase lock has been achieved, and rotate the received constellation appropriately. Alternatively, differential encoding can be used, as discussed in Chapter 11, to overcome this problem, albeit at the cost of a differential encoding SNR or BER penalty.

8.6 Summary

TCM has proved to be a useful coding technique over high SNR bandlimited channels, in particular telephone lines. The original TCM schemes proposed lead to a power efficiency improvement of some 4dB over uncoded schemes for a reasonable decoder complexity. Modern advances have improved this figure slightly but at the cost of a substantial increase in coder complexity. TCM is a rapidly evolving area, in particular for fading mobile channels and is fully explained in two dedicated publications [5, 7]. In this chapter our intention has been to introduce the reader to the principle, and its application to QAM without going into great detail as to the mechanics of the coding scheme. Instead we supply a substantial reference list to allow the reader to investigate TCM to whatever depth they require.

The decoding and demodulation of TCM schemes is typically performed using maximum likelihood sequence estimation (MLSE) based on the Viterbi algorithm. A few associated issues of MLSE for equalisers have been touched upon in Section 7.6, but for a full treatment the reader is referred to references [11]–[16].

In the next chapter we detail the first and most widespread use of TCM, the high bit rate transmission of information over telephone lines, and we show how the combination of quadrature modulation and advanced TCM schemes with channel equalisers has dramatically increased the amount of data which can be transmitted via such a channel.

Bibliography

[1] **J.L.Massey**, "Coding and modulation in digital communications", *Proc. 1974 Int. Zurich seminar on digital communications*, Zurich, Switzerland, ppE2(1)-E2(4).

[2] **H.Imai and S.Hirakawa**, "A new multilevel coding method using error correction codes", *IEEE Tran. Inf. Theory, Vol-IT23*, 1977, pp371-377.

[3] **G.Ungerboeck**, "Channel coding with multilevel/phase signals", *IEEE Tran. Inf. Theory, Vol-IT28*, Jan 1982, pp55-67.

[4] **G.Ungerboeck**, "Trellis-coded modulation with redundant signal sets. Parts 1 and 2", *IEEE Comms Magazine*, Vol.25, No.2, Feb 1987, pp5-21.

[5] **E.Biglieri and M.Luise**, "Coded modulation and bandwidth efficient transmission", *Proc. 5th Int. Workshop*, Elsevier, Netherlands, 8-12 Sept 1991.

[6] **IEEE Comms. Magazine**, "Special issue on coded modulation", *Vol.29, No.12*, Dec.1991.

[7] **E.Biglieri, D.Divsalar, P.J.McLane and M.K.Simon**, "Introduction to trellis coded modulation with applications", *MacMillan Publishing Co.*, New York, 1991.

[8] **G.D.Forney, R.G.Gallager, G.R.Lang, F.M.Longstaff and S.U.Qureshi**, "Efficient modulation for band-limited channels", *IEEE J-SAC*, Vol.SAC-2, No.5, Sept 1984, pp632-647.

[9] **C.E.Shannon and W.Weaver**, "A mathematical theory of communication", Urbana,IL: Univ. Illinois Press, 1949.

[10] **J.M.Wozencraft and R.S.Kennedy**, "Modulation and demodulation for probabilistic coding", *IEEE Trans. Inf. Theory*, Vol.IT-12, 1966, pp291-297.

[11] **J.M.Wozencraft and I.M.Jacobs**, "Principles of communications engineering", *J. Wiley*, 1965.

[12] **R.E.Blahut**, "Theory and practice of error control codes", Addison-Wesley, 1983.

[13] **R.E.Berlekamp**, "Algebraic coding theory", *McGraw Hill*, 1968.

[14] **W.W.Peterson**, "Error correcting codes", *Cambridge, Mass. MIT Press*, 1961.

[15] **A.M.Michelson and A.M.Levesque**, "Error control techniques for digital communications", *J. Wiley*, 1985.

[16] **K.H.H.Wong and L.Hanzo**, in R.Steele (Ed.) "Mobile radio communications", *Pentech Press*, 1992, Chapter 4, pp347-488.

[17] **M.Oeder**, "Rotationally invariant trellis codes for mPSK modulation", *Proc. IEEE ICC'85*, Chicago, June 1985, pp552-556.

[18] **L-F.Wei**, "Trellis-coded modulation with multidimensional constellations", *IEEE Trans Inf. Theory*, Vol.IT-33, No.4, July 1987, pp483-501.

Chapter 9

QAM Modems for Band-Limited AWGN Channels

9.1 Introduction

The most widely used AWGN communication channel is the conventional telephone line. Since its amplitude and group-delay characteristics vary slowly, mainly due to aging, humidity, etc., telephone lines can be considered as linear and time-invariant. They are typically band-limited to 300-3000 Hz and have SNR values around 30 dB. The international lines must comply with the CCITT M1020 Recommendation, the amplitude and group-delay characteristics of which were shown in Figure 2.5.

The early history of modems for AWGN channels is comprehensively documented in Reference [1]. Early data transmission modems designed in the 1950s used frequency shift keying (FSK) at 300 bps for switched telephone lines and at 1200 bps for private or leased lines. From the 1960s onward, in conjunction with the up-grading of the telephone network, the equalised bandwidth was gradually extended to 1200 Hz, 1600 Hz and 2400 Hz. This allowed the signalling rates to increase from 1200 Hz to 2400 Hz, while the higher SNR values facilitated the transmission of several bits per sample.

An important mile-stone was the launch of the first four-phase

Rate (bps)	Baudrate (Bd)	Constellation	Standard	Features
2400	1200	4-DPSK	V.26, 1968	fixed EQ
4800	1600	8-DPSK	V.27, 1972	manual EQ
9600	2400	16-QAM	V.29, 1976	adapt. EQ
9600	2400	32-QAM, TC	V.32, 1984	adapt. EQ
14 400	2400	128-QAM, TC	V.33, 1988	adapt. EQ

Table 9.1: Summary of Modem Features

2400 bps modem in 1962, which was later standardised in the V.26 CCITT Recommendation. This was followed in 1967 by the introduction of the eight-phase differential phase shift keying (8-DPSK), 4800 bps modem using a signalling rate of 1600 Bd and 3 bits/sample transmissions. To achieve this signalling rate over leased lines a manual channel equaliser (EQ) was needed, as specified by the V.27 CCITT Recommendation. However, with rapid advances in digital equalisation, the V.27bis and V.27ter Recommendations quickly followed, proposing adaptive channel equalisation, which allowed operation via switched telephone lines.

In 1971 the first 4 bits/symbol 16-QAM modem was developed, which deployed an advanced channel equaliser to achieve a signalling rate of 2400 Bd. This modem transmitted at 9600 bps over point-to-point 4-wire leased lines and it was standardised in 1976 in the CCITT V.29 Recommendation. This development was further improved to facilitate 9600 bps transmissions via 2-wire switched telephone lines and it was standardised in the V.32 Recommendation in 1984. Although the basic configuration uses a square-shaped 16-QAM constellation, it also has a 32-point trellis-coded option to improve its robustness against channel errors. The most advanced QAM scheme at the time of writing, standardised in 1988 in the V.33 Recommendation, is the 14 400 bps point-to-point 4-wire modem, which is recommended for leased lines. It uses trellis-coded (TC) 128-QAM for 14 400 bps transmissions, but it also allows trellis-coded 64-QAM transmissions at a fall-back rate of 12 000 bps over lower quality channels. The history of point-to-point multi-level modems is summarised in Table 9.1.

9.2 Transmission Bitrate Limits

As we have seen before, in case of square QAM constellations both the I and Q components assume the equi-probable, equi-spaced transmission levels of $\pm d$, $\pm 3d \ldots \pm (2^m - 1)d$, where m is the number of bits per quadrature component. The average energy per quadrature component is then [1]

$$S_m = (4^m - 1)/3, \tag{9.1}$$

which gives for 16-QAM $S_2 = 5d^2$ and for 64-QAM $S_3 = 21d^2$. Then the total constellation energy is $E_{16\text{-QAM}} = 10d^2$ and $E_{64\text{-QAM}} = 42d^2$. From Equation 9.1 follows that

$$S_{m+1} = 4S_m + 1, \tag{9.2}$$

and hence when increasing the number of bits per quadrature component by one, the average energy is increased by about a factor of four or 6 dB.

The channel capacity C of the AWGN channel band-limited to B Hz was determined by Shannon [2] as follows:

$$C = B \log_2(1 + S/N) \text{ bit/sec.} \tag{9.3}$$

Observe that for high $SNR = S/N$ values and constant AWGN power N the channel capacity doubles when the signal power S is quadrupled by transmitting an additional bit per quadrature component, for example when transmitting 64-QAM in place of 16-QAM. In other words, an additional 6 dB channel SNR is required, if the channel capacity is to be doubled by transmitting two extra bits per complex QAM phasor. This fact manifests itself, for example, in an approximately 6 dB shift of the 4 bit/symbol 16-QAM BER curve to higher SNRs, when using 6 bit/symbol 64-QAM transmissions. Assuming that sampling takes place at the Nyquist-rate of $f_s = 2B$, the maximum information conveyed by a QAM channel symbol per quadrature component is

$$\frac{C}{2B} = \frac{1}{2} \log_2(1 + \frac{S}{N}) \text{ bit/quad.comp..} \tag{9.4}$$

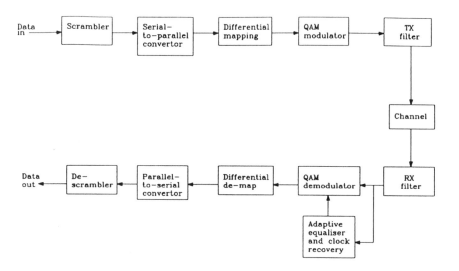

Figure 9.1: General Modem Schematic for Band-Limited AWGN Channels

Using a lower number of bits/quadrature component clearly does not fully exploit the maximum capacity of the channel. Accordingly, in the band-limited telephone channel the achievable transmission rate depends on the number of bits per symbol, which is governed by the channel SNR available.

In the following sections we consider how modems have evolved towards high capacity systems by considering recent CCITT recommendations for modems [5], commencing with the V.29 modem.

9.3   V.29 Modem

The 9600 bps V.29 modem was recommended for use over point-to-point four-wire leased telephone lines, but its users are not precluded from using it over lower quality links. There are provisions for optional fall-back rates of 7200 and 4800 bps, when the channel conditions are hostile. A generic block diagram for all the modems we consider in this chapter is shown in Figure 9.1.

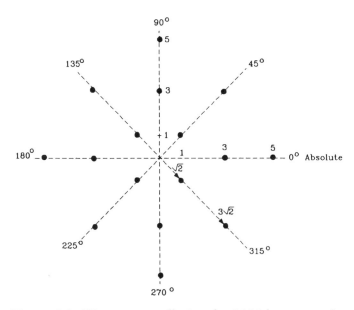

Figure 9.2: Phasor constellation for 9600 bps operation

9.3.1 Signal Constellation

The 9600 bps input data stream is "scrambled" using a linear feed-back shift register in order to assist the carrier and clock recovery operation by preventing a long sequence of logical "1"s or "0"s. The scrambled data sequence is then converted into 4 bit/symbol called "quadbits", which are Gray coded onto the signal constellation depicted in Figure 9.2. The first bit (Q_1) of every symbol determines the amplitude of the signal element to be transmitted, but the amplitude is also dependent on the instantaneous absolute phase, and the two different sets of amplitudes used are given in Table 9.2. The remaining three bits Q_2, Q_3 and Q_4 are differentially Gray coded onto the phase positions, as summarized in Table 9.3. After differential mapping of the bits, 16-QAM modulation is carried out using the signal constellation of Figure 9.2 at a signalling rate of 2400 Bd.

At the fall-back rate of 7200 bps the bit Q_1 is permanently set to zero, limiting the amplitude to either $\sqrt{2}$ or 3, depending on the phase information, as seen in Figure 9.3. Otherwise the mapping

Absolute phase	Q_1	Relative signal element amplitude
$0°, 90°, 180°, 270°$	0	3
	1	5
$45°, 135°, 225°, 315°$	0	$\sqrt{2}$
	1	$3\sqrt{2}$

Table 9.2: Phasor-Amplitude Mapping for the V.29 Modem

Q2	Q3	Q4	Phase change
0	0	1	$0°$
0	0	0	$45°$
0	1	0	$90°$
0	1	1	$135°$
1	1	1	$180°$
1	1	0	$225°$
1	0	0	$270°$
1	0	1	$315°$

Table 9.3: Phasor-Phase Mapping for the V.29 Modem

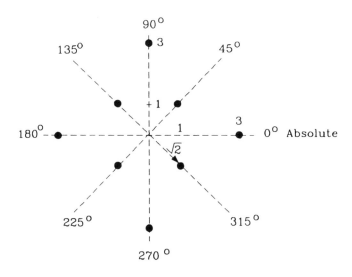

Figure 9.3: Signal Space Diagram at 7200 bps

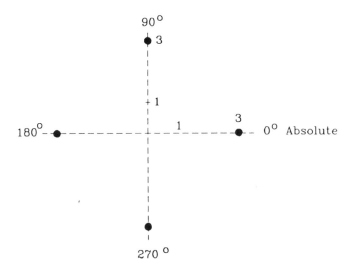

Figure 9.4: Signal Space Diagram at 4800 bps

Data bits		Quadbits				Phase change
		Q1	Q2	Q3	Q4	
0	0	0	0	0	1	0°
0	1	0	0	1	0	90°
1	1	0	1	1	1	180°
1	0	0	1	0	0	270°

Table 9.4: Mapping table for 4800 bps operation

is identical to that of the 9600 bps constellation. The bit rate is $2400 Bd \times 3$ bits/symbol=7200bps. In case of 4800 bps transmissions $Q_1 = 0$ and $Q_4 = (\overline{Q_2 \oplus Q_3})$ are set, where $\oplus$ means modulo 2 addition and (¯) is the inverse of ( ), yielding the mapping summarized in Table 9.4. The resulting constellation is shown in Figure 9.4 and the 2 bits/symbol transmissions at 2400Bd yield a bit rate of 4800bps.

9.3.2 Training Signals

The operation of the adaptive channel equaliser, carrier recovery and timing recovery circuits is aided by the transmission of specific training signals which allow characterisation of the telephone line

Training Segments	Type of line signal	No. sym. intervals	Approx. time (ms)
Segment one	No transmitted energy	48	20
Segment two	Alternations	128	53
Segment three	Equaliser conditioning pattern	384	160
Segment four	Scrambled all binary "1"s	48	20
Total signal	Total synchronising signal	608	253

Table 9.5: Training Signals for the V.29 Modem

in terms of its impulse response, and the establishment of timing references. These are summarised in Table 9.5 for the V.29 modem. The training sequence is split into four segments, each containing different signals. Segment one contains no energy and forms a so-called pre-cursor. Segment two consists of the alternate sequence of phasors A and B for the duration of 128 symbol intervals, where phasors A and B are depicted in Figure 9.5 for the transmission rates of 9600, 7200 and 4800 bps, respectively. Observe in the figure that symbol A determines the absolute phase reference of 180°. The Segment two sequence toggles between two distinct phasor states at a signalling rate of 2400Bd, hence it is periodic at 1200 Hz, therefore having a strong 1200 Hz frequency domain component which assists timing recovery, as explained in Chapter 6. By the time that segment two is finished the timing recovery must be established.

Segment three of the training pattern is designed to initialise the adaptive channel equaliser by transmitting a pseudo-random (PR) sequence of phasors C and D. This pseudo-random sequence can be used to sound the channel. Observe in Figure 9.5 that the phasor D is transmission rate dependent. The PR sequence generator uses the polynomial $p(x) = 1 + x^{-6} + x^{-7}$, and is shown in Figure 9.6, where $\oplus$ represents modulo 2 addition. Every time the PR sequence contains a zero, phasor C is transmitted, while for a logical "1" phasor

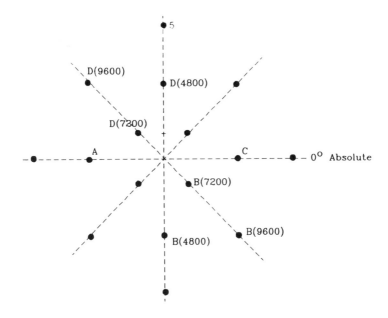

Figure 9.5: Signal Space Diagram Showing Synchronizing
Signal Points

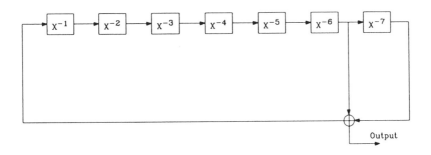

Figure 9.6: Pseudo-Random Sequence Generator

D is sent. The seven-stage PR sequence generator is initialised to 0101010, yielding an initial sequence of CDCDCDC... and continues for 384 symbol durations. Since these phasors are widely spaced in the signal constellation, the transmitted signal becomes similar to that of the 2400Bd BPSK transmissions. These phasors have large Euclidean distances between them and hence are unlikely to be corrupted by AWGN. The same phasors can be used to assist initial equaliser convergence as explained in Chapter 7.

In Segment four of the training sequence 48 scrambled binary "1"s are transmitted for further updating and fine tuning of the clock and carrier recovery circuits. This is because the initial clock and carrier recovery during segment two was performed without equalisation. Now that equalisation is present it is possible to fine-tune these timing recovery circuits. The total training lasts 608 symbol durations amounting to about 253 ms.

9.3.3   Scrambling and Descrambling

Data scrambling and descrambling is invoked in order to assist the clock and carrier recovery circuits by preventing the transmission of long sequences of all "1"s or all "0"s. Its operation is based on the generator polynomial

$$g(x) = 1 + x^{-18} + x^{-23} . \tag{9.5}$$

The scrambler performs a logical operation on the data bits to be transmitted using the generator polynomial $g(x)$. Figure 9.7 shows a suitable circuit structure where D_i are the input data bits and D_s the output data stream. At the beginning of transmissions the switch on the scrambler is set to "0" causing the scrambler to be filled with logical "0"s. During this period the input data bits D_i are part of the training sequence and can be sent unscrambled since the input "0"s do not affect the sequence D_s. During normal data transmission the scrambled data is fed back to the shift register by setting the switch to D_s. Descrambling is carried out by the circuit of Figure 9.8 by performing the inverse operation using the generator polynomial of Equation 9.5.

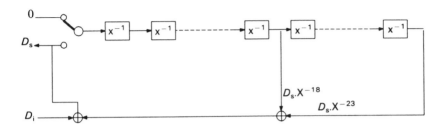

Figure 9.7: V.29 Scrambler

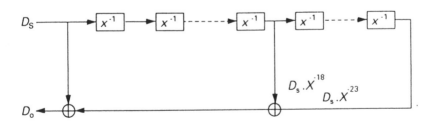

Figure 9.8: V.29 Descrambler

9.3.4   Channel Equalisation and Synchronisation

The use of channel equalisation is compulsory in the modem and the receiver has to be provided with appropriate means of detecting whether the channel has changed significantly since the equaliser training sequence was sent. In this instance the equalisation will no longer be correct, and the receiver sends a training sequence to the original transmitter which indicates to this transmitter that in response it should send another training sequence to the receiver. Upon re-synchronisation the modem also has to be able to detect the four-segment initial synchronisation signal sequence described earlier in Table 9.5. When detecting the reception of the training sequence, say from modem A to modem B, then modem B has to initiate the transmission of its own training pattern.

If modem A does not receive a synchronising signal from modem B within the interval of the maximum expected turn-around delay, which is typically 1.2 sec, it sends another synchronising signal. Also, if modem A fails to synchronise on its received sequence, it transmits another four-segment sequence. The carrier frequency is 1700 Hz and the transmitted spectrum measured when transmitting continuous scrambled logical "1" must have an essentially linear phase over the range of 200–2700 Hz. The energy density has to be attenuated at the frequencies of 500 Hz and 2900 Hz by 4.5 ± 2.5 dB with respect to its level at the carrier frequency.

9.4   V.32 Modem

9.4.1   General Features

The V.32 Recommendation [5] proposes a family of two-wire duplex modems for transmission rates of up to 9600 bps for the general switched telephone network as well as for point-to-point leased telephone circuits. The signalling rate is 2400 Bd and transmission rates of 9600 bps as well as 4800 bps are supported using a variety of QAM constellations. At 9600 bps either square QAM or trellis-coded 32-QAM are used. There is provision for both manual as well as for automatic transmission rate selection. The carrier frequency is 1800 Hz and the spectrum, when transmitting logical "1"s, has to

Inputs		Previous outputs		16-QAM outputs		32-QAM outputs		Signal State
$Q1_n$	$Q2_n$	$Y1_{n-1}$	$Y2_{n-1}$	$Y1_n$	$Y2_n$	$Y1_n$	$Y2_n$	
0	0	0	0	0	1	0	0	B
0	0	0	1	1	1	0	1	C
0	0	1	0	0	0	1	0	A
0	0	1	1	1	0	1	1	D
0	1	0	0	0	0	0	1	A
0	1	0	1	0	1	0	0	B
0	1	1	0	1	0	1	1	D
0	1	1	1	1	1	1	0	C
1	0	0	0	1	1	1	0	C
1	0	0	1	1	0	1	1	D
1	0	1	0	0	1	0	1	B
1	0	1	1	0	0	0	0	A
1	1	0	0	1	0	1	1	D
1	1	0	1	0	0	1	0	A
1	1	1	0	1	1	0	0	C
1	1	1	1	0	1	0	1	B

Table 9.6: Differential Coding for the V.32 Modem

be attenuated by 4.5 ± 2.5 dB at frequencies of 600 and 3000 Hz, when compared to the carrier frequency.

9.4.2 Signal Constellation and Bit Mapping

9.4.2.1 Non-Redundant 16-QAM

The 9600 bps non-redundant square 16-QAM uses a partially differential bit mapping onto the phasor constellation. The scrambled data stream is divided into groups of four bits and the first two bits $Q1_n$ and $Q2_n$ of the nth symbol are differentially encoded to generate the bits $Y1_n$ and $Y2_n$ according to Table 9.6 where the signal state applies to 4800bps. Following this the bits $Y1_n$, $Y2_n$, $Q3_n$ and $Q4_n$ are then mapped onto the square 16-QAM constellation, as shown in Figure 9.9. In case of 4800 bps transmissions the two-bit symbols are generated by differentially encoding $Q1_n$ and $Q2_n$ into $Y1_n$ and $Y2_n$, as specified in Table 9.6. The corresponding phasor subset designated by states A, B, C and D coincides with four of the 16-QAM phasors and is also shown in Figure 9.9.

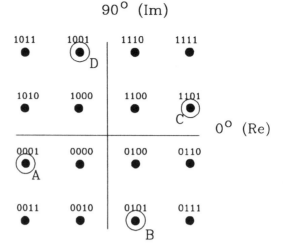

The binary numbers denote $Y1_n$ $Y2_n$ $Q3_n$ $Q4_n$

Figure 9.9: V.32 16-Point Phasor Constellation with Non-Redundant Coding for 9600 bps and Subset A B C D of States Used at 4800 bps and for Training

9.4.2.2 Trellis-Coded 32-QAM

The fundamentals of trellis-coded modulation (TCM) were discussed in Chapter 8, here we focus our attention on its employment in the V.32 modem. The general structure of a trellis-coded 32-QAM modulator is shown in Figure 9.10 [3]. When using $(m + 1) = 5$ bits per QAM symbol, the signal constellation is constituted by $2^{m+1} = 32$ phasors as displayed in Figure 9.11. In our specific case the 32 phasors are subdivided into eight subsets $D0 \ldots D7$, each constituted by four phasors, which are as far apart from each other, as possible. This is shown in Figure 9.12, where the three most significant bits $Y0_n, Y1_n$ and $Y2_n$ are the subset identifiers. Phasors of a subset are encoded by the two least significant bits $Q3_n$ and $Q4_n$.

Phasors of different subsets might be close to each other, hence they are easily corrupted and therefore they need error correction coding. The two most significant bits $Q1_n$ and $Q2_n$ of the four-bit input symbol are therefore $R = 2/3$-rate, constraint length $\nu = 3$ convolutionally coded to yield three bits $Y0_n, Y1_n,$ and $Y2_n$, which select a specific subset, i.e. D-group, of the 32-QAM constellation.

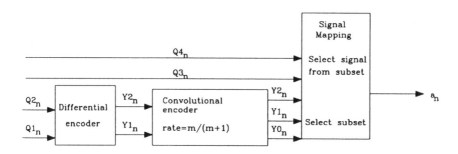

Figure 9.10: General Structure of Encoder Modulator for Trellis-Coded 32-QAM Modulation [3]©IEEE, 1987, Ungerboeck

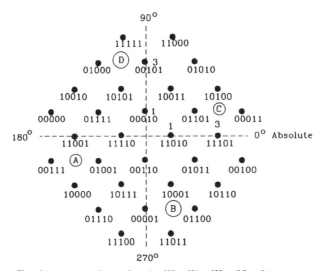

The binary numbers denote YO_n $Y1_n$ $Y2_n$ $Q3_n$ $Q4_n$

Figure 9.11: V.32 32-Point Signal Structure with Trellis-Coding for 9600 bps and States A B C D Used at 4800 bps and for Training

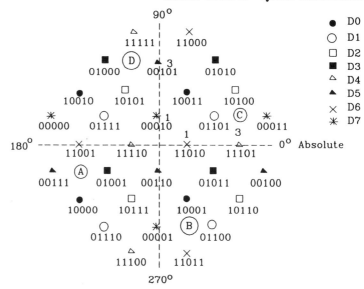

Figure 9.12: V.32 Trellis-Coded Signal Subsets $D0 \ldots D7$

Accordingly, the constraint length $\nu = 3$ code has $\nu = 3$ storage elements and $2^\nu = 8$ trellis states.

TCM schemes have been shown to have significant coding gains over uncoded constellations [3], but Ungerboeck also demonstrated (see Section 8.5) that they are more sensitive to carrier phase offsets than the less dense uncoded constellations. Therefore, in general it is advantageous to design TCM codes having as many rotationally invariant, phase symmetric phasor positions as possible. This would ensure shorter bursts of errors and faster recovery after temporary loss of synchronisation. However, the overall TCM scheme must be rendered transparent to the data, i.e. insensitive to phase rotations, by means of differential encoding and decoding which typically incurs a BER penalty.

A TCM scheme was found by Wei [4] for the 32-QAM constellation of Figure 9.11 that could achieve a coding gain of 4 dB using an 8-state, constraint length $\nu = 3$ code, while retaining 90° phase symmetry. This convolutional encoder contained non-linear elements, as seen in Figure 9.13.

The 32-QAM trellis-coded scheme generates the bits $Y1_n$ and $Y2_n$ from the first two input bits $Q1_n$ and $Q2_n$ by differential coding as

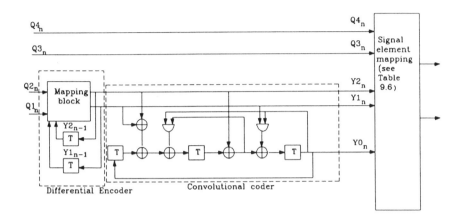

Figure 9.13: Trellis-Coding at 9600 bps [4]©IEEE, 1984, Wei

seen in Table 9.6. The differentially encoded bits $Y1_n$ and $Y2_n$ are then input to the $R = 2/3$-rate systematic convolutional encoder depicted in Figure 9.13. The figure also shows the differential encoding and the mapping onto the 32-QAM signal constellation.

Since the convolutional encoder is systematic, its input bits $Y1_n$ and $Y2_n$ are copied to its output and the simple Boolean logic seen in Figure 9.13 specifies the necessary operations to generate the parity bit $Y0_n$. Finally, the bits $Y0_n$, $Y1_n$, $Y2_n$, $Q3_n$ and $Q4_n$ are mapped onto the trellis-coded 32-QAM constellation displayed in Figure 9.11. Observe that at the fall-back rate of 4800 bps the same states A, B, C and D are used, as in case of the non-redundant constellation of Figure 9.9 but these now do not coincide with any of the legitimate 32-QAM phasors. The I and Q quadrature component coordinates of these states are identical to those of the corresponding states in Figure 9.9 and hence they are distinctly different from the 32-QAM constellation points.

9.4.3 Scrambler and Descrambler

In the V.32 modem each transmission direction uses a different scrambler. The calling modem uses the same scrambler as the V.29 Re-

commendation shown in Figure 9.7, specified by the generator polynomial of Equation 9.5, namely $g_1(x) = 1 + x^{-18} + x^{-23}$. At the
calling modem scrambling is performed by dividing the message data
polynomial by the generator polynomial and the coefficients of the
quotient constitute the scrambled data. The answering modem com-
putes the de-scrambled data signal by multiplying the received data
with the generator polynomial $g_1(x)$, while scrambling is carried out
using:

$$g_2(x) = 1 + x^{-5} + x^{-23}. \tag{9.6}$$

This long division can be carried out by means of a similar circuit
to that of Figure 9.7, however, the feed-back taps of the linear shift
register are at the positions given by the generator polynomial $g_2(x)$.

The initial set-up and training procedures of the V.32 modem are
much more complicated than for the V.29 modem, which were briefly
described in the previous section. These training procedures tend to
use the signalling states A, B, C and D or some subset of them to
assist the initial set-up of the carrier and clock recovery circuitries,
as well as that of the adaptive channel equaliser.

Since this book is concerned with QAM modulation, we will not
consider further standardised features of the V.32 modem. The interested reader is referred to the newest edition of the CCITT V-Series
Recommendations [5].

9.5   V.33 Modem

9.5.1   General Features

The 14 400 bps V.33 modem is designed primarily for special quality four-wire leased telephone lines, which comply with the CCITT
M.1020 Recommendation shown in Chapter 2. It has a 12 000 bps
fall-back rate and includes an eight-state trellis-coded modulator and
an optional multiplexer to combine data rates of 2400 bps, 4800 bps,
7200 bps, 9600 bps and 12 000 bps. The carrier frequency is 1800 Hz
and the signalling rate is 2400 Baud. The scrambler's and descrambler's generator polynomial is identical to that of the V.29 modem,
namely $g(x) = 1 + x^{-18} + x^{-23}$.

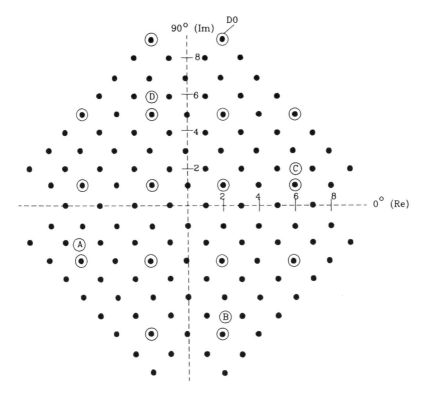

Figure 9.14: Signal Space Diagram and Mapping for Trellis-
Coded Modulation at 14 400 bps

9.5.2 Signal Constellations and Bit Mapping

The 14 400 bps scrambled data stream is divided into groups of
six consecutive bits and the first two bits $Q1_n$ and $Q2_n$ are differentially encoded into $Y1_n$ and $Y2_n$, as we have seen in Table 9.6
for the V.32 modem. The differentially encoded bits $Y1_n$ and $Y2_n$
are convolutionally encoded using the same systematic, non-linear
convolutional encoder as in case of the V.32 modem, which was portrayed in Figure 9.13. The $R = 2/3$-rate systematic convolutional
encoder generates the parity bit $Y0_n$, which is concatenated to the
differential encoder's output bits $Y1_n$ and $Y2_n$ and to the uncoded
input bits $Q3_n$, $Q4_n$, $Q5_n$ and $Q6_n$. This seven-bit sequence $Q6_n$,
$Q5_n$, $Q4_n$, $Q3_n$, $Y2_n$, $Y1_n$, $Y0_n$ is then mapped onto the 128-QAM
signal constellation seen in Figure 9.14.

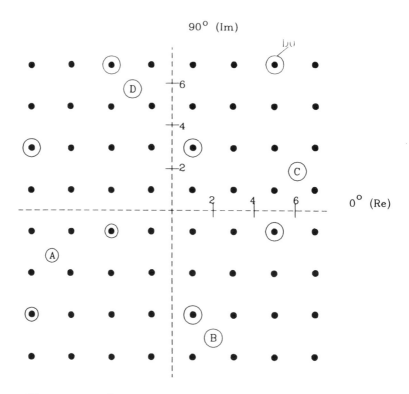

Figure 9.15: Signal Space Diagram and Mapping for Trellis-Coded Modulation at 12 000 bps

Similarly to the V.32 trellis-coded constellation, the three least significant protected bits $Y2_n$, $Y1_n$ and $Y0_n$ are used as subset identifiers to select one of the eight trellis subsets. For example, in Figure 9.14 the circled phasors belong to the subset identified by $[Y2_n, Y1_n, Y0_n] = [110]$. The remaining four unprotected bits are used to encode the 16 phasor positions within the trellis-coded subset. Since these phasors are sufficiently far apart in the signal constellation, they are less prone to noise corruption and hence they can be transmitted unprotected.

At the 12 000 bps fall-back rate the modem operates using 6 bits/-symbol transmissions and the phasor constellation depicted in Figure 9.15. The input data rate of 12 000 bps would only require 5 bits/symbol at the Baud-rate of 2400 Bd, but the previously described trellis-coding scheme generates and attaches the parity bit

Training Segments	Type of line signal	No. sym. intervals	Approx. time (ms)
Segment one	Alternations ABAB	256	106
Segment two	Equaliser conditioning A,B,C,D	2976	1240
Segment three	Rate sequence	64	27
Segment four	Scrambled all binary "1"s	48	20
Total	Total synchronizing signal time	3344	1393

Table 9.7: V.33 Training Sequence

$Y0_n$ to protect the differentially coded subset partitioning bits $Y2_n$ and $Y1_n$. Apart from removing the bit $Q6_n$ and using the constellation of Figure 9.15, the 12 000 bps scheme is identical to the 14 400 bps scheme, but with its increased noise protection distances amongst constellation points allows the modem to operate at lower signal-to-noise ratios. The 12 000 bps set-partitioning scheme is based again on the three convolutionally coded least significant bits $Y2_n$, $Y1_n$ and $Y0_n$ of the circled phasors in Figure 9.15.

9.5.3 Synchronising Signals

Before the transmission of useful data the modem requires a variety of training signals in order to condition its carrier and clock recovery circuits, as well as the adaptive channel equaliser. The standardised initial synchronising signals are summarised in Table 9.7. Segment one of the training pattern is constituted by 256 alternations between the signal constellation states A and B, depicted in Figures 9.14 and 9.15 which occupy the same positions as in the V.32 recommendations and hence coincide with four of the legitimate non-redundant 16-QAM phasors. This segment assists the initial carrier and clock recovery, as detailed in Chapter 6. This is followed by Segment two, consisting of a scrambled pseudo-random sequence of the states A, B, C and D shown in Figures 9.14 and 9.15, which is

transmitted at 4800 bps and designed to support the initial setup of
the adaptive equaliser as highlighted in Chapter 7. Segment three is
designed to convey a 16-bit binary sequence, which is scrambled and
transmitted eight times at 4800 bps using differentially encoded bits.
This sequence carries transmission rate, multiplex setup or other
configuration information. Finally, Segment four contains scrambled
binary "1"s transmitted at the rate specified in Segment three. This
segment is used to fine-tune the clock and carrier recovery circuits
because the linear distortions of the channel should now be equalised
and so the clock and carrier references established over the unequalised channel can now be more reliably set. Scrambling is invoked in
order to introduce signal transitions into long strings of logical "1"s
or "0"s.

V.33 modems are provided with adaptive channel equalisers. The
receiver must be able to detect loss of equalisation and initiate a
re-synchronisation procedure. Upon initiating a re-synchronisation
sequence the initiating modem expects to receive a synchronising
signal from the remote modem within the maximum turn-around
delay.

9.6 Summary

In this chapter we have examined QAM schemes for AWGN telephone lines. Because of the need to ensure standardisation to allow
a wide range of users to share information without concern about
compatibility, the modulation schemes used within these modems
have been recommended by the CCITT. The latest modems use high
level constellations, complex trellis coded systems and long training
sequences in order to maximise the transmission rate facilitated by
a bandlimited transmission medium.

This consideration of one of the most widespread uses of QAM
modems concludes our section on QAM for Gaussian channels. In the
remaining chapters we concentrate on hostile fading mobile channels.
We start the next section by considering the theoretical performance
of certain QAM constellations over mobile radio channels and then
continue to investigate means whereby the receiver can learn of the
distortions imposed by the channel.

Bibliography

[1] **G.D. Forney, R.G. Gallager, G.R. Lang, F.M. Longstaff and S.U. Qureshi**, "Efficient Modulation for Band-Limited Channels", *IEEE Tr. on Selected Areas in Comms*, vol. SAC-2, no. Sept. 1984, pp. 632-647, Sept. 1984

[2] **C.E. Shannon and W. Weaver**, "A Mathematical Theory of Communication", Urbana, Illinois Press, 1949

[3] **G. Ungerboeck**, "Trellis-Coded Modulation with Redundant Signal Sets, Part I and II", *IEEE Comms Magazine*, vol. 25, no. 2, pp. 5-21, Febr. 1987

[4] **L.F. Wei**, "Rotationally-Invariant Convolutional Channel Coding with Expanded Signal Space, Part I and II", *IEEE Tr. on Selected Areas in Comms*, vol. SAC-2, pp. 659-686, Sept. 1984

[5] **International Consultative Committee for Telephone and Telegraph Recommendations**, "V.29 - V.33", *Geneva*.

Chapter 10

Square QAM for Rayleigh fading channels

10.1 Square 16-QAM Performance over Rayleigh-fading Channels

Having considered the BER versus channel SNR performance of QAM transmissions via AWGN channels in Chapter 5, we now turn to the analysis of the square 16-QAM constellation of Figure 3.3 over Rayleigh fading channels [4, 5, 9]. Our discussion in this Chapter assumes that the reader has already consulted Chapter 5. Assuming a so-called non-frequency-selective, narrow-band fading channel, where the signal bandwidth is much lower than the coherence bandwidth of the channel, all frequency components of the transmitted signal undergo the same attenuation and phase shift. The multipath components in the received signal are not resolvable and the channel transfer function is given by

$$c(t) = \alpha(t) \cdot e^{j\,\Phi(t)}, \tag{10.1}$$

where $\alpha(t)$ represents the Rayleigh-fading envelope and $\Phi(t)$ the phase of the channel, which is uniformly distributed over $[-\pi, \pi]$. If additionally the fading is slow, so that $\alpha(t) = \alpha$ and $\Phi(t) = \Phi$ for the duration of one signalling interval, the received signal $r(t)$ at the channel's output is:

$$r(t) = \alpha \cdot e^{j\,\Phi} \cdot m(t) + n(t), \tag{10.2}$$

where $m(t)$ is the transmitted modulated signal and $n(t)$ is an AWGN process.

In Chapter 5 we derived the following $C1$ and $C2$ BER results for the AWGN channel using the Gaussian Q-function [3]:

$$P_{1G} = \frac{1}{2}Q\{\frac{d}{\sqrt{N_0/2}}\} + \frac{1}{2}Q\{\frac{3d}{\sqrt{N_0/2}}\} = \frac{1}{2}[Q\{\sqrt{\frac{E_0}{5N_0}}\} + Q\{3\sqrt{\frac{E_0}{5N_0}}\}].$$

(10.3)

and

$$P_{2G} = Q\{\sqrt{\frac{E_0}{5N_0}}\}.$$

(10.4)

where $E_0 = 10d^2$ is the average constellation energy.

Assuming perfectly phase-coherent reception, no fade compensation, and rewriting Equations 10.3 and 10.4 in terms of the instantaneous SNR γ via Rayleigh-fading channels, we get:

$$P_{1R}(\gamma) = \frac{1}{2}[Q\{\sqrt{\gamma/5}\} + Q\{3\sqrt{\gamma/5}\}],$$

(10.5)

and

$$P_{2R}(\gamma) = Q\{\sqrt{\gamma/5}\}.$$

(10.6)

As the fading envelope fluctuates, the instantaneous SNR γ is also changing. The average BER is found by calculating the bit error probability at a given instantaneous SNR γ and averaging it over all possible $SNRs$. This is carried out by multiplying the bit error probability $P(\gamma)$ at the instantaneous SNR γ with the occurrence probability of the specific SNR γ expressed in terms of its probability density function (PDF) $C(\gamma)$ and then averaging, i.e. integrating, this product over all possible values of γ:

$$P_{be} = \int_0^\infty P(\gamma) \cdot C(\gamma)d\gamma.$$

(10.7)

The random variable $\gamma = \alpha^2 \cdot E_0/N_0$ is a transformed form of the fading envelope α and the PDF of α, $C(\alpha)$ is known to be Rayleigh [1], [2]:

$$C(\alpha) = (\frac{\alpha}{\alpha_0{}^2})e^{-\alpha^2/2\alpha_0{}^2},$$

(10.8)

where α_0^2 is the identical variance of the independent quadrature components constituting the fading envelope α, while the second moment of α is given by $E(\alpha^2) = \overline{\alpha^2} = 2\alpha_0^2$ giving the variance of the envelope itself.

Let us now compute the PDF of γ, $C(\gamma)$, given that $C(\alpha)$ is Rayleigh distributed, and $\gamma = \alpha^2.E_o/N_o$ is a second order function of α. The following theorem can be invoked [3]:

Theorem

Let α be a continuous random variable with the PDF $C(\alpha)$, and let $\gamma = \alpha^2.E_o/N_o$ be a transformation of α. In order to determine the PDF of γ, $C(\gamma)$, we solve the equation $\gamma = \alpha^2.E_o/N_o$ for α in terms of γ. If α_1 and α_2 are the only real solutions then

$$C(\gamma) = C(\alpha_1)|\frac{d\alpha_1}{d\gamma}| + C(\alpha_2)|\frac{d\alpha_2}{d\gamma}|. \tag{10.9}$$

As $\gamma = \alpha^2 \cdot E_0/N_0$ has two real roots, α_1 and α_2, but the Rayleigh distribution does not exist in the negative amplitude domain, α_2 can be eliminated and hence $C(\gamma)$ is given by

$$C(\gamma) = C(\alpha_1) \cdot |\frac{d\alpha_1}{d\gamma}|. \tag{10.10}$$

When taking into account that

$$\alpha = \sqrt{\frac{N_0}{E_0}} \cdot \gamma^{\frac{1}{2}} \tag{10.11}$$

and that

$$\frac{d\alpha_1}{d\gamma} = \frac{1}{2}\sqrt{\frac{N_0}{E_0\gamma}} \tag{10.12}$$

we arrive at

$$C(\gamma) = \frac{1}{2\alpha_0^2}\frac{N_0}{E_0\gamma} \cdot e^{\frac{-N_0\gamma}{2E_0\alpha_0^2}}. \tag{10.13}$$

If we define the average SNR Γ as:

$$\Gamma = \overline{\gamma} = E\{\alpha^2\frac{E_0}{N_0}\} = \overline{\alpha^2}\frac{E_0}{N_0} = 2\alpha_0^2\frac{E_0}{N_0}, \tag{10.14}$$

where we exploited the fact that $E(\alpha^2) = \overline{\alpha^2} = 2\alpha_0^2$ for a Rayleigh *PDF*, then from Equations 10.13 and 10.14 the transformed *PDF* $C(\gamma)$ is given by

$$C(\gamma) = \frac{1}{\Gamma}e^{-\gamma/\Gamma}, \tag{10.15}$$

which is known as the Chi-square distribution [2], with the instantaneous $SNR \; \gamma \geq 0$.

The $C1 \; BER$ over Rayleigh-fading channels is found by substituting the $PDF \; C(\gamma)$ from Equation 10.15 and the instantaneous bit
error probability $P_{1R}(\gamma)$ over Rayleigh-fading channels from Equation 10.5, into Equation 10.7, yielding:

$$P_{1R}(\Gamma) = \frac{1}{2\Gamma} \int_0^\infty [Q\{\sqrt{\gamma/5}\} + Q\{3\sqrt{\gamma/5}\}] \cdot e^{-\gamma/\Gamma} d\gamma . \qquad (10.16)$$

The $C2 \; BER$ cannot be formulated without considering the effect
of a particular level of channel attenuation on the demodulation process. The demodulation is now carried out on an attenuated signal
constellation. Therefore we multiply the decision boundaries specified in Equation 4.6 for the $C2$ bits in the I and Q components by
the average attenuation $\overline{\alpha}$:

$$
\begin{array}{llllll}
\text{if} & & I,Q & \geq & 2\overline{\alpha}d & \text{then} \quad i_2, q_2 = 1 \\
\text{if} & -2\overline{\alpha}d \leq & I,Q & < & 2\overline{\alpha}d & \text{then} \quad i_2, q_2 = 0 \qquad (10.17) \\
\text{if} & -2\overline{\alpha}d > & I,Q & & & \text{then} \quad i_2, q_2 = 1.
\end{array}
$$

Considering the case when the transmitted bit i_2 or q_2 is a logical
0 and assuming that $\alpha < 2\overline{\alpha}$, the protection distance between the
received phasor αd and the decision boundary $2\overline{\alpha}d$ is $d_1 = (2\overline{\alpha}d - \alpha d)$.
Upon substituting d_1 into Equation 4.7 instead of d, we get the $C2$
BER for the transmission of a logical 0 as

$$
\begin{aligned}
P_{2,0,<2} &= Q\{\frac{d_1}{\sqrt{N_0/2}}\} \\
&= Q\{\frac{d(2\overline{\alpha} - \alpha)}{\sqrt{N_0/2}}\}. \qquad (10.18)
\end{aligned}
$$

From $E_0 = 10d^2$ we have $d = \sqrt{E_0/10}$, and whence:

$$P_{2,0,<2} = Q\{(2\overline{\alpha} - \alpha)\sqrt{\frac{E_0}{5N_0}}\}. \qquad (10.19)$$

From $\gamma = \alpha^2 E_0/N_0$ we get $E_0/N_0 = \gamma/\alpha^2$, and therefore:

$$
\begin{aligned}
P_{2,0,<2} &= Q\{(\frac{2\overline{\alpha} - \alpha}{\alpha})\sqrt{\frac{\gamma}{5}}\} \\
&= Q\{(\frac{2\overline{\alpha}}{\alpha} - 1)\sqrt{\frac{\gamma}{5}}\}. \qquad (10.20)
\end{aligned}
$$

Upon substituting Equations 10.20 and 10.15 into Equation 10.7 we get one component of the total $C2$ error probability. First the upper integration boundary of Equation 10.7 is derived for $\alpha \leq 2\overline{\alpha}$ as

$$\gamma = \alpha^2 E_0/N_0 \leq 4(\overline{\alpha})^2 E_0/N_0 . \tag{10.21}$$

By taking into account that for a Rayleigh distribution we have [1] $\overline{\alpha} = \alpha_0\sqrt{\pi/2}$, and we arrive at:

$$\gamma = 4(\alpha_0\sqrt{\frac{\pi}{2}})^2\frac{E_0}{N_0} = 2\alpha_0{}^2\frac{E_0}{N_0}\pi = \Gamma\pi, \tag{10.22}$$

and

$$P_{2,0,<2}(\Gamma) = \int_0^\infty P(\gamma)C(\gamma)d\gamma = \int_0^{\Gamma\pi} Q\{(\frac{2\overline{\alpha}}{\alpha} - 1)\sqrt{\frac{\gamma}{5}}\} \cdot \frac{1}{\Gamma}e^{-\gamma/\Gamma}d\gamma. \tag{10.23}$$

Similarly, for $d_1 = (2\overline{\alpha}d - \alpha d) < 0$, i.e. for $\alpha > 2\overline{\alpha}$, we have

$$P_{2,0,>2} = 1 - [1 - Q\{-\frac{2\overline{\alpha}d - \alpha d}{\sqrt{N_0/2}}\}] = 1 - Q\{\frac{d(2\overline{\alpha} - \alpha)}{\sqrt{N_0/2}}\}. \tag{10.24}$$

Exploiting $d = \sqrt{E_0/10}$ we have

$$P_{2,0,>2} = 1 - Q\{\sqrt{\frac{E_0}{5N_0}}(2\overline{\alpha} - \alpha)\}, \tag{10.25}$$

and by taking into account that $E_0/N_0 = \gamma/\alpha^2$ we arrive at:

$$P_{2,0,>2} = 1 - Q\{(\frac{2\overline{\alpha}}{\alpha} - 1)\sqrt{\frac{\gamma}{5}}\}. \tag{10.26}$$

The lower integration limit is now identical to the previously computed upper one, i.e. $\gamma = \pi\Gamma$, and the total probability of receiving a logical one in the $C2$ subchannel instead of the transmitted logical zero is given by:

$$P_{2,0}(\Gamma) = P_{2,0,<2}(\Gamma) + P_{2,0,>2}(\Gamma). \tag{10.27}$$

Upon substituting Equations 10.23 and 10.26 into Equation 10.27 we get:

$$\begin{aligned} P_{2,0}(\Gamma) &= \frac{1}{\Gamma}\int_0^{\pi\Gamma} Q\{(\frac{2\overline{\alpha}}{\alpha} - 1)\sqrt{\frac{\gamma}{5}}\}e^{-\gamma/\Gamma}d\gamma \\ &+ \frac{1}{\Gamma}\int_{\pi\Gamma}^\infty [1 - Q\{(\frac{2\overline{\alpha}}{\alpha} - 1)\sqrt{\frac{\gamma}{5}}\}]e^{-\gamma/\Gamma}d\gamma. \end{aligned} \tag{10.28}$$

In the reverse situation, when a transmitted $C2$ logical one is corrupted into a logical zero, the protection distance is $d_1 = 3\alpha d - 2\overline{\alpha}d$, which is positive, if $3\alpha d > 2\overline{\alpha}d$, i.e., $\alpha/\overline{\alpha} > 2/3$. The AWGN has to overcome this protection distance to cause an error, and hence the error probability for a positive protection distance d_1 is

$$P_{2,1,>2/3} = Q\{(\frac{3\overline{\alpha}}{\alpha} - 2)\sqrt{\frac{\gamma}{5}}\}. \tag{10.29}$$

If the protection distance d_1 is negative, then $3\alpha d < 2\overline{\alpha}d$, i.e., $\alpha/\overline{\alpha} < 2/3$. In this situation the decisions are always erroneous when the noise resides above the level $-(3\alpha d - 2\overline{\alpha}d)$, which is expressed with the aid of the Gaussian Q function as:

$$P_{2,1,<2/3} = Q\{\frac{-(3\alpha d - 2\overline{\alpha}d)}{\sqrt{N_0/2}}\} = Q\{\frac{-d(3\alpha - 2\overline{\alpha})}{\sqrt{N_0/2}}\}$$

or

$$P_{2,1,<2/3} = 1 - Q\{(\frac{3\overline{\alpha}}{\alpha} - 2)\sqrt{\frac{\gamma}{5}}\}. \tag{10.30}$$

Before computing the total $C2$ bit error probability for the transmission of a logical *one*, we determine the integration limit for Equation 10.7. Since $\alpha > 2\overline{\alpha}/3$,

$$\gamma = \alpha^2 \frac{E_0}{N_0} = (\frac{2}{3}\overline{\alpha})^2 \frac{E_0}{N_0} = \frac{4}{9}(\overline{\alpha})^2 \frac{E_0}{N_0}. \tag{10.31}$$

By exploiting for the Rayleigh distribution that [1] $\overline{\alpha} = \alpha_0 \sqrt{\pi/\gamma}$, we get:

$$\gamma = \frac{4}{9}\alpha_0{}^2 \frac{\pi}{\gamma} \frac{E_0}{N_0} = \Gamma \frac{\pi}{9}. \tag{10.32}$$

Therefore:

$$P_{2,1}(\Gamma) = P_{2,1,<2/3}(\Gamma) + P_{2,1,>2/3}(\Gamma), \tag{10.33}$$

or

$$\begin{aligned} P_{2,1}(\Gamma) &= \frac{1}{\Gamma}\int_0^{\pi\Gamma/9} Q\{(\frac{3\overline{\alpha}}{\alpha} - 2)\sqrt{\frac{\gamma}{5}}\}e^{-\gamma/\Gamma}d\gamma \\ &+ \frac{1}{\Gamma}\int_{\pi\Gamma/9}^{\infty}[1 - Q\{(\frac{3\overline{\alpha}}{\alpha} - 2)\sqrt{\frac{\gamma}{5}}\}]e^{-\gamma/\Gamma}d\gamma. \end{aligned} \tag{10.34}$$

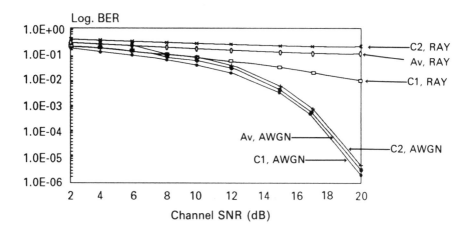

Figure 10.1: Square 16-QAM BER versus channel SNR curves for AWGN and Rayleigh channels

For random transmitted data the overall $C2$ subchannel error probability is given by:

$$P_{2R}(\Gamma) = \frac{1}{2}[P_{2,1}(\Gamma) + P_{2,0}(\Gamma)]. \qquad (10.35)$$

When we evaluated the $C1$ and $C2$ bit error probabilities from Equations 10.16 and 10.35, respectively, we received nearly identical curves to those, depicted in Figure 10.1 denoted by C1,Ray and C2,Ray, for our simulations. The average C1 and C2 BER curve is represented by AV,Ray in the figure. For comparison we also included the corresponding AWGN curves denoted by C1,AWGN and C2,AWGN as well as the average BER AV,AWGN, of the two subchannels. We noted in Chapter 5 that the $C1$ and $C2$ BER differences are consistent but not drastic when transmitting square 16-QAM signals via the AWGN channel. The discrepancy becomes more dramatic over the Rayleigh fading channel. While the $C1$ BER is monotonously decreasing, the $C2$ curve shows a high residual BER. This is because due to the received signal envelope fluctuations the multilevel QAM constellation collapses towards the origin of the coordinate system, causing excessive BERs for the low-protection $C2$ subchannel. The high-protection $C1$ subchannel withstands the channel fading better and hence its behaviour is mostly governed by the AWGN. Automatic gain control (AGC) techniques with and without channel-sounding side-information for fading compensation are reported in references [4]-[6] allowing the reduced residual BERs to be efficiently combatted by appropriate FEC methods.

In the closing part of this section, we briefly note that for the integral of the product of the Gaussian Q-function and the Rayleigh PDF, there exists closed form solutions. The closed form C2 bit error probability can be derived as follows:

$$
\begin{aligned}
P_{2R}(\alpha_0) &= \int_0^\infty Q\left\{\frac{\alpha d}{\sqrt{N_o/2}}\right\} C(\alpha) d\alpha \\
&= \int_0^\infty Q\left\{\frac{\alpha d}{\sqrt{N_o/2}}\right\} \frac{\alpha}{\alpha_0^2} \cdot e^{\frac{-\alpha^2}{2\alpha_0^2}} d\alpha.
\end{aligned}
\tag{10.36}
$$

We exploit the fact that [10]

$$
\int_0^\infty [1 - erf(\beta x)] e^{-\mu x^2} \cdot x \, dx = \frac{1}{2\mu}\left(1 - \frac{\beta}{\sqrt{\mu + \beta^2}}\right)
\tag{10.37}
$$

where the relationship between the Gaussian error function $erf(x)$ and the Q-function is given by [3]

$$
1 - erf(x) = 2 \cdot Q\{\sqrt{2}x\}.
\tag{10.38}
$$

Upon rewriting Equation 10.36 in a more convenient form we have

$$
P_{2R}(\alpha_0) = \frac{1}{2\alpha_0^2} \int_0^\infty 2 \cdot Q\left\{\sqrt{2}\frac{d}{\sqrt{N_o}}\alpha\right\} \cdot \alpha \cdot e^{\frac{-\alpha^2}{2\alpha_0^2}} d\alpha
\tag{10.39}
$$

and exploiting Equation 10.38 gives

$$
P_{2R}(\alpha_0) = \frac{1}{2\alpha_0^2} \int_0^\infty 2 \cdot \left(1 - erf\left\{\frac{d}{\sqrt{N_o}}\alpha\right\}\right) \cdot \alpha \cdot e^{\frac{-\alpha^2}{2\alpha_0^2}} d\alpha
\tag{10.40}
$$

Assigning $\beta = d/\sqrt{N_o}$ and $\mu = 1/2\alpha_0^2$ in order to enable us to use the closed form formula of Equation 10.37 we get

$$
P_{2R}(\alpha_0) = \frac{1}{2\alpha_0^2}\frac{1}{2\mu}\left(1 - \frac{\beta}{\sqrt{\mu + \beta^2}}\right)
\tag{10.41}
$$

and after substituting back $\beta = d/\sqrt{N_0}$ and $\mu = 1/2\alpha_0^2$ we arrive at

$$
\begin{aligned}
P_{2R}(\alpha_0) &= \frac{\alpha_0^2}{2\alpha_0^2} \left(1 - \frac{\frac{d}{\sqrt{N_o}}}{\sqrt{\frac{1}{2\alpha_0^2} + \frac{d^2}{N_o}}} \right) \\
&= \frac{1}{2} \left[1 - \sqrt{\frac{2\alpha_0^2 \frac{d^2}{N_o}}{1 + 2\alpha^2 \frac{d^2}{N_o}}} \right].
\end{aligned}
\tag{10.42}
$$

The derivation of the $C1$ bit error probability follows similar lines but is beyond the scope of this book.

10.2   Square 64-QAM Performance over Rayleigh-Fading Channels

Adopting an approach similar to that used for the $16 - QAM$ in the Section 10.1 the formula for the $C1$ BER can be obtained by substituting the Gaussian channel result of Equation 4.22, repeated below for convenience

$$
P_{C1}(\gamma) = \frac{1}{4} Q[\sqrt{\frac{\gamma}{21}}] + \frac{1}{4} Q[\sqrt{\frac{3\gamma}{21}}] + \frac{1}{4} Q[\sqrt{\frac{5\gamma}{21}}] + \frac{1}{4} Q[\sqrt{\frac{7\gamma}{21}}].
\tag{10.43}
$$

from Section 4.3 into Equation 10.7 along with the transformed PDF $C(\gamma)$ in Equation 10.15, in order to arrive at:

$$
P_{C1}(\Gamma) = \frac{1}{4\Gamma} \int_0^\infty \{ Q[\sqrt{\frac{\gamma}{21}}] + Q[3\sqrt{\frac{\gamma}{21}}] + Q[5\sqrt{\frac{\gamma}{21}}] + Q[7\sqrt{\frac{\gamma}{21}}] \} e^{-\gamma/\Gamma} d\gamma.
\tag{10.44}
$$

This simple derivation is achieved because the $C1$ decision boundaries constituted by the coordinate axis and shown in Figure 4.2 of Chapter 5 are unaltered by the fading. However, the probability of bit error for the $C2$ and $C3$ subchannels cannot be derived without considering the effects of fading on each phasor and decision boundary individually.

When calculating the probability of bit error for $C2$, we acknowledge that although the received phasors are attenuated by the instantaneous α value, the receiver is arranged to demodulate with reference to the expected value $2\alpha_0$. The effect of fading must be computed individually for each phasor. For P_6 the modified protection distance d_1 measured from the decision boundary $4\overline{\alpha}d$ is seen from the phasor constellation depicted in Figure 4.2 to be $d_1 = 4\overline{\alpha}d - 3\alpha d$. If the modified protection distance is overcome by noise, erroneous decisions occur. If the modified protection distance $d_1 < 0$, then in the absence of noise the decisions are consistently erroneous. In the presence of noise the phasors can be carried back into the error-free decision domain by sufficiently large negative noise samples. In both cases the error probability is equivalent to the noise samples exceeding the protection distance, irrespective of its actual value. In terms of the $Q[\,]$ function we have

$$P_{e6}(\gamma) = Q[(\frac{4\overline{\alpha}}{\alpha} - 3)\sqrt{\frac{\gamma}{21}}].\tag{10.45}$$

For the phasor P_5 the modified protection distance from the $C2$ decision boundary $4\overline{\alpha}d$ is $d_1 = 4\overline{\alpha}d - \alpha d$. Observe that the effect of the instantaneous attenuation α is now less profound than for P_6, where it is multiplied by a factor of three. Using this d_1 value in the argument of the $Q[\,]$ function gives

$$P_{e5}(\gamma) = Q[(\frac{4\overline{\alpha}}{\alpha} - 1)\sqrt{\frac{\gamma}{21}}].\tag{10.46}$$

The modified protection distance from the $C2$ decision boundary at $4\overline{\alpha}d$ for P_7 is seen from the phasor constellation of Figure 4.2 to be $d_1 = 4\overline{\alpha}d - 5\alpha d$, which yields an error probability of

$$P_{e7}(\gamma) = Q[(\frac{4\overline{\alpha}}{\alpha} - 5)\sqrt{\frac{\gamma}{21}}].\tag{10.47}$$

The phasor P_8 has the highest distance from the coordinate axis, therefore it is profoundly effected by the instantaneous fading. It has an associated protection distance of $d_1 = 4\overline{\alpha}d - 7\alpha d$ which results in an error probability of

$$P_{e8}(\gamma) = Q[(\frac{4\overline{\alpha}}{\alpha} - 7)\sqrt{\frac{\gamma}{21}}].\tag{10.48}$$

The partial $C2$ error probabilities from Equations 10.45-10.48 have to be substituted in Equation 10.7 along with Equation 10.15 in order to deliver the average square 64-QAM $C2$ BER for Rayleigh fading channels:

$$
\begin{aligned}
P_{C2}(\Gamma) &= \frac{1}{4\Gamma}\{ \int_0^\infty Q[(\frac{4\overline{\alpha}}{\alpha} - 1)\sqrt{\frac{\gamma}{21}}]e^{-\gamma/\Gamma}d\gamma \\
&+ \int_0^\infty Q[(\frac{4\overline{\alpha}}{\alpha} - 3)\sqrt{\frac{\gamma}{21}}]e^{-\gamma/\Gamma}d\gamma \\
&+ \int_0^\infty Q[(\frac{4\overline{\alpha}}{\alpha} - 5)\sqrt{\frac{\gamma}{21}}]e^{-\gamma/\Gamma}d\gamma \\
&+ \int_0^\infty Q[(\frac{4\overline{\alpha}}{\alpha} - 7)\sqrt{\frac{\gamma}{21}}]e^{-\gamma/\Gamma}d\gamma\}.
\end{aligned}
\tag{10.49}
$$

The $C3$ subchannel performance is computed similarly, but for each phasor there are two modified protection distances, d_1 and d_2. For example, for the phasor P_6 in Figure 4.2 we find $d_1 = 6\overline{\alpha}d - 3\alpha d$ and $d_2 = 3\alpha d - 2\overline{\alpha}d$, representing the distances from the $C3$ decision boundaries at $6\overline{\alpha}d$ and $2\overline{\alpha}d$, respectively. When exposed to AWGN, the decisions are erroneous on one hand, if the modified protection distance d_1 is exceeded by the noise samples. This holds for negative d_1 values as well. Erroneous decisions are also encountered, if the phasor P_6 is carried across the $C3$ decision boundary at $2\overline{\alpha}d$ by sufficiently large negative noise samples. This happens, whenever the noise value resides below the level $-d_2$. Accordingly, the $C3$ bit error probability for P_6 is

$$
P_{e6}(\gamma) = Q[(\frac{6\overline{\alpha}}{\alpha} - 3)\sqrt{\frac{\gamma}{21}}] + Q[(3 - \frac{2\overline{\alpha}}{\alpha})\sqrt{\frac{\gamma}{21}}].
\tag{10.50}
$$

Considering the case of the phasor P_5 the modified protection distances are $d_1 = 2\overline{\alpha}d - \alpha d$ and $d_2 = 6\overline{\alpha}d - \alpha d$, respectively. Erroneous decisions are engendered, if the protection distance d_1 is exceeded by noise, but noise samples larger than d_2 carry the phasors into another error-free decision domain. Whence the error probability is given by

$$
P_{e5}(\gamma) = Q[(\frac{2\overline{\alpha}}{\alpha} - 1)\sqrt{\frac{\gamma}{21}}] - Q[(\frac{6\overline{\alpha}}{\alpha} - 1)\sqrt{\frac{\gamma}{21}}]
\tag{10.51}
$$

When the phasor P_7 is transmitted the situation is characterised by the distances $d_1 = 6\overline{\alpha}d - 5\alpha d$ and $d_2 = 5\alpha d - 2\overline{\alpha}d$, and hence

$$
P_{e7}(\gamma) = Q[(\frac{6\overline{\alpha}}{\alpha} - 5)\sqrt{\frac{\gamma}{21}}] + Q[(5 - \frac{2\overline{\alpha}}{\alpha} - 1)\sqrt{\frac{\gamma}{21}}].
\tag{10.52}
$$

Finally, for the phasor P_8 we find $d_1 = 7\alpha d - 6\overline{\alpha}d$ and $d_2 = 7\alpha d - 2\overline{\alpha}d$, where errors are caused by noise samples below the level $-d_1$. Should, however, the noise vector fall below $-d_2$, the phasors are switched to another error-free decision domain across the decision boundary at $2\overline{\alpha}d$, therefore

$$P_{e8}(\gamma) = Q[(7 - \frac{6\overline{\alpha}}{\alpha})\sqrt{\frac{\gamma}{21}}] - Q[(7 - \frac{2\overline{\alpha}}{\alpha})\sqrt{\frac{\gamma}{21}}]. \qquad (10.53)$$

Let us assume again that random sequences are sent, i.e., the probability of each phasor $P_1 \ldots P_{64}$ in Figure 4.2 occurring is identical, and further, let us exploit the symmetry of the signal constellation. On substituting Equations 10.50-10.53, along with Equation 10.15, into Equation 10.7 we obtain the average $C3$ bit error probability as a function of the average SNR Γ, viz.:

$$\begin{aligned}
P_{C3}(\Gamma) = \frac{1}{4\Gamma}\{ &\int_0^\infty [Q[(\frac{6\overline{\alpha}}{\alpha} - 3)\sqrt{\frac{\gamma}{21}}] + Q[(3 - \frac{2\overline{\alpha}}{\alpha})\sqrt{\frac{\gamma}{21}}]]e^{-\gamma/\Gamma}d\gamma \\
+ &\int_0^\infty [Q[(\frac{2\overline{\alpha}}{\alpha} - 1)\sqrt{\frac{\gamma}{21}}] - Q[(\frac{6\overline{\alpha}}{\alpha} - 1)\sqrt{\frac{\gamma}{21}}]]e^{-\gamma/\Gamma}d\gamma \\
+ &\int_0^\infty [Q[(\frac{6\overline{\alpha}}{\alpha} - 5)\sqrt{\frac{\gamma}{21}}] + Q[(5 - \frac{2\overline{\alpha}}{\alpha} - 1)\sqrt{\frac{\gamma}{21}}]]e^{-\gamma/\Gamma}d\gamma \\
+ &\int_0^\infty [Q[(\frac{7-6\overline{\alpha}}{\alpha})\sqrt{\frac{\gamma}{21}}] - Q[(7 - \frac{2\overline{\alpha}}{\alpha})\sqrt{\frac{\gamma}{21}}]]e^{-\gamma/\Gamma}d\gamma \}.
\end{aligned}$$

$$(10.54)$$

In summary, the square 64-QAM $C1$, $C2$ and $C3$ subchannel performances over Rayleigh-fading channels are given by Equations 10.44, 10.49 and 10.54, respectively. The equivalent BER vs. channel SNR curves are plotted in Figure 10.2, which again coincide within a fraction of a dB with our simulation results. The BER differences between the three classes become more profound in case of Rayleigh channels than via the AWGN channel. This is in harmony with our experience in case of the $16 - QAM$ BER curves displayed in Figure 10.1. The BER of the $C1$ subchannel is well suited for FEC-coded speech or image transmission, while the $C2$ and $C3$ performances have to be improved by fading-compensating automatic gain control and optional diversity reception for FEC techniques to become efficient [4]-[6].

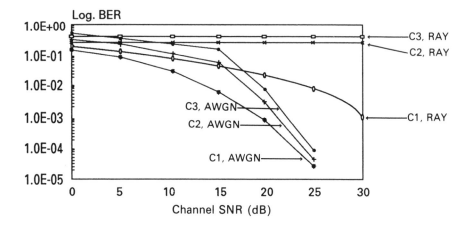

Figure 10.2: Square 64-QAM BER versus channel SNR curves for AWGN and Rayleigh channels

10.3   Reference Assisted Coherent QAM

Two powerful methods have been proposed in order to ensure coherent QAM operation in fading environments. Both these techniques deliver channel measurement information in terms of attenuation and phase shift due to fading. The first is transparent tone in band (TTIB) assisted modulation, where a pilot carrier is inserted typically in the centre of the modulated spectrum. At the receiver the signal is extracted and used to estimate the channel induced attenuation and phase rotation.

The other technique is called pilot symbol assisted modulation (PSAM) where known channel sounding phasors are periodically inserted into the transmitted time-domain signal sequence. Similarly to the frequency domain pilot tone, these known symbols deliver channel measurement information.

10.3.1 Transparent Tone In Band Modulation[11]

10.3.1.1 Introduction

Transparent tone in band (TTIB) assisted modulation has been proposed for various mobile radio applications by McGeehan, Bateman et al [11]–[18]. TTIB schemes place a pilot tone within the spectrum of the transmitted signal which can be used for a range of applications from in-band signalling in telephone systems through fading compensation in mobile radio systems [18], to coherent data transmissions [16, 19] to aid the operation of direct conversion receivers. Further related contributions can be found in References [20]–[26].

In the following discussion of TTIB schemes we follow McGeehan and Bateman's approach [11] and concentrate on the use of TTIB in a mobile radio environment. TTIB schemes constitute a frequency domain alternative to pilot symbol assisted modulation (PSAM) [24] (see Section 10.3.2.1). In TTIB systems for mobile radio applications a spectral gap of a certain bandwidth is created in the centre of the signal spectrum to allow insertion of the pilot tone. The pilot tone is often chosen to be the carrier frequency as this can then assist the receiver in the process of coherent demodulation. The use of coherent demodulation overcomes the carrier recovery problems highlighted in Chapter 6 and allows the use of the maximum least distance square constellations discussed in the previous two sections over mobile radio channels.

Further advantages can be achieved if the separation of the two subbands created by dividing the spectrum is made to be a subharmonic of the symbol timing. This allows relatively straightforward clock recovery procedures to be employed. Finally, since the amplitude and phase of the transmitted pilot symbol are known to the receiver, extrication of this pilot symbol allows an estimate of the complex fading channel envelope which removes the need for AGC. However, this will only be possible if the channel is exhibiting flat fading, i.e. all the other frequency components of the signal suffer the same amplitude and phase shift.

The disadvantages of this system are that the bandwidth requirements are slightly increased, and higher transmitter and receiver complexity are required to perform the necessary spectral operations. Furthermore, increased transmitted power is required for the transmission of the pilot tone, and although this is typically at a lower level than the power level of the transmitted signal, at very low levels the pilot signal can become corrupted by noise, reducing the reliability of the fading estimates. Furthermore, the inclusion of the pilot tone increases the signal envelope fluctuations which results in increased out of band emissions due to the amplifier non-linearities, as discussed in Chapter 5.

10.3.1.2   Principles of TTIB

The basic principles of TTIB transmission are shown in Figure 10.3, while the corresponding frequency domain manipulations are portrayed in Figure 10.4, with the ten stages in processing shown in each of the figures.   The input waveform is firstly filtered by the LPF in order to remove high frequencies which might lead to aliasing. In Figure 10.4 both the lower subband (L) and upper subband (U) occupy half the total bandwidth B, but there is no reason why the signal could not be split into a number of unequal sidebands apart from the implementational practicalities. The ideal LPF, LPF2 removes U and passes L to the transmitter. Then U is frequency translated using a carrier frequency f_T leading to the spectrum shown at stage three. This is then bandpass filtered by BPF1 before being recombined with L for transmission. At stage five, the frequency gap between L and U is f_G, extending the total transmission bandwidth to $B + f_G$. Next the pilot carrier frequency f_P is added to the composite signal. If the total bandwidth $(B + f_G)$ is less than the coherence bandwidth of the channel then both the received spectrum and the received pilot tone suffer the same attenuation and phase shift and so the same correction factor can be used to remove the fading from both the pilot and the signal spectrum.

At the receiver, the pilot signal is extricated using BPF3, while L is retained by LPF3 and U by BPF2. If the frequency f_T is known to the receiver, and there is perfect alignment between nominal and actual frequencies giving $f_R = f_T$ then the original signal spectrum can be recovered at stage ten. Before a decision is made as to the transmitted signal, the extricated pilot tone is used to remove

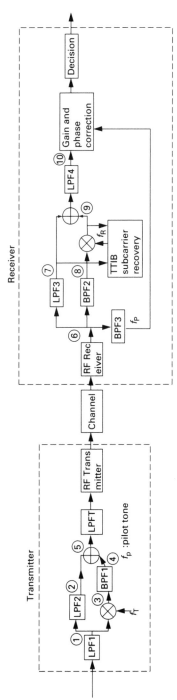

Figure 10.3: TTIB System Schematic [11]©IEEE, 1984, McGeehan, Bateman

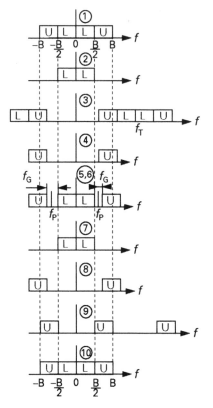

Figure 10.4: TTIB Processed Spectra [11]©IEEE, 1984, McGeehan, Bateman

the estimated effect of the complex channel fading by deriving an amplitude and phase correction factor. The bandwidth of BPF3 is an important system parameter as if it is made too small then Doppler shift and oscillator drift may prevent recovery of the pilot tone, whereas if it is too large it will process an excessive amount of channel noise degrading the reliability of the channel estimate and hence the system performance.

The TTIB receiver typically relies on signals seven and nine in order to recover the TTIB subcarrier f_T used by the transmitter in the frequency translation process. The manner in which this is performed is discussed in the next subsection.

In practice there is usually a frequency offset Δw between the TTIB subcarrier f_T at the transmitter, and that at the receiver, denoted f_R. The effect of this frequency offset of $\Delta w = 2\pi\Delta f = 2\pi(f_T - f_R)$ will also be addressed in the next subsection, while a practical subband splitting technique known as quadrature mirror filtering (QMF) which does not require infinitely steep cutoff filters will be discussed in the next but one subsection.

10.3.1.3 TTIB Subcarrier Recovery

In order to eliminate interferences between the L and U subbands and achieve perfect signal reconstruction it is crucial to combine their frequency and phase coherently. Because the received pilot tone has been subject to up and down conversions in the transmitter and receiver, respectively, and the multipath channel might have introduced some random frequency offset, the pilot will be prone to some frequency error and so cannot be relied upon in producing the receiver's TTIB subcarrier f_R. The channel effects and RF up and down conversions have an identical influence over L and U, whereas the TTIB subcarrier offset affects only U, as shown in Figure 10.4.

To overcome this problem the TTIB subcarrier recovery method shown in Figure 10.5 is used [11]. Its operation relies on the characteristics of the signals labelled seven and nine, which are identical to those shown in Figures 10.3 and 10.4. Observe in Figure 10.5 that U is phase shifted by 90 degrees and then both signals seven and nine are input to a limiter or null comparator in order to remove any modulation or channel imposed phase variations. The two signals are then multiplied together to create the difference and sum of their frequency components. The loop filter removes the sum of the frequencies, but retains the difference, which is then input to a voltage controlled oscillator (VCO) which generates the frequency and phase coherent local TTIB carrier $f_R = f_T$.

The operation of the TTIB subcarrier recovery system is best understood if a single tone of

$$i(t) = a_i \cos(w_i t + \alpha_i) \tag{10.55}$$

is used to excite the transmitter, where a_i, w_i and α_i are the amplitude, frequency and initial phase of the tone, respectively. We also assume that overlapping regions of the L and U subbands do contain

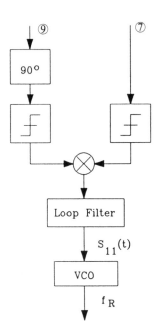

Figure 10.5: TTIB Subcarrier Recovery [11]©IEEE, 1984, McGeehan, Bateman

some signal energy. We choose w_i specifically to satisfy this condition and assume that the L and U subband filters have attenuations of A_1 and A_2, respectively at this transition band frequency.

Initially, the U subband tone is frequency translated using the TTIB subcarrier of

$$C_T(t) = \cos(w_T t + \alpha_T) \tag{10.56}$$

having a frequency of w_T and initial phase of α_T. It is then added to the L tone giving a signal at point five of Figure 10.3 as follows

$$S_5(t) = A_1 a_i \cos(w_i t + \alpha_i) + A_2 a_i \cos[(w_i + w_T)t + \alpha_i + \alpha_T] \tag{10.57}$$

where due to the filter delay τ_1 introduced by both LPF2 and BPF1, and the delay τ_2 introduced by the transmitter filter LPFT in Figure 10.3, the time axis must be translated such that t becomes $t - \tau_1 - \tau_2$. Whilst it might seem unlikely that LPF2 and BPF1 would have identical delays, we will show how this might be arranged using QMF in the next section.

The received signal is corrupted by the complex fading introducing an envelope factor of $\alpha(t)$ and a phase factor of $\psi(t)$. It also has a residual oscillator error of Δw due to up and down conversion. The signal received at stage six of Figure 10.3 is therefore given by

$$
\begin{aligned}
S_6(t) &= A_1 a_i \alpha(t) \cos[w_i t + \alpha_i + \psi(t) + \Delta wt] \\
&\quad + A_2 a_i \alpha(t) \cos[(w_i + w_T)t + \alpha_i + \alpha_T + \psi(t) + \Delta wt].
\end{aligned}
\tag{10.58}
$$

The TTIB subcarrier at the receiver is given by

$$
C_R(t) = \cos(w_R t + \alpha_R)
\tag{10.59}
$$

where α_R is its initial phase and w_R is its angular frequency. Then the signal at stage seven in Figure 10.3, the output of LPF3, becomes

$$
S_7(t) = A_3 A_1 a_i \alpha(t) \cos[w_i t + \alpha_i + \psi(t) + \Delta wt]
\tag{10.60}
$$

where A_3 is the attenuation of LPF3 at $(w_i + \Delta w)$ and the time t is now redefined as $t - \tau_1 - \tau_2 - \tau_3$, with τ_3 being the identical delay of LPF3 and BPF2. After passing $S_6(t)$ through BPF2 we get

$$
S_8(t) = A_4 A_2 a_i \alpha(t) \cos[(w_i + w_T)t + \alpha_i + \alpha_T + \psi(t) + \Delta wt]
\tag{10.61}
$$

where A_4 is the attenuation of BPF2 at $(w_i + w_T + \Delta w)$. By mixing $S_8(t)$ with the output signal from the VCO having a free running frequency of w_R and an initial phase of α_R, components are generated at the difference frequency of $(w_i + w_T - w_R)$ and the sum frequency $(w_i + w_T + w_R)$, with the latter term being removed by LPF4. Ignoring, therefore, the latter term, the difference frequency term at position nine is then given by

$$
\begin{aligned}
S_9^{diff}(t) &= A_4 A_2 a_i \alpha(t) \cos[(w_i + w_T - w_R)t + \alpha_i + \alpha_T - \alpha_R \\
&\quad + \psi(t) + \Delta wt - w_R(\tau_1 + \tau_2 + \tau_3)].
\end{aligned}
\tag{10.62}
$$

The last term of $w_R(\tau_1 + \tau_2 + \tau_3)$ in Equation 10.62 is introduced now because the time variable t is defined for the received components as $[t - (\tau_1 + \tau_2 + \tau_3)]$ due to the filtering delays incurred, but the time associated with the receiver's frequency is not delayed. In order to phase and frequency coherently combine L and U given by $S_7(t)$ and $S_9^{diff}(t)$ then $w_T = w_R$ and $\alpha_T - \alpha_R - w_R(\tau_1 + \tau_2 + \tau_3) = 0$ must be satisfied. As portrayed in Figure 10.5, initially $S_9(t)$ is phase shifted by $90°$ in order to rotate the cos() function and generate a sin() function. Then both $S_7(t)$ and the phase-shifted $S_9(t)$ are input to a limiter which removes any envelope fluctuations, and the amplitude-limited signals are multiplied together. Both the sum and differences of their arguments are generated, but the loop filter of Figure 10.5 admits only their difference $S_11(t)$ to the VCO, hence we arrive at:

$$S_{11}(t) = \sin[(w_T - w_R)t + (\alpha_T - \alpha_R) - w_R(\tau_1 + \tau_2 + \tau_3)] \quad (10.63)$$

Observe that $S_{11}(t)$ is independent of any channel fading since $\psi(t)$ was cancelled, but retains the frequency and phase error terms between the transmitter and receiver.

After the addition of $S_7(t)$ and $S_9(t)$ and the removal of the unwanted mixer output component by LPF4, the recovered signal can be derived from Equations 10.60 and 10.62 as

$$S_{10}(t) = (A_1A_3 + A_2A_4)\alpha(t)\, a_i \cos(w_i t + \alpha_i + \Delta wt). \quad (10.64)$$

If, by appropriate filter design $A_1A_3 + A_2A_4 = 1$ is maintained, the recovered signal is corrupted by the channel amplitude fading $\alpha(t)$ and the frequency offset Δw only. However, the TTIB processing itself appears perfectly transparent. Since the pilot signal and the information signal suffer the same attenuation in a flat fading narrowband channel, the channel sounding information derived by the pilot can be used to remove the effects of the fading from the information sequence.

10.3.1.4   TTIB Schemes Using Quadrature Mirror Filters

Quadrature mirror filters (QMFs) [27] allow relatively straightforward TTIB implementations. A variety of suitable QMF designs have been proposed by Johnston [28]. The fundamental property of QMFs is that the lower (L) and upper (U) sidebands are symmetrical around the joint cutoff frequency of the LPF and HPF stages. Hence, despite their overlapping transition region they do not introduce aliasing distortions and automatically ensure identical signal delays for both subband signals. Furthermore, since both stages retain signal energy from the transition band, their output signals in this frequency band will be highly correlated with each other. Through the use of correlation techniques we can combine these two correlated subbands perfectly after the removal of the pilot tone at the receiver.

The number of subbands is not limited to two, m cascaded stages of QMFs can be used to provide 2^m subbands. With an increased number of subbands the system becomes more complex, but as each subband becomes narrower in comparison to the coherence bandwidth of the mobile radio channel, and the number of pilots which can be inserted increases, the channel is effectively sounded across the signal's bandwidth making it possible to dispense with a channel equaliser. However, the increased number of pilots reduces the spectral efficiency of the transmission. In Chapter 15 we will introduce an orthogonal transformation-based band splitting technique which might employ 128 subchannels and a large number of pilot tones.

In this section we consider the twin band, QMF based TTIB processing shown in Figure 10.6. In this Figure a complex baseband spectrum is seen which is split by the QMF HP and LP stages. In part (c) the subbands are split apart to make room for the pilot tone.

In order for distortion free signal reconstruction to occur using QMFs the QMF structure must have an all pass transfer function given by

$$|H_{LP}(f)|^2 + |H_{HP}(f)|^2 = 1. \qquad (10.65)$$

In order to maintain linear phase both the HP and LP impulse responses must be symmetric. Finally, the alias free condition will be met if the impulse responses satisfy the condition

$$h_{LP}(n) = (-1)^n h_{HP}(n). \qquad (10.66)$$

Assuming a complex baseband input spectrum of $I(f)$ the QMF outputs can be written as

$$\begin{aligned} I_{LP}(f) &= I(f) \cdot H_{LP}(f) \\ I_{HP}(f) &= I(f) \cdot H_{HP}(f). \end{aligned} \qquad (10.67)$$

In order to shift $I_{LP}(f)$ and $I_{HP}(f)$ sufficiently far apart to create a spectral gap for the pilot symbol we multiply both transfer functions

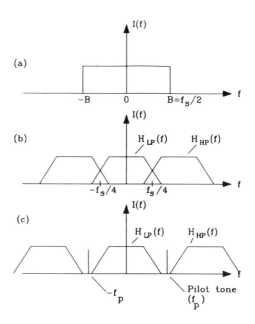

a) Complex baseband spectrum
b) QMF high pass and low pass transfer functions
c) Addition of pilot tone to spectral gap created

Figure 10.6: QMF Splitting of a TTIB Signal

by $e^{\pm jw_T t}$, where $2w_T$ is the required width of the spectral notch. This leads to a transmitted signal of

$$T(f) = I(f)[H_{LP}(f)e^{-jw_T t} + H_{HP}(f)e^{jw_T t}]. \qquad (10.68)$$

These operations are summarised in Figure 10.7 where the complex baseband spectra are also shown at the various stages of the processing. Note that due to the half band splitting the subband signals must be decimated by two and in general the connections between blocks represent complex signals. Bateman [19] suggested a QMF-based TTIB receiver structure, but Cavers [24] proposed an improved alternative. Here we explain Caver's structure, but use Bateman's frequency domain approach in our descriptive analysis.

As previously detailed, the transmitted signal $T(f)$ is subjected to amplitude fading and phase rotation by the mobile radio channel. However, in this analysis we neglect these effects since they

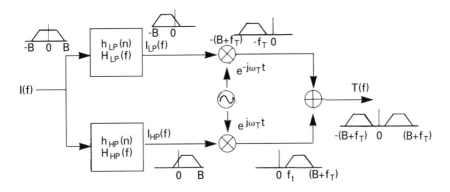

Figure 10.7: TTIB Transmitter Scheme [19]©IEEE, 1990, Bateman

are considered in the previous subsection, and concentrate purely on the signal reconstruction. For perfect, alias free signal regeneration, the sidebands must be shifted back to their original position, and this operation is typically performed in two steps. This is shown in Figure 10.8 where the QMF based TTIB receiver's schematic is shown along with the typical baseband spectral representation of the various stages of processing.

Initially, after removing the pilot tone, the subband components of the received signal $R(f)$ are translated back close to their original positions by being shifted using a frequency of $\pm w_R = \pm(w_T + \Delta w)$, where Δw represents the frequency difference $(w_R - w_T)$ due to misalignment between the transmitter and receiver oscillators. These translated signals can be expressed in terms of the transmitted signal $T(f)$ and noise $N(f)$ using

$$R(f) = T(f) + N(f) \tag{10.69}$$

so that

$$\begin{aligned} R_{LP}(f) &= R(f).e^{j(w_T+\Delta w)t} &= [T(f)+N(f)]e^{j(w_T+\Delta w)t} \\ R_{HP}(f) &= R(f).e^{-j(w_T+\Delta w)t} &= [T(f)+N(f)]e^{-j(w_T+\Delta w)t}. \end{aligned}$$
$$\tag{10.70}$$

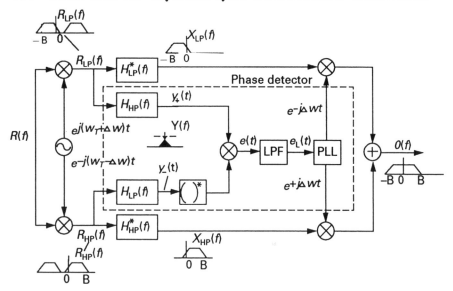

Figure 10.8: QMF based TTIB receiver structure [19]
©IEEE, 1990, Bateman

Upon substituting $T(f)$ from Equation 10.68 into Equation 10.70 we obtain

$$
\begin{aligned}
R_{LP}(f) &= I(f).H_{LP}(f)e^{j\Delta wt} + I(f).H_{HP}(f).e^{j(2w_T+\Delta w)t} + \\
&\quad N(f)e^{j(w_T+\Delta w)t} \\
R_{HP}(f) &= I(f).H_{LP}(f).e^{-j(2w_T+\Delta w)t} + I(f).H_{HP}(f)e^{-j\Delta wt} + \\
&\quad N(f)e^{-j(w_T+\Delta w)t}.
\end{aligned}
$$

(10.71)

It can be seen in Figure 10.8 that one of the side lobes of each of the spectra $R_{LP}(f)$ and $R_{HP}(f)$ is now shifted back to their original positions, apart from a small frequency error Δw. Filtering $R_{LP}(f)$ and $R_{HP}(f)$ with the filter characteristics $H_{LP}(f)$ and $H_{HP}(f)$, respectively, removes the incorrectly positioned side lobes and retains the required ones, yielding

$$
\begin{aligned}
X_{LP} &= R_{LP}(f).H^*_{LP}(f) \\
&= I(f).|H_{LP}(f)|^2 e^{j\Delta wt} + N(f).H^*_{LP}(f)e^{j(w_T+\Delta w)t} \\
X_{HP} &= R_{HP}(f).H^*_{HP}(f) \\
&= I(f).|H_{HP}(f)|^2 e^{-j\Delta wt} + N(f).H^*_{HP}(f)e^{j(w_T+\Delta w)t}.
\end{aligned}
$$

(10.72)

The remaining operations in Figure 10.8 are concerned with the removal of the residual frequency error Δw and the reconstruction of the original full band signal. Assuming that the frequency error can be extricated from $R_{LP}(f)$ and $R_{HP}(f)$ by exploiting the correlations inherent in their overlap transition bands (which we will address later) then the output signal $O(f)$ can be written as

$$O(f) = X_{LP}(f).e^{-j\Delta wt} + X_{HP}(f).e^{j\Delta wt}. \tag{10.73}$$

Substituting Equation 10.72 into Equation 10.73 yields

$$O(f) = I(f)[|H_{LP}(f)|^2 + |H_{HP}(f)|^2] + \\ N(f).H_{LP}^*(f).e^{jw_Tt} + N(f).H_{HP}^*(f).e^{-jw_Tt} \tag{10.74}$$

where the filtered and phase shifted noise term of

$$N_F(f) = N(f).H_{LP}^*(f).e^{jw_Tt} + N(f).H_{HP}^*(f).e^{-jw_Tt} \tag{10.75}$$

is identical to $N(f)$ since it has the same total bandwidth, the filters $H_{LP}(f)$ and $H_{HP}(f)$ have complimentary transfer functions and the noise in the two sidebands is uncorrelated due to their narrow overlapping regions. Taking the all-pass nature of the QMFs given in Equation 10.65 into account, Equation 10.74 can be written as

$$O(f) = I(f) + N(f) \tag{10.76}$$

which is the original input signal plus the additive noise. Therefore, the QMF based TTIB transceiver ensures perfectly transparent baseband processing.

10.3.1.5 Residual Frequency Error Compensation [24]

As mentioned earlier, the compensation of the residual frequency error Δw is based on the correlation of the spectral components of the HP and LP transition regions. If this region does not contain any significant energy , some deterministic signal can be added, although this reduces the overall power efficiency [13].

The filters $H_{HP}(f)$ and $H_{LP}(f)$ in the phase detector section of Figure 10.8 extract the transition band components of the L and U band signals $R_{LP}(f)$ and $R_{HP}(f)$, respectively, which were given in Equation 10.71. Due to the anti-symmetric filter arrangement in the phase detector compared to the filters in the corresponding branches of the transmitter, the combined frequency response $H(f)$ of the TTIB transmitter and the receiver's concatenated phase detector becomes identical in both branches, and is described by

$$H(f) = H_{LP}(f) \cdot H_{HP}(f). \tag{10.77}$$

This anti-symmetrical filter arrangement blocks all frequency components outside the transition band, and the input signal with spectrum $I(f)$ generates an output having a spectrum of

$$\begin{aligned} Y(f) &= I(f) \cdot H(f). \\ &= I(f).H_{LP}(f) \cdot H_{HP}(f). \end{aligned} \tag{10.78}$$

In the time domain this corresponds to

$$y(t) = i(t) * h(t) = \int_{-\infty}^{\infty} i(t - \tau)h(\tau)d\tau \tag{10.79}$$

where $y(t)$, $i(t)$ and $h(t)$ are the time domain representations of $Y(f)$, $I(f)$ and $H(f)$, respectively.

If the transmission channel is non-ideal, the received signal $r(t)$ differs from the transmitted signal $t(t)$ which is described by the following relationship

$$r(t) = \alpha(t) \cdot e^{j\psi(t)} \cdot t(t) + n(t) \tag{10.80}$$

where $\alpha(t)$, $\psi(t)$ and $n(t)$ represent the fading envelope, the fading phase, and the additive noise, respectively. These quantities are considered to be slowly varying with time which allows us to drop their dependency on t within a symbol period. The signal $y(t)$ in Equation 10.79 is subjected to the channel effects portrayed in Equation 10.80, but due to the oscillator frequency error $\Delta w = (w_T - w_R)$ between the transmitter and receiver, a further phase component Δwt must be taken into account, yielding the phase shifted signals $y_+(t)$ and $y_-(t)$ as follows

$$\begin{aligned} y_+(t) &= \alpha \cdot e^{j(\psi + \Delta wt)} \cdot y(t) + n_+(t) \\ &= \alpha \cdot e^{j\psi} \cdot e^{j\Delta wt} \cdot y(t) + n_+(t) \\ y_-(t) &= \alpha \cdot e^{j(\psi - \Delta wt)} \cdot y(t) + n_-(t) \\ &= \alpha \cdot e^{j\psi} \cdot e^{-j\Delta wt} \cdot y(t) + n_-(t) \end{aligned} \tag{10.81}$$

where $n_\pm(t)$ now represents the phase shifted additive noise components. After taking the conjugate of $y_-(t)$ in Equation 10.81 and multiplying $y_+(t)$ and $y_-^*(t)$ as shown in Figure 10.8 we derive the error signal

$$\begin{aligned} e(t) &= y_+(t) \cdot y_-^*(t) \\ &= \alpha^2 \cdot e^{j2\Delta wt} \cdot |y(t)|^2 + \alpha \cdot e^{j\psi} \cdot e^{j\Delta wt} \cdot y(t) \cdot n_-^*(t) + \\ &\quad \alpha \cdot e^{-j\psi} \cdot e^{j\Delta wt} \cdot y^*(t) \cdot n_+(t) + n_+(t) \cdot n_-^*(t). \end{aligned}$$

(10.82)

In the case of low channel noise we can approximate this equation by

$$e(t) \approx \alpha^2 \cdot e^{j2\Delta wt} \cdot |y(t)|^2 \qquad (10.83)$$

which upon evaluating the phase $\Phi = 2\Delta wt$ and halving the frequency allows the receiver to phase and frequency coherently recombine the L and U subbands by shifting the signals $X_{LP}(f)$ and $X_{HP}(f)$ in Figure 10.8 back to their original positions. Note, however, that there is a phase ambiguity of π in the phase detection process since shifts of both Φ and $\pi + \Phi$ produce the same signal $e(t)$. In this situation the TTIB receiver could erroneously invert the polarity of the output signal $O(t)$. This problem can be overcome through the use of differential coding, although this does incur a performance penalty as discussed in Chapter 4.

10.3.1.6 TTIB System Parameters [26]

The performance of a TTIB-based 16 level QAM scheme has been reported in Reference [26] where initially an AWGN channel was assumed and the hardware was constructed using a TMS320C25 digital signal processing device. With a perfectly coherent, synchronous implementation the SNR degradation due to device imperfections was about 0.5dB when compared to the theoretical performance. When TTIB notch-width based timing recovery was used along with perfect carrier recovery, a further 0.5dB degradation was incurred.

When evaluating the TTIB performance using pilot-based carrier recovery, further degradations were introduced which were dependent on the level of the pilot signal transmitted. At higher pilot levels the system is less prone to channel noise, but also less power efficient. If a constant total power level is assumed, there is an optimum trade-off between pilot and information signal power. Furthermore, by narrowing the pilot filter bandwidth, less noise is introduced and the pilot signal's SNR is improved, but the maximum fading rate which can be followed is reduced. In their implementation, Martin and Bateman [26] found a bandwidth of 300Hz to be most appropriate.

They also found that at a pilot power level of -3dB relative to the signal, the 16-QAM BER against SNR performance was very similar to the perfectly coherent scheme, if the pilot power was not included when calculating the E_b/N_o ratio. When the pilot power was included, a performance penalty of about 2.5dB was incurred. At a pilot level of -6dB relative to the mean information power a further 1dB loss in SNR was added which was deemed acceptable by the authors.

When the performance of the TTIB modem was evaluated over a fading channel at a frequency of 70MHz, the pilot level of -3dB was still adequate and yielded a 2.5dB E_b/N_o penalty for fading rates between 1 and 100Hz. However, for higher fading rates the pilot filter bandwidth limited the possible range of fading fluctuations and impaired the performance unless a higher notch width was introduced. The BER versus channel SNR performance of the TTIB assisted 16-QAM modem proposed by Martin and Bateman [26] is shown in Figure 10.9 for Rayleigh fading channels exhibiting Doppler frequencies of 1, 10 and 100Hz.

Clearly, TTIB assisted coherent QAM ensures high-integrity information transmission via fading channels by providing both amplitude and phase references for the receiver. These references assist the receiver in attaining coherent demodulation against a pilot scaled set of demodulation thresholds at a moderate complexity. Having discussed the insertion of channel sounding information in the spectral domain we now focus our attention on a time-domain technique called pilot symbol assisted modulation.

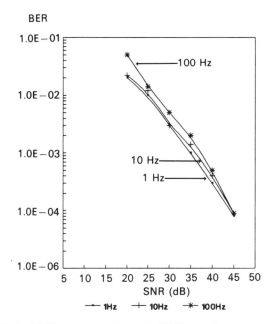

Figure 10.9: BER versus channel SNR performance of TTIB assisted 16-QAM with f_P=70MHz, $f_{Doppler}$=1, 10 and 100Hz. [26]©IEEE, 1991, Martin, Bateman

10.3.2 Pilot Symbol Assisted Modulation [33]

10.3.2.1 Introduction

As we have seen in Chapter 5, the BER of the square constellation 16-QAM and 64-QAM is sufficiently low for example for speech transmission over AWGN channels, but as shown in Chapter 10 it becomes prohibitively high for transmission over Rayleigh-fading channels. This is particularly so for the lower integrity C2 subchannel in case of 16-QAM and for the C2 and C3 subchannels of 64-QAM, resulting in the average BER becoming unacceptably high.

As shown in the previous section, one way to improve the BER of the square constellation over fading channels is to use transparent tone-in-band (TTIB) transmission. This results in higher out-of-band emissions and hence higher adjacent channel interferences, whilst also increasing complexity. An alternative technique which is analogous to TTIB but instead of transmitting constantly in part of the available spectrum, transmits periodically in all the available spectrum is refered to as pilot symbol assisted modulation (PSAM) [29]–[31], [32]. This method relies upon the insertion of known phasors into the stream of useful information symbols for the purpose of channel sounding. These pilot symbols allow the receiver to extract channel attenuation and phase rotation estimates for each received symbol, facilitating the compensation of the fading envelope and phase. Closed form formulae for the BER of PSAM were provided by Cavers [33] for binary phase shift keying (BPSK), and quadrature phase shift keying (QPSK), while for 16-QAM he derived a tight upper-bound of the symbol error rate (SER).

10.3.2.2   PSAM System Description

Following Caver's approach [33], the block diagram of a general PSAM scheme is depicted in Figure 10.10, where the pilot symbols p are cyclically inserted into the data sequence prior to pulse shaping, as demonstrated by Figure 10.11. A frame of data is constituted by M symbols, and the first one in every frame is assumed to be the pilot symbol $b(0)$, followed by $(M-1)$ useful data symbols $b(1), b(2) \ldots b(M-1)$.

Detection can be carried out by matched filtering, and the output of the matched filter is split into data and pilot paths, as seen in Figure 10.10. The set of pilot symbols can be extracted by decimating the matched filter's sampled output sequence using a decimation factor of M. The extracted sequence of pilot symbols must then be interpolated in order to derive a channel estimate $v(k)$ for every useful received information symbol $r(k)$. Decision is carried out against a decision level reference grid, scaled and rotated according to the instantaneous channel estimate $v(k)$.

Observe in Figure 10.10 that the received data symbols must be delayed according to the interpolation and prediction delay incurred. This delay becomes longer, if interpolation is carried out using a longer history of the received signal to yield better channel estimates. Consequently, there is a trade-off between processing delay and accuracy. The interpolation coefficients can be kept constant over a whole pilot-period of length M, but better channel estimates can be

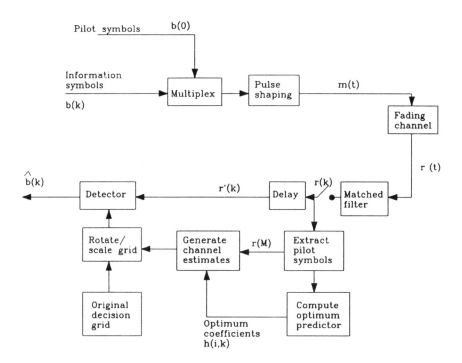

Figure 10.10: PSAM Schematic Diagram [33]©IEEE, 1991, Cavers

obtained if the interpolator's coefficients are optimally updated for every received symbol.

The complex envelope of the modulated signal can be formulated as:

$$m(t) = \sum_{k=-\infty}^{\infty} b(k)p(t - kT), \qquad (10.84)$$

where $b(k) = -3, -1, 1$ or 3 represents the quaternary I or Q components of the 16-QAM symbols to be transmitted, T is the symbol duration and $p(t)$ is a band-limited unit-energy signalling pulse, for which we have:

$$\int_{-\infty}^{\infty} |p(t)|^2 dt = 1. \qquad (10.85)$$

The value of the pilot symbols $b(kM)$ can be arbitrary, although sending a sequence of known pseudo-random symbols avoids the

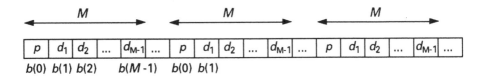

Figure 10.11: Insertion of Pilot Symbols

transmission of a periodic tone, which would increase the detrimental adjacent channel interference [30].

The narrowband Rayleigh channel is assumed to be "flat"-fading, which implies that all frequency components of the transmitted signal suffer the same attenuation and phase shift. This condition is met if the transmitted signal's bandwidth is much lower than the channel's coherence bandwidth. The received signal is then given by:

$$r(t) = c(t) \cdot m(t) + n(t), \qquad (10.86)$$

where $n(t)$ is the AWGN and $c(t)$ is the channel's complex gain. Assuming a Rayleigh-fading envelope $\alpha(t)$, uniformly distributed phase $\phi(t)$ and a residual frequency offset of f_0, we have:

$$c(t) = \alpha(t)e^{j\phi(t)} \cdot e^{j\omega_0 t} \qquad (10.87)$$

The matched filter's output symbols at the sampling instant kT are then given as:

$$r(k) = b(k) \cdot c(k) + n(k). \qquad (10.88)$$

Without imposing limitations on the analysis, Cavers [33] assumed that in every channel sounding block $b(0)$ was the pilot symbol and considered the detection of the useful information symbols in the range $\lfloor -M/2 \rfloor \leq k \leq \lfloor (M - 1)/2 \rfloor$, where $\lfloor \bullet \rfloor$ is the integer of $\bullet$. Optimum detection is achieved if the corresponding channel gain $c(k)$ is estimated for every received symbol $r(k)$ in the above range. The channel gain estimate $v(k)$ can be derived as a weighted sum of the surrounding K received pilot symbols $r(iM)$, $\lfloor -K/2 \rfloor \leq i \leq \lfloor K/2 \rfloor$, as shown below:

$$v(k) = \sum_{i=\lfloor -K/2 \rfloor}^{\lfloor K/2 \rfloor} h(i,k) \cdot r(iM), \qquad (10.89)$$

and the weighting coefficients $h(i,k)$ explicitly depend on the symbol position k within the frame of M symbols.

The estimation error $e(k)$ associated with the gain estimate $v(k)$ is computed as:

$$e(k) = c(k) - v(k). \qquad (10.90)$$

10.3.2.3 Channel Gain Estimation

While previously proposed PSAM schemes used either a low-pass interpolation filter [30] or an approximately Gaussian filter [31], Cavers deployed an optimum Wiener filter to minimise the channel estimation error variance $\sigma^2_e(k) = E\{e^2(k)\}$, where $E\{\ \}$ represents the expectation. This well-known estimation error variance minimisation problem can be formulated as follows:

$$\begin{aligned}
\sigma_e^2(k) &= E\{e^2(k)\} = E\{[c(k) - v(k)]^2\} \\
&= E\left\{ \left[c(k) - \sum_{i=\lfloor -K/2 \rfloor}^{\lfloor K/2 \rfloor} h(i,k) \cdot r(iM) \right]^2 \right\}. \qquad (10.91)
\end{aligned}$$

In order to find the optimum interpolator coefficients $h(i,k)$, minimising the estimation error variance $\sigma^2_e(k)$ we consider estimating the kth sample and set:

$$\frac{\partial \sigma_e^2(k)}{\partial h(i,k)} = 0 \quad \text{for} \quad \lfloor -K/2 \rfloor \le i \le \lfloor K/2 \rfloor. \qquad (10.92)$$

Then using Equation 10.91 we have:

$$\frac{\partial \sigma^2_e(k)}{\partial h(i,k)} = E\left\{ 2\left[c(k) - \sum_{i=\lfloor -K/2 \rfloor}^{\lfloor K/2 \rfloor} h(i,k) \cdot r(iM) \right] \cdot r(jM) \right\} = 0. \qquad (10.93)$$

After multiplying both square bracketed terms with $r(jM)$, and computing the expected value of both terms separately, we arrive at

$$E\{c(k) \cdot r(jM)\} = E\{ \sum_{i=\lfloor -K/2 \rfloor}^{\lfloor K/2 \rfloor} h(i,k) \cdot r(iM) \cdot r(jM)\}. \qquad (10.94)$$

Observe that

$$\Phi(j) = E\{c(k) \cdot r(jM)\} \qquad (10.95)$$

is the cross-correlation of the received pilot symbols and complex channel gain values, while

$$R(i,j) = E\{r(iM) \cdot r(jM)\} \qquad (10.96)$$

represents the pilot symbol autocorrelations, hence Equation 10.94 yields:

$$\sum_{i=\lfloor -K/2 \rfloor}^{\lfloor K/2 \rfloor} h(i,k) \cdot R(i,j) = \Phi(j), \quad j = \lfloor -\frac{k}{2} \rfloor \ldots \lfloor \frac{k}{2} \rfloor. \qquad (10.97)$$

If the fading statistics can be considered stationary, the autocorrelations $R(i,j)$ will only depend on the difference $|i - j|$, giving $R(i,j) = R(|i-j|)$. Therefore Equation 10.97 can be written as:

$$\sum_{i=\lfloor -K/2 \rfloor}^{\lfloor K/2 \rfloor} h(i,k) \cdot R(|i-j|) = \Phi(j), \quad j = \lfloor -K/2 \rfloor \ldots \lfloor K/2 \rfloor, \qquad (10.98)$$

which is a form of the well-known Wiener-Hopf equations [34], often used in estimation and prediction theory [2].

This set of K equations contains K unknown prediction coefficients $h(i,k)$, $i = \lfloor -K/2 \rfloor \ldots \lfloor K/2 \rfloor$, which must be determined in order to arrive at a minimum error variance estimate of $c(k)$ by $v(k)$. First the correlation terms $\Phi(j)$ and $R(|i-j|)$ must be computed and to do this the expectation value computations in Equations 10.95 and 10.96 need to be restricted to a finite duration window. This approach is referred to as the *autocorrelation method* [2].

The set of Equations 10.98 can also be expressed in a convenient matrix form as:

$$\begin{bmatrix} R(0) & R(1) & R(2) & \ldots & R(K) \\ R(1) & R(0) & R(1) & \ldots & R(K-1) \\ R(2) & R(1) & R(0) & \ldots & R(K-2) \\ \vdots & \vdots & \vdots & \ldots & \vdots \\ R(K) & R(K-1) & R(K-2) & \ldots & R(0) \end{bmatrix} \qquad (10.99)$$

$$
\cdot \begin{bmatrix} h\left(\lfloor -\frac{K}{2}\rfloor, k\right) \\ h\left(\lfloor -\frac{K}{2}+1\rfloor, k\right) \\ h\left(\lfloor -\frac{K}{2}+2\rfloor, k\right) \\ \vdots \\ h\left(\lfloor \frac{K}{2}\rfloor, k\right) \end{bmatrix} = \begin{bmatrix} \Phi\left(\lfloor -\frac{K}{2}\rfloor\right) \\ \Phi\left(\lfloor -\frac{K}{2}+1\rfloor\right) \\ \Phi\left(\lfloor -\frac{K}{2}+2\rfloor\right) \\ \vdots \\ \Phi\left(\lfloor \frac{K}{2}\rfloor\right) \end{bmatrix},
$$

which can be solved for the optimum predictor coefficients $h(i,k)$ by matrix inversion using Gauss-Jordan elimination or any appropriate recursive algorithm.

Once the optimum predictor coefficients $h(i,k)$ are known, the minimum error variance channel estimate $v(k)$ can be derived from the received pilot symbols using Equation 10.89, as also demonstrated by Figure 10.10.

10.3.2.4   PSAM Parameters

Cavers [33] provided a range of results for a variety of PSAM parameters. As regards to the pilot spacing M, the optimum value is determined by the Nyquist rate of the fading envelope. Inserting pilot symbols less frequently results in a significant increase in BER due to the inability to track the fading, while an unnecessarily frequent insertion wastes energy without significantly improving the BER performance.

The typical energy loss and Doppler frequency interdependence can be highlighted by the following simple example. Let us assume a fast moving vehicle with a Doppler frequency of $f_D = 100\,Hz$, and a TDMA multi-user signalling rate of 100 ksymbols/s, yielding a normalised Doppler shift of $f_d \cdot T = 10^{-3}$. This would require a Nyquist frequency of $f_N = 2 \cdot 10^{-3}$, implying a pilot spacing of $M = 500$, which results in an energy loss of only 0.2 %. If the signalling rate reduces to 10 ksymbols/s, the relative frequency of the pilot symbol insertion must be increased ten-fold in order for the pilot symbols to appear in the same positions in terms of absolute time, facilitating equally frequent channel sounding, as in the case of 100 ksymbols/s signalling. The corresponding pilot insertion frequency of $M = 50$ implies an energy loss of about 2 %. However, when using the PSAM scheme in a single-user scenario with a low signalling rate of, say, 2 ksymbols/s, the energy loss due to five times more frequent channel sounding associated with $M = 10$ becomes 10 %.

As seen in Figure 10.10, the operation of the PSAM scheme is prone to a delay of $KM/2$ symbols, which might become an impediment in case of speech transmissions. Due to this start-up delay the first $KM/2$ modulation symbols are corrupted by fading and hence must be discarded. This might effect for example, some $7 \cdot 10/2 = 35$ start-up symbols for the specific case of $K = 7$ and $M = 10$.

Clearly, the design of the predictor coefficients $h(i, k)$ depends on a variety of PSAM system parameters, such as K and M, as well as on channel conditions, such as the prevailing SNR and normalised Doppler shift. The symbol error rate performance upper bounds derived by Cavers [33] for 16-QAM cannot be approached if the above conditions are drastically different from those for which the predictor coefficients were optimised. Best results can be attained using adaptive predictors updating their parameters on-line, as signalling and channel conditions vary.

A further advantage of PSAM is that it generates an absolute phase reference and hence differential encoding of the data is not required. In contrast, TTIB transmissions require a perfect phase lock to be maintained [35], which assumes differential coding, associated with some SNR penalty. In a more recent paper [36] Cavers investigated the performance of PSAM schemes under dispersive channel conditions introduced by frequency selective fading channels in case of BPSK and QPSK. He found that the performance gains are sensitive to delay spread, but PSAM always ensured a better performance than differential coding. Recently Seymour and Fitz [37] recognized that ignoring the transmitted information symbols in the predictor is wasteful. This is because the modulated received information symbols also carry channel-specific information. Exploiting this property allows for more sparse pilot insertion, thereby saving modulation energy, or achieving slightly better BER performance.

10.3.2.5 PSAM Performance

In this Section we embarked on the performance evaluation of two low-complexity square-constellation pilot-assisted modems, namely

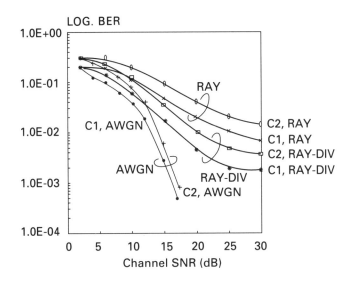

Figure 10.12: Square 16-QAM/PSAM BER versus channel
SNR curves for AWGN and Rayleigh channels
with and without diversity at 4 mph, 1.9 GHz
and 100 kBd

that of a 16-QAM/PSAM and a 64-QAM/PSAM scheme. The pilot separation of the 16-QAM scheme was $M = 10$, while that of
the 64-QAM modem was $M = 5$ at a pedestrian speed of 4 mph,
propagation frequency of 1.9 GHz and signalling rate of 100 kBd.
The channel magnitude and phase fluctuation was linearly interpolated between two adjacent pilot symbols. The performance of
these schemes is displayed in Figures 10.12. and 10.13. This
low-complexity approach typically failed to track the amplitude and
phase trajectory upon emerging from a deep fade, which manifests itself in a residual bit error rate, but overall provided a significant performance improvement, when compared to the scenarios portrayed
earlier in Figures 10.1 and 10.2 without PSAM.

The performance of a combined 16-QAM/PSAM/TCM scheme
over Rayleigh fading channels is reported in Figure 11.8 of Chapter 11,
where three PSAM modulation schemes having a net throughput of 2
bits/symbol are studied comparatively. Specifically, uncoded QPSK,
2/3-rate coded 8PSK-TCM and 1/2-rate square 16-QAM/TCM are
compared and the 16-QAM/TCM scheme has the best performance,

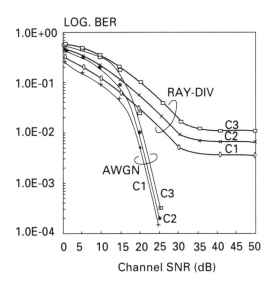

Figure 10.13: Square 64-QAM/PSAM BER versus channel SNR curves for AWGN and Rayleigh channels with diversity at 4 mph, 1.9 GHz and 100 kBd

since it has no unprotected bits.

10.4 Summary

In this Chapter we started by considering the theoretical performance of 16 and 64-level square QAM over mobile radio channels. The results showed a significant drop in performance compared to transmission over the Gaussian channels considered in the previous section of this book.

We then continued to consider two particular schemes of QAM transmission over mobile radio channels whereby an attempt was made to transmit some information to the receiver concerning the instantaneous state of the mobile radio channel. Transparent tone in band attempted to split the transmitted spectrum into two, to increase the spacing between these two parts, and to insert a continuous tone which the receiver could use to estimate the channel response. Such a scheme was shown to be complex and a number of problems with it were detailed. Pilot symbol assisted modulation inserted a known symbol periodically into the data stream. Since the receiver had been pre-programmed as to what this symbol was and when it would appear it could use this information to estimate the channel response at that particular instance. Advanced extrapolation techniques could then be used to predict the channel response between any two of these periodic symbols. Both schemes were shown to have some success in overcoming the worst problems of the mobile radio channel although both had the disadvantage of increasing the required bandwidth due to the transmission of redundant information.

In the next Chapter we consider a completely different means of overcoming the problem of a rapidly changing channel. This is through the use of a different QAM constellation known as Star QAM, which through its symmetry and use of differential coding, removes the need for the receiver to estimate the channel response at all.

Bibliography

[1] **W.Y.C. Lee**, "Mobile Communication Engineering", McGraw-Hill, 1982

[2] **R. Steele**, "Mobile Radio Communications", Pentech Press, U.K., 1992

[3] **K.S.Shanmugan**, "Digital and analogue communications systems", *J.Wiley*, New York, 1979.

[4] **L. Hanzo, R. Steele and P.M. Fortune**, "A Subband Coding, BCH Coding and 16-QAM System for Mobile Radio Speech Communications", *IEEE Tr. on Veh. Techn.*, Nov. 1990, Vol 39, No 4, pp 327-340

[5] **L. Hanzo, R. Salami, R. Steele and P.M. Fortune**, "Transmission of Digitally Encoded Speech at 1.2 KBd for PCN", *IEE Proceedings, Part I*, Vol. 139, No. 4, Aug. 1992, pp 437-447

[6] **R. Stedman, H. Gharavi, L. Hanzo and R. Steele**, "16-QAM Transmission of Sub-band Coded Images via Microcellular Mobile Channels", accepted by *IEEE Tr. on Video Systems*, 1992

[7] **W.T. Webb, L. Hanzo and R. Steele**, "Bandwidth-Efficient QAM Schemes for Rayleigh-Fading Channels", *IEE Proc. Pt I*, Vol 138, No 3, June, 1991, pp 169-175

[8] **J.G. Proakis**, "Digital Communications", McGraw-Hill, 1983

[9] **P.M Fortune, L. Hanzo and R. Steele**, "On the computation of 16-QAM and 64-QAM performance in Rayleigh-fading channels", *IEICE Transactions on Comms*, Vol. E75-B, No. 6, June 1992, pp 466-475

[10] **I.S.Gradshteyn and I.M.Ryzhik**, "Table of integrals, series and products", *Academic Press*, 1980, p649.

[11] **J.P.McGeehan and A. Bateman**, "Phase-locked transparent tone in band (TTIB): A new spectrum configuration particularly suited to the transmission of data over SSB mobile radio networks", *IEEE Trans Comm, Vol.COM-32*, pp81-87, 1984.

[12] **G.J.Saulnier and W.Raffety**, "Pilot-aided modulation for narrow-band satellite communications", *Proc. Mobile Satellite Conf. 1988*, pp329-336.

[13] **A.Bateman and J.P.McGeehan**, "Feedforward transparent tone in band for rapid fading protection in multipath fading", *IEE Int. Conf. Comms. Vol.68, 1986*, pp9-13.

[14] **A.Bateman and J.P.McGeehan**, "The use of transparent tone in band for coherent data schemes", *IEEE Int. Conf. Comms., Boston, Mass.*, 1983.

[15] **A.Bateman, G.Lightfoot, A.Lymer and J.P.McGeehan**, "Speech and data transmissions over a 942MHz TAB and TTIB single sideband mobile radio system", *IEEE Trans Veh. Tech., Vol.VT-34* pp13-21, 1985.

[16] **A.Bateman and J.P.McGeehan**, "Data transmissions over UHF fading mobile radio channels", *Proc IEE Pt.F, Vol.131*, 1984, pp364-374.

[17] **J.P.McGeehan and A.Bateman**, "A simple simultaneous carrier and bit synchronisation system for narrowband data transmissions", *Proc. IEE, Pt.F, Vol.132*, pp69-72, 1985.

[18] **J.P.McGeehan and A.Bateman**, "Theoretical and experimental investigation of feedforward signal regeneration", *IEEE Trans. Veh. Tech., Vol.VT-32*, pp106-120, 1983

[19] **A.Bateman**, "Feedforward transparent tone in band: Its implementation and applications", *IEEE Trans. Veh. Tech. Vol.39, No.3*, Aug 1990, pp235-243.

[20] **M.K.Simon**, "Dual pilot tone calibration technique", *IEEE Trans. Veh. Tech., Vol.VT-35, No.2*, May 1986, pp63-70.

[21] **M.P.Fitz**, "A dual-tone reference digital demodulator for mobile communications", *IEEE Tran. Veh. Tech., Vol.VT-42, No.2*, May 1993, pp156-166.

[22] **S.Gamnathan and K.Feher**, "Pilot tone aided QPRS systems for digital audio broadcasting", *IEEE Trans. on Broadcasting, Vol.38, No.1*, March 1992, pp1-6.

[23] **F.Davarrin**, "Mobile digital communications via tone calibration", *IEEE Trans. Veh. Tech., Vol.VT-36, No.2*, May 1987, pp55-62.

[24] **J.K.Cavers**, "The performance of phase locked transparent tone in band with symmetric phase detection", *IEEE Trans. on Comms., Vol.39, No.9*, Sept 1991, pp1389-1399.

[25] **J.K.Cavers**, "Performance of tone calibration with frequency offset and imperfect pilot filter", *IEEE Tran. Veh. Tech., Vol.40, No.2*, May 1991, pp426-434.

[26] **P.M.Martin and A.Bateman**, "Practical results for a modem using linear mobile radio channels", *Proc. IEEE VTC'91*, St Louis, USA, pp386-392.

[27] **D.Esteban and C.Galand**, "Application of quadrature mirror filters to split band voice coding schemes", *Proc. ICASSP'77*, CT, pp191-195.

[28] **J.D.Johnston**, "A filter family designed for use in quadrature mirror filter banks", *Proc. ICASSP'80*, pp294-295.

[29] **J.H. Lodge, M.L. Moher**: "Time Diversity for Mobile Satellite Channels Using Trellis Coded Modulations", *IEEE Global Telecommun. Conf.*, Tokyo, 1987

[30] **M.L. Moher, J.H. Lodge**: "TCMP – A Modulation and Coding Strategy for Rician Fading Channels", *IEEE J. Select. Areas Commun.*, Vol. 7, pp. 1347-1355, Dec. 1989

[31] **S. Sampei, T. Sunaga:** "Rayleigh Fading Compensation Method for 16-QAM in Digital Land Mobile Radio Channels", *Proc. IEEE Veh. Technol. Conf.*, San Francisco, CA, May 1989, pp. 640-646

[32] **L. Hanzo, R. Salami, R. Steele, P.M. Fortune:** "Transmission of Digitally Encoded Speech at 1.2 KBaud for PCN", *IEE-Proc., Part-I.* Vol. 139, No. 4, pp. 437-447, Aug. 1992

[33] **J.K. Cavers:** "An Analysis of Pilot Symbol Assisted Modulation for Rayleigh Fading Channels", *IEEE Tr. on Veh. Techn.*, Vol. 40, No. 4, pp. 686-693, Nov. 1991

[34] **S. Haykin:** *Adaptive Filter Theory*, Prentice Hall, 1991

[35] **J.K. Cavers:** "The Performance of Phase Locked Transparent Tone-In-Band with Symmetric Phase Detection", *IEEE Trans. Commun.*, Vol. 39, pp. 1389-1399, Sept. 1991

[36] **J.K. Cavers:** "Pilot Symbol Assisted Modulation in Fading and Delay Spread", *Proc. of IEEE VTC'93, Secancus, N.J., USA*, 18-20 May 1993, pp. 13-16

[37] **J.P. Seymour, M.P. Fitz:** "Improved Carrier Synchronisation Techniques for Mobile Communications", *Proc. of IEEE VTC'93, Secancus, N.J., USA*, 18-20 May 1993, pp. 901-904

Chapter 11

Star QAM schemes for Rayleigh fading channels

11.1 Introduction

In Chapter 10 we considered the transmission of coherently detected maximum least distance square QAM signals over Rayleigh fading channels. We have shown that adequate BER performance can only be achieved through deploying either frequency-domain pilots (TTIB) or using time-domain pilot signals (PSAM). The channel attenuation and phase rotation information derived using these techniques facilitates fading compensation and coherent detection at moderate implementational complexity. In many applications, such as light-weight hand-held portable telephones, power consumption, weight and low-cost construction are crucial issues, and hence lower complexity modem schemes are desirable. In this case it may be preferable to reduce the system performance slightly in order to be able to employ a low-complexity non-coherent differentially encoded QAM constellation, such as the circular or Star QAM scheme proposed in this chapter. We can then dispense with TTIB, PSAM, or AGC reference schemes, and no longer require carrier recovery. Consequently, the result is an attractive low-complexity system. In this chapter we investigate the properties and performance of a variety of Star QAM systems and then consider constellation distortion and practical issues.

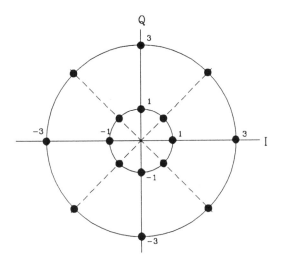

Figure 11.1: Transmitted differential Star QAM constellation

11.2 Star 16-QAM transmissions over mobile channels

In Section 4.1 we presented a brief discussion on the most appropriate choice of constellation f ˜ a range of channel conditions, and showed the superiority of the Type III rectangular constellation of Figure 4.1 over the Type I circular or star constellation **for AWGN channels**. The QAM constellation which we advocate **for Rayleigh fading channels** is shown in Figure 11.1. This constellation does not have a minimum least free distance between points in the manner of the square constellation of Chapter 10, but does allow efficient differential encoding and decoding methods to be used which remove the need for AGC and carrier recovery and thus go some way towards mitigating the effects of Rayleigh fading. The structure of this constellation will be further investigated throughout this section.

11.2.1 Differential coding

In the case of PLL type carrier tracking some form of differential encoding is essential as the Rayleigh fading channel can introduce phase shifts in excess of 50 degrees between consecutive symbols in the case of slow signalling rates, making it extremely difficult to establish an absolute phase reference. The encoding method used in the Star QAM system is as follows. Of the four bits in each symbol, b_1, b_2, b_3 and b_4, the first is differentially encoded onto the QAM phasor amplitude so that a "1" causes a change to the amplitude ring which was not used in the previous symbol, and a "0" causes the current symbol to be transmitted at the same amplitude as the previous symbol. The remaining three bits are differentially Gray encoded onto the phase so that, for example, "000" would cause the current symbol to be transmitted with the same phase as the previous one, "001" would cause a 45 degree phase shift relative to the previous symbol, "011" a 90 degree shift relative to the previous symbol, and so on.

11.2.2   Differential decoding

Using the above differential encoding technique, decoding data is now reduced to a comparison test between the previous and current received symbols. Suppose we fix the transmitted rings at amplitude levels A_1 and A_2. Let the received phasor amplitudes be Z_t and Z_{t+1} at time t and t+1, respectively. The demodulator must identify whether there has been a significant change in amplitude in order to regenerate a logical "1". This is equivalent to asking whether the amplitude of the phasor at the transmitter changed rings at time t+1 compared to time t. The algorithm employed at the demodulator uses two adaptive thresholds to carry out its decisions. If

$$Z_{t+1} \geq \left(\frac{A_1 + A_2}{2} \right) Z_t \tag{11.1}$$

or if

$$Z_{t+1} < \left(\frac{2}{A_1 + A_2} \right) Z_t \tag{11.2}$$

then a significant change in amplitude is deemed to have occurred and bit b_1 is set to logical "1" at time t+1. Notice that the thresholds are dependent on Z_t, and as the amplitude of the phasors change in fading conditions so do the thresholds. Should both of Inequalities 11.1 and 11.2 fail to be satisfied, b_1 is assigned logical "0".

If the received symbol phases are θ_t and θ_{t+1} at time t and t+1, respectively, the demodulated angle is

$$\theta_{dem} = (\theta_{t+1} - \theta_t) \bmod 2\pi. \qquad (11.3)$$

This angle is then quantised to the nearest multiple of 45 degrees and a lookup table is consulted in order to derive the remaining three output bits, b_2, b_3 and b_4. This differential system can considerably improve the BERs compared to the square constellation because it eliminates the long error bursts that occur when a false lock was inflicted. Of considerable importance is that with differential amplitude encoding there is no longer any need for AGC. This not only simplifies the system, but also removes errors caused by an inability of the AGC to follow the fading envelope.

11.2.3 Effect of oversampling

In mobile radio channels the fading continues to cause problems because there are changes in channel amplitude and phase during symbol periods, which in general move the differentially decoded phasors nearer to the decision boundaries. The most likely cause of error in the Star QAM system is when both the noise, and the change in the phasor's amplitude or phase due to fading, combine to drive the incoming signal level over a decision boundary. As the Rayleigh fading envelope is bandlimited by the normalised Doppler frequency, it is highly correlated and predictable, particularly at low vehicular speeds. Hence a correction factor may be applied to the incoming signal in order to compensate for the changes in the fading envelope during the last symbol period. Such a system must be fast acting so that the sudden change from an amplitude decrease to an amplitude increase experienced at the bottom of a fade can immediately be detected and compensated. Methods such as using the differential of the PLL error signal in order to change the step size of the phase correction signal tend to overshoot at sudden changes and exhibit damped second-order system behaviour.

In order to overcome this problem a simple oversampling receiver can be used. In this system n observations equally spaced in time are made per symbol period. At SNRs above 30dB the current phasor can be modified to compensate for the fading. This is done by finding

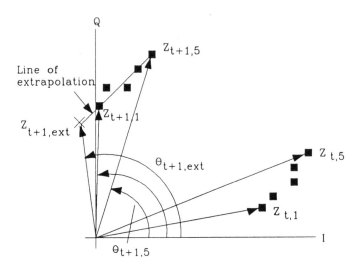

Figure 11.2: Correction for changes in fading envelope

the change in the incoming symbol phase and amplitude over the current symbol period. We do this by subtracting the phase at the end of the symbol from the phase at the beginning of the symbol, and subtracting the amplitude at the end of the symbol from the amplitude at the beginning of the symbol.

The situation is shown in Figure 11.2. We use the same notation as before, but with the addition of subscript n to the symbols, to signify the nth observation of the symbol at time t. Thus

$$Z_{t+1,diff} = Z_{t+1,n} - Z_{t+1,1} \qquad (11.4)$$

where *diff* means differential, and

$$\theta_{t+1,diff} = \theta_{t+1,n} - \theta_{t+1,1}. \qquad (11.5)$$

These changes can be used to extrapolate back from the first observation in the current symbol to the point in time when the last observation from the previous symbol was made.

With the aim of improving the accuracy of Inequalities 11.1 and 11.2 we replace Z_t by its last oversampled value, namely $Z_{t,n}$ and we use an estimate of Z_{t+1} which is formed by extrapolation as

$$Z_{t+1,ext} = Z_{t+1,1} - \frac{Z_{t+1,diff}}{n} \qquad (11.6)$$

rather than Z_t. Notice that $Z_{t+1,1}$ is the first sample of Z_{t+1} and is closest in time to $Z_{t,n}$. By subtracting the average change in Z_{t+1} over a symbol period, i.e. $\frac{Z_{t+1,diff}}{n}$ from $Z_{t+1,1}$, we obtain an estimate of Z_{t+1} had it been transmitted at time t. This is beneficial as there may have been significant amplitude and phase changes between time t and t+1 as can be seen in Figure 11.2.

After determining bit b_1 with the aid of Inequalities 11.1 and 11.2 using the modified Z_t and Z_{t+1} values, we determine bits b_2, b_3 and b_4 by formulating

$$\theta_{dem} = (\theta_{t+1,ext} - \theta_{t,n}) \ mod \ 2\pi. \qquad (11.7)$$

where $\theta_{t+1,ext}$ and $\theta_{t,n}$ are the phase angles associated with $Z_{t+1,ext}$ and $Z_{t,n}$. Again θ_{dem} is quantised and used to address a lookup table which provides values of b_2, b_3 and b_4.

In the above description it has been assumed that no pulseshaping or filtering was employed so that square pulseshapes result. This is impractical because of the spectral spillage caused by such modulation. The oversampling system can work with practical pulseshaping systems. With pulseshaping the oversampling system needs to perform an inverse operation before predicting the change undergone in the channel. At the receiver an attempt is made to reconstruct the transmitted waveform. This is done by passing the estimated received and regenerated data in square waveform through an identical filter to the transmitter filter. The difference between this reconstructed waveform and the received waveform can then be used to estimate the average change that has taken place over the symbol period, and thus form some estimate of the Rayleigh fading. This estimate can then be used in the decoding of the next symbol, with extrapolation techniques instigated as required. Simulations showed the degradation in BER over unfiltered transmissions to be negligible.

11.2.4 Star 16-QAM Performance

Previous QAM systems tended to exhibit a residual BER at high SNRs due to the rapidly changing Rayleigh channel, rather than the

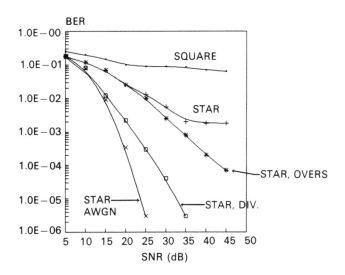

Figure 11.3: BER versus channel SNR results for various 16-
QAM systems

additive noise. With this system the residual BER is reduced by approximately two orders of magnitude. The simulation results of this
system when the 16-QAM carrier was 1.9GHz, the symbol rate was
16kSym/s, the mobile's speed was 30mph and the channel exhibited
Rayleigh fading with additive white Gaussian noise (AWGN) are
given in Figure 11.3. The receiver operated as described above, with
the oversampling ratio set at n=8. Non-linear filtering as introduced
in Chapter 5 was employed at the transmitter. Both transmitter and
receiver used a fourth-order Butterworth lowpass filter with a 3dB
point at 1.5 times the Baud rate, i.e. 24kHz.

The variation of BER versus channel SNR is shown in curve (c) in
Figure 11.3. Also shown as bench markers are the results for the similar complexity coherent non-differential square QAM constellation
using no fading compensation AGC, TTIB or PSAM (curve (a)) and
the Star 16-QAM with differential encoding (curve (b)) both over
a Rayleigh fading channel, and the Star 16-QAM with differential
encoding over an AWGN channel (curve (e)). The performance of

the system having differential encoding and oversampling (curve(c)) can be considerably enhanced by the use of spatial diversity, where two antennas and receiver circuits are used. For these simulations, switched diversity was used, whereby for each phasor received, the receiver with the incoming phasor of largest magnitude was selected. Both receivers must have their own differential decoders. Curve (d) shows the performance of this second order diversity assisted system.

As can be seen, a very substantial improvement in BER has been obtained over the coherent non-compensated square 16-QAM scheme having similar complexity by using Star QAM, and at high SNRs oversampling gave a further significant gain. By introducing second-order switched diversity the system operated with a channel SNR of only 5dBs above that for an AWGN channel for a BER of 10^{-3}.

11.3 Trellis coded modulation for QAM

In an attempt to further reduce the BER achieved by the Star 16-QAM schemes proposed in the previous section, we turned our attention towards various FEC coding schemes. Papers published by Ungerboeck and others [1] suggest that for an AWGN channel, significant coding gains can be achieved by expanding the symbol set size and using the extra bit(s) gained for channel coding. In its most common form this is known as Trellis Code Modulation (TCM). TCM schemes employ redundant non-binary modulation in combination with a finite state encoder which governs the selection of the modulation signals to generate coded signal sequences. This process is described in Chapter 8.

Historically TCM was conceived to operate with modems over AWGN channels. Here it could be assumed that an accurate phase reference was established and maintained and so there was no problem with false locking. One of the properties of TCM systems is that they exhibit invariance to 180 degree rotations, i.e. if lock is established 180 degrees from the correct lock position their operation will be unaffected. Systems have been suggested [2] having non-linear convolutional encoders which exhibit invariance to all 90 degree rotations, but no systems exhibiting invariance to 45 degree rotations

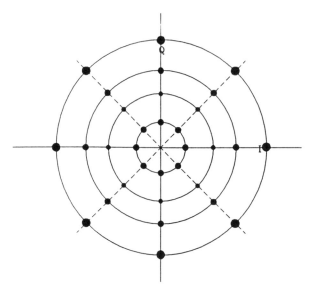

Figure 11.4: Star 32 TCM constellation

have been published. This means that TCM cannot be used as it stands with the Star 16-QAM system, as half of the possible lock points will lead to incorrect system operation.

In order to maintain phase invariance to 45 degree rotations it is necessary to introduce differential coding whereby we associate each TCM word with a phase and amplitude change, rather than to an absolute phase and amplitude as is normally done. The constellation we opt for is a four ring Star scheme with 8 points on each level, i.e. the 32-level Star QAM shown in Figure 11.4. This arrangement does not have a constant free distance amongst constellation points, but it does enable the TCM codewords to be optimally and differentially mapped onto the constellation. Based on our experiments we discovered that sub-optimal mappings involving constellations, for example, that have 4,6,10,12 points on the first,second, third and fourth rings, respectively, where the rings are numbered starting with the inner ring, have poorer results than a constellation having 8 points on each of its four rings. Diagonal interleaving over approximately three fades was used in order to randomise errors. Simulations of TCM revealed marginal improvements in BER at very high SNRs compared to 16-level Star QAM, although significant degradation in

BER was experienced at the lower SNRs encountered in practice. This degradation at lower SNRs was because the BERs on which the convolutional decoder was operating were so high that the decoder often chose the incorrect path through the trellis and thus increased the number of errors. It was not until the BER fell below a certain level that the convolutional coding system was able to reduce the number of errors. TCM systems only proved beneficial when switched diversity was used, achieving a residual BER of 5×10^{-5} at SNRs above 35dB. This was because current TCM systems have been optimized for AWGN.

11.4 Block Coding

In our next endeavour in attempting to reduce the Star 16-QAM BER block coding [4], rather than convolutional coding [4], was employed by expanding the signal set to cope with the extra bits required for the FEC code. A 2/3 coding rate was considered to be appropriate, causing the number of QAM levels to increase from 16 to 64. An extension of the Star constellation was selected having 4 amplitude rings with 16 points equi-spaced on each ring. Again, this was not optimal as regards to the minimum distance criterion, but simulations showed it to perform better in fading environments than constellations which were optimal for AWGN.

For block codes to perform well in the Rayleigh fading environment it is necessary to add interleaving to the system in order to randomly distribute the errors in time. The block code and the interleaving process introduce a delay, and the maximum permissible delay depends on the type of information to be transmitted. The integrity constraints of computer data transmissions are at least three orders of magnitude higher than those of digital speech transmissions. Fortunately, data channels can accept longer interleaving delays which allow effective randomisation of the bursty error statistics of the Rayleigh fading channel. This considerably increases the ability of the forward error correction (FEC) decoder to decrease the BER. For each transmission rate, propagation frequency, vehicular speed and interleaver algorithm there is a minimum interleaving depth or delay to transform the BER statistics of a fading channel into a good approximation of those encountered in a Gaussian channel. For a specific combination of system parameters, an interleaved FEC codeword has to overbridge a number of channel fades.

For the propagation frequencies 1.7 to 1.9 GHz used for personal communications networks (PCN) the wavelength is about 17cm and there is approximately one fade every 8.5 cm distance. If the data transmission rate is 64 kbit/s, yielding a signalling rate of 16 ksamples/s for the uncoded 16-level QAM, then when the mobile station is travelling at 30mph or 13.3m/s, there are approximately 100 QAM samples transmitted between two deep fades which are about half a wavelength apart. Diagonal interleaving over six fades randomises the bursty error statistics and has a delay of approximately 600 QAM samples corresponding to about 40 ms. This delay is typically acceptable for speech communications [5]. By increasing the interleaving depth to much higher values associated with higher delay which is acceptable for data transmission, the BER is further improved.

We consider Bose-Chaudhuri-Hocquenghem (BCH) block codes [4] to have favourable properties for PCN transmissions. They can correct both random and bursty errors and also their error detection capability allows the BCH decoder to know when the received codeword contains more errors than the correcting power of the code can cope with. Provided a systematic BCH code is used, the information part of the coded word can be separated from the parity bits without attempting error correction which would precipitate more errors due to the fact that the codec's error correction power was exceeded and hence the decoding operation would be erroneous.

A special subclass of BCH codes is the maximum minimum distance Reed-Solomon(RS) codes [4]. These codes operate on non-binary symbols and have identical error-locator and symbol fields. The non-binary RS codes are optimum due to their maximum distance property, and may also be sufficiently long to overbridge channel fades without additional interleaving. However, they are more complex to implement than binary BCH codes. To explore both ends of the complexity/performance trade-off we selected an extremely long and complex RS code, the $RS(252, 168, 42)$ code over Galois field $GF(256)$ using 8 bit symbols, the moderately long as less complex $RS(44, 30, 7)$ code over $GF(64)$, as well as the low complexity short binary $BCH(63, 45, 3)$ code. All these codes have an approximately equal coding rate of $R = 0.7$. The nomenclature used here is $RS(m, n, k)$ where m is the number of encoded symbols, n is the number of information symbols and k is the number of corrected symbols in a codeword. Every field element of the finite field $GF(2^l)$ is represented by an l-bit non-binary symbol in the case of RS codes.

11.5   64-level TCM

As a bench-mark scheme for the block coded arrangements a 64-level 2/3 rate convolutional coding system was devised. However, TCM as outlined in Chapter 8 cannot be used directly as it doubles the symbol set size, and here we have a quadrupling of the set size from 16 to 64 levels. Nevertheless, the principles of TCM can be retained. The 64 possible code words were divided into sixteen groups of four so-called D groups [1]. TCM only adds FEC coding to those bits that have the highest probability of error. With four input bits and six bits per symbol we can add half-rate convolutional coding to the more vulnerable two bits and leave the other two that are more widely spaced uncoded. The two coded bits plus the two FEC parity bits can specify one of sixteen groups, and the uncoded two bits can specify one of four points within this group. The four points in each group are spaced as far apart across the constellation as possible so that there is little chance of one of these four points being mistakenly received as another in the presence of noise.

In Figure 11.5 we display the constellation of 64 points representing the 64 possible transmitted phasors. Figure 11.5 may also be viewed as a lookup table for the differential encoding. The six bits span the decimal range 0-63 as they vary from 000000-111111. If this decimal number is in the range 0-3,4-7,8-11,...60-63 we select subgroup D0,D1,D2...D15, respectively. In each subgroup we map each of the four possible numbers onto one of the four points in that subgroup. This is done by starting on the positive x axis and the

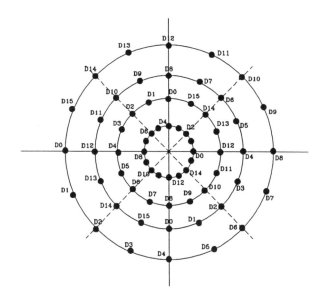

Figure 11.5: Star 64 TCM constellation

innermost circle, and rotating anti-clockwise. The first point in the subgroup that we come across is given the lowest number for that subgroup. Thus if we consider subgroup D0, we would assign the point on the positive x axis the value 0, i.e. it is the point we map to when the incoming six bits are 000000. The point on the positive y axis and the second circle becomes 1 corresponding to incoming bits 000001, the point on the negative x axis becomes 2 corresponding to 000010, and the point on the negative y axis becomes 3 corresponding to 000011. This is repeated for all subgroups. Thus the D4 point on the negative y axis corresponds to 19 or 010011. Once we have identified the phasor for the incoming codeword, we can use this to derive the differential signal which we must add onto the previous constellation point transmitted as a reference in order to derive the constellation point that we transmit. The representation is as follows.

A point on the inner ring causes us to transmit the current symbol with an identical amplitude to the previous symbol transmitted.

A point on the second ring causes us to transmit the current symbol with an amplitude on the next amplitude ring up from the previous symbol transmitted. If the previous symbol amplitude was that of the outermost ring then a change is made to the innermost ring, i.e. wrap-round occurs.

A point on the third ring causes an increase of two rings in amplitude from the previous amplitude transmitted again with wrap-round, and so on.

A point at 0 degrees on the positive x-axis represents no phase change from the previous point transmitted. A point at 22.5 degrees represents a phase change of +22.5 degrees relative to the previous point transmitted. A point at 45 degrees represents a phase change of +45 degrees relative to the previous point transmitted and so on.

As an example, if the last phasor transmitted was that corresponding to the point labelled D13 at 22.5 degrees on the second ring and the input bits were 000010, we decode these input bits as the D0 point on the negative x axis. Thus we increase the ring size by three, wrapping round from the D13 point to the innermost ring, and rotate this point by 180 degrees to end up at the unlabelled D9 point between the corresponding D8 and D10 points on the innermost ring at -157.5 degrees. This is the phasor transmitted.

This heuristic representation has been used as it allows set partitioning into the D groups to be carried out in the same way as for conventional non-differential TCM.

The half rate coder chosen was of constraint length K=5 with generator polynomials

$$g1 = 1 + X^3 + X^4$$

and

$$g2 = 1 + X + X^2 + X^4$$

as recommended for the GSM system [7]. These generator polynomials are optimal for random error statistics. The encoded bits are diagonally interleaved prior to the mapping shown in Figure 11.5. This interleaving was the same as used with the block codes.

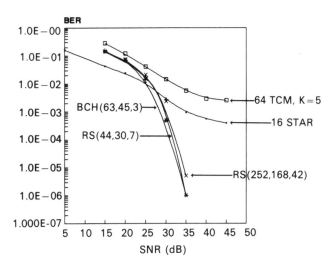

Figure 11.6: TCM and block coded performance

11.6 Bandwidth efficient coding results

The above 64-level $R = 2/3$, $K = 5$ TCM system contrived in the previous section performed worse than the Star 16-QAM at all SNRs, as shown in Figure 11.6. When using separate block coding and absorbing the parity bits by constellation expansion at the cost of higher channel BERs and implementational complexity, but without bandwidth expansion as described in Section 11.4, decreased the BER dramatically compared to both our 64-TCM $K = 5$ system and to the uncoded Star 16-QAM scheme. The $BCH(63, 45, 3)$ code and the $RS(44, 30, 7)$ code had nearly identical performances, in spite of the considerably higher block length and complexity of the RS code. The $RS(252, 168, 42)$ code offers an extra 2 dB SNR gain for a large increase in complexity. We therefore favour the BCH code which provides virtually error-free communications for channel SNR values in excess of 30-35 dB, a value that may be realisable in the small microcells to be ultimately found in a fully developed PCN. By using error correction coding and compensating for the increased bit rate by deploying higher level modulation, we are able to provide transmissions of higher integrity, but with identical bandwidth compared to an uncoded system. The transmitted power and system complexity are also increased.

11.7 Overall coding strategy

We now consider 16 and 64-level QAM schemes which are error protected, where the FEC coding now decreases the useful information transmission rate whilst increasing the integrity of the transmitted data. The previous 64-level QAM scheme having a 2/3 rate code had its code rate reduced to 1/2 whilst maintaining constant transmission rate, but decreasing the primary information rate. We selected this overall 1/2 coding rate as it is widely used in mobile radio [6, 4]. A further coding rate reduction does not bring substantial coding gains and squanders channel capacity which cannot be compensated for by using more modulation levels. We also employed a 3/4 rate code in conjunction with the Star 16-QAM in order to provide the same overall bit rate as the coded 64-level QAM.

Our results are depicted in Figure 11.7. The uncoded Star 16-QAM and the 64-level QAM/RS(44, 30, 7) curves are repeated for comparison along with the 64-level QAM/RS(60, 30, 15) and 16-level QAM/RS(60, 44, 8) arrangements. Observe that the error correction power of the 64-QAM/RS(60,30,15) scheme is about twice as strong as that of the 16-QAM/RS(60,44,8) system. However, 64-QAM has typically more than twice the symbol error rate of 16-QAM and this is why the 16-QAM arrangement is likely to out-perform the coded 64-QAM scheme. There is a consistent and remarkable improvement in both the 16-level QAM and 64-level QAM performance. For SNRs in excess of 25 dB there is an almost 5 dB extra SNR gain improvement due to the stronger RS code in case of the 64-level QAM scheme. By employing error correction coding, the performance of the 16-level QAM arrangement is dramatically improved and becomes superior to that of the 1/2-rate coded 64-level QAM system. Depending on the integrity required, an SNR value of 25 dB is sufficient for reliable signalling via the $16 - QAM/RS$(60, 44, 8) system.

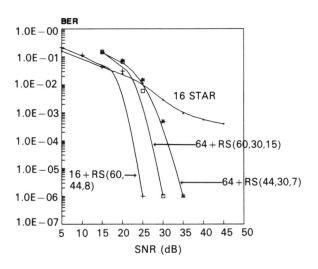

Figure 11.7: Overlaid block coding performance

11.7.1 Square 16-QAM/PSAM/TCM Scheme

The previously considered differential 32-TCM and 64-TCM Star QAM schemes failed to improve the Star 16-QAM performance partly due to the lack of fading compensation, and partly because of the ambitious goal of providing a 4 bit/symbol net transmission rate. Clearly, the expanded 64-TCM constellation had reduced the ability of the scheme to withstand fading compared to the 16-QAM schemes.

Ho, Cavers and Varaldi [9] embarked on a comparison of three modulation schemes with a net throughput of 2 bits/symbol. These were uncoded QPSK, rate 2/3 8PSK-TCM as proposed by Ungerboeck [1], and rate 1/2 square 16-QAM/TCM combined with PSAM. The pilot symbol assisted fading estimates allowed the authors to improve the power efficiency over uncoded QPSK via fading channels.

The proposed square 16-QAM/TCM scheme was based on separate four-state TCM of the I and Q components. Ho *et al* compared the BER versus channel SNR performance of their three schemes for a variety of fading rates, using a pilot periodicity of M=7 and a k=11th order channel predictor. The authors also provided best case

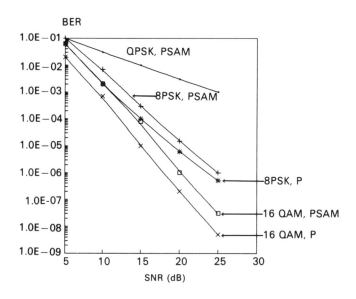

Figure 11.8: BER performance of coded 8PSK and coded 16QAM [9] ©IEEE, 1992, Ho et al

performance estimates when using the actual complex fading sample for channel estimation. Their results are shown in Figure 11.8, where P represents a perfect channel estimate.

Observe that the best performance was achieved by 16-QAM/-TCM/PSAM, since there are no unprotected bits transmitted over the channel. For BER values below 10^{-6} 16-QAM was about 5dB more power-efficient than 8-PSK, and about 25dB more efficient than uncoded QPSK. As regards power amplifier design, it is important to compare these schemes on the basis of peak power. If all three schemes are allocated the same peak power, their corresponding peak-to-average power ratios can be used in order to derive their resulting average power. Ho *et al* report that for a 50% excess bandwidth raised cosine pulseshaping, the corresponding peak-to-average ratios are 2.45dB, 2.75dB and 5.31dB for QPSK, 8-PSK and 16-QAM, respectively. For a fair comparison the BER curves of Figure 11.8 must be shifted to the right by the above SNR values. After such a shift the 16-QAM still has a 2.44dB peak power advantage

at a BER of 10^{-6}. These figures were confirmed by other researchers [10, 11].

11.8   Distorted Constellation Star QAM

11.8.1   Introduction

In Chapters 4 and 10 we have shown that the maximum distance
square 16-QAM scheme has two subchannels with different integrities, which we have referred to as the C1 and C2 subchannels. The
BER advantage of the C1 channel over the C2 channel is not dramatic for AWGN channels, but is more significant over Rayleigh fading channels. The different subchannel integrities can be equalised
using matched FEC codes. However, in the case of coded speech it
is often advantageous to exploit the unequal BERs by transmitting
the more vulnerable speech data via the C1 channel, while the more
robust speech data is sent via the C2 subchannel [12]-[15]

In the 16-level Star QAM systems each bit in the 4-bit symbol
has an approximately equal probability of being in error. In general
this is a desirable feature as data can be transmitted without applying any special mapping strategy and this normally yields the best
overall bit error rate (BER). There are situations, however, where
equal BERs for all bits is disadvantageous. For example, when the
data applied to the Star QAM modem is from an n-bit PCM source,
where the most significant bit corresponds to an 2^{n-1} higher voltage
than the least significant bit, then the MSB needs to be received with
a concomitant lower BER than the least significant bit (LSB). For
information sources having a hierarchical structure in their data it is
necessary to employ source matched channel coding strategies in order to ensure that the recovered data has the requisite performance
after decoding. This procedure employing a range of channel codecs
or an adaptive channel codec, is complex and expensive. We seek a
simpler solution here, investigating whether distorting the Star constellation may yield an acceptable performance without the need for
complex source-matched channel coding.

11.8.2 Distortion of the Star

As it is desirable for the average of the four individual BERs to remain as low as possible, only minor distortions to the Star QAM constellation are considered, as it was found to be well suited to the Rayleigh fading environment. Accordingly the twin-level circular constellation is retained, along with the differential Gray coding of the constellation points.

Within these confines two forms of distortion are considered. One is to change the spacing between the inner and outer rings, and the other is to no longer equi-space the eight points around each ring. Simulations were performed using random data, encoded onto the Star QAM constellation and transmitted on a 1.9GHz carrier at a Baud rate of 16kSym/sec corresponding to 64kbits/s. The mobile's speed was a constant 30mph. Appropriate Rayleigh fading and Gaussian noise was generated leading to an average channel SNR of 30dB. The data was differentially decoded and the BER was calculated.

11.8.2.1 Amplitude Distortion

Bearing in mind the structure of the Star QAM constellation of Figure 11.1, increasing the spacing between the two rings of the Star QAM constellation potentially improves the performance of bit b_1 at the expense of the other three bits. Bit b_1 is expected to have improved integrity because more noise is required to move it across the decision boundary. The remaining three bits will suffer because they are moved closer together on the inner ring, increasing the probability of phase error for inner-inner, inner-outer and outer-inner ring transitions, and decreasing the probability of error only for the outer-outer ring transition. In the case of random data all transitions are equally likely.

The simulation results for the variation of the BER of each of the four bits and the average BER as the ratio of the distance between the rings was varied is shown in Figure 11.9. Whilst bits b_2, b_3 and b_4 generally exhibited increasing BER as would be expected, bit b_1 had a minimum BER at a ring ratio of 3, where the inner ring has a magnitude of 1 and the outer ring a magnitude of 3. The reason that the BER did not continue to fall with increasing ring ratio is that as the inner ring shrinks at the expense of the growth of the outer ring, constellation points on the inner ring become increasingly susceptible to noise, considerably distorting their amplitude and phase value. So although transitions from inner to outer and outer to inner rings have a low probability of being decoded incorrectly, there is a relatively high probability that an inner to inner ring transition will be incorrectly decoded as either an inner to outer or outer to inner transition. Decoding this change as an outer to inner transition is possible because the receiver does not decide upon which ring the previous symbol sent was on, but looks for a significant change in amplitude between previous and current symbols. This avoids error propagation due to incorrect decisions. Simulations with the receiver attempting to make a decision as to the ring on which the previous symbol resided in order to eliminate the incorrect decoding of an inner-inner ring transition as an outer-inner ring transition showed that this scheme exhibited worse performance than the original system because of the error propagation associated with incorrect decisions.

It can be seen that there is little scope for changing the ring ratio. Variations between 1.5 and 3 would be acceptable. A ring ratio of 1.5 allows the largest variation in terms of BER between bits, with bit b_1 having a BER about 6 times greater than bits b_2 and b_4.

The average BER exhibited a minimum at a ring ratio of 2, rising slowly as the ring ratio was increased, and rising more quickly as the ring ratio was decreased. A theoretical analysis performed by Chow *et al* [16] for AWGN also came to similar conclusions. However, with their only being a 0.9dB difference between ring ratios of 2 and 3, performance gains made by optimising this ring ratio will be small.

The second form of constellation distortion considered is to change the angles between each of the points on a ring. The current system has a spacing of 45 degrees between each adjacent point. By increasing this angular spacing for some points and decreasing it for others, the BER of certain bits can be altered. The bit mapping onto the phasor points for one of the rings on the current system is shown in Figure 11.10. In all cases the bit mapping on the other ring has constellation points at identical angular spacing. Only 3 bits are

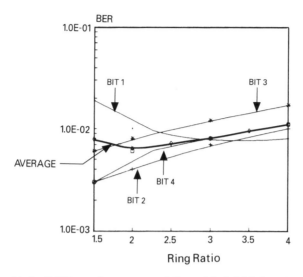

Figure 11.9: BER performance of Star 16-QAM for ring ratio variations between 1.5 and 4 at 30mph, 1.9GHz, 16ksymbols/s, and SNR=30dB

shown against each point, corresponding to bits b_2, b_3 and b_4 as b_1 is used to differentiate between the rings. It is important to remember that this diagram represents a differential mapping system. That is, a phase point at an angle of 45 degrees, say, implies that the current symbol should be transmitted with a phase shift of $+45$ degrees relative to the previous symbol transmitted, interpreted as modulo 360 degrees. In all subsequent simulations the ring ratio was held at a value of 3.

11.8.2.2 Phase Variations

As can be seen in Figure 11.10 the 8 points on a circle can be split into two groups of 4 points each. In each of these subgroups, separated by the dashed line in the figure, the first bit, namely bit b_2 in the 4 bits mapping scheme, is the same, i.e., a logical 1 to the left of the dashed line and a logical 0 to the right of the line. The integrity of b_2 can be increased by further separating these subgroups as shown

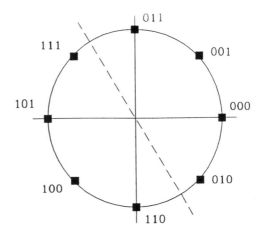

Figure 11.10: Mapping for standard Star system

in Figure 11.11. Here the angle θ is our variable parameter. We note from the geometry of Figure 11.11 that the angle ϕ is given by

$$\phi = 60^{\circ} - \frac{\theta}{3} \qquad (11.8)$$

where ϕ in common with all the angles quoted throughout, is in degrees. Hence, for example, for the undistorted case of $\theta = 45^{\circ}$ we have that $\phi = 45^{\circ}$, as expected. The variation of BER against θ is given in Figure 11.12 for our initial conditions of SNR=30dB, 30mph, 1.9GHz and 16ksymbols/s. Bit b_1 is not shown because it remained constant with variations in θ as would be expected. It is apparent that as θ increased above about 100 degrees, the average BER rose steeply and this factor probably precludes operation in this region. Indeed, the average BER was at a minimum for $\theta = 45^{\circ}$, and the price paid for a different BER on each bit was a higher average BER. As desired, the BER performance of bit b_2 was improved at the expense of bits b_3 and b_4. For values of θ in excess of 80 degrees there was no longer any significant improvement in the BER of bit b_2. At this point there is a ratio of about 4 between the BER of bit b_2 and bits b_3 as well as b_4. With the ring ratio held at 3, bit b_1 had a performance similar to bits b_3 and b_4.

There is a further distortion that can be applied to the constellation. This is shown in Figure 11.13 where each of the two groups of 4

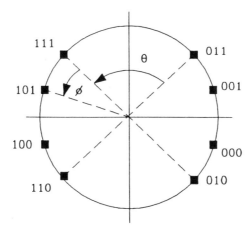

Figure 11.11: Bit b_2 distortion system

points are divided into two further sub-groups. In each of these sub-groups bit b_4 has a constant value. Thus we would expect to increase the performance of bit b_4 at the expense of bit b_3 by increasing the angle α. This is because the protection distance between opposite values of b_4 is now increased, while that between opposite values of b_3 is decreased. The angles in Figure 11.13 are related by

$$\phi = 90° - \frac{\theta + \alpha}{2}. \qquad (11.9)$$

Again, for the undistorted case of $\theta = \alpha = 45°$, Equation 11.9 gives $\phi = 45°$. The BER performance of this system for different values of θ is shown in Figures 11.14 to 11.16. The BER performance for only bits b_3 and b_4 are displayed as the BER for bits b_1 and b_2 remained constant. The trend in all graphs is the same, a sharply rising average BER, and only a slowly falling BER for b_4. This suggests that only small increases in terms of α are acceptable. For example a value of $\alpha = 50°$ when $\theta = 90°$ gives a ratio of 6.5 between the BER of bit b_4 and that of bits b_2 and b_3. Similarily, for the same distortion a BER ratio of 1.5 accrues between bit b_4 and bit b_1. In this instance the average BER is degraded by a factor of 1.75 which corresponds to about 2.5dB.

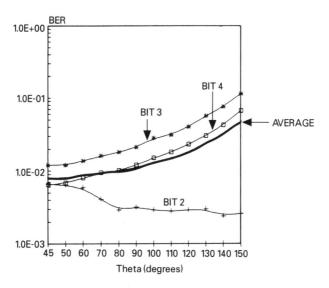

Figure 11.12: BER versus distortion angle θ for bits 2, 3, and 4 of the Star 16-QAM constellation at 30mph, 1.9GHz, 16ksymbols/s and SNR=30dB

11.9   Practical Considerations

11.9.1   Introduction

In previous chapters, it was assumed that no hardware imperfections were introduced. This gave an optimistic estimate of the performance. Possible imperfections include a finite number of quantisation levels, I-Q crosstalk, AM-AM and AM-PM conversion non-linearities and a finite oversampling ratio. Even if it appeared possible to implement a modem which, as far as the QAM technique employed is concerned, appears perfect, it may be sensible to reduce the performance in order to achieve a simpler and cheaper design. In this section the effects of a number of imperfections which are likely to occur in a hardware modem are investigated, in order to establish hardware parameters.

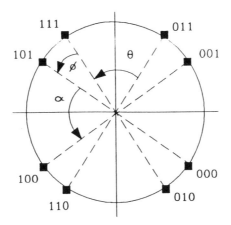

Figure 11.13: Bit b_4 distortion system

11.9.2 Hardware imperfections

11.9.2.1 Quantisation Levels

Typical QAM modems employ digital baseband circuitry, and so analogue-to-digital (A-D) conversion is required at the input of the receiver. It is important that an adequate number of bits is chosen for this convertor. If too low a number of bits are chosen then the performance will suffer badly, and if too many are chosen then the hardware complexity and cost will rise substantially whilst the maximum operating speed will fall. Initial quantisation level simulations assumed that the received signal level after pre-amplification would fall within a certain range. The quantisation levels are spread evenly throughout this dynamic range, and the incoming signal is rounded to the nearest quantisation level. Peak clipping occurs if the signal exceeds this range. Results of simulations carried out using a variety of quantisation levels are shown in Figure 11.17.

For these simulations data was transmitted at 128ksymbols/s, at a mobile speed of 30mph, and a propagation frequency of 1.9GHz. Non-Linear Filtering (NLF) was used to shape the transmitted data and a fourth order Butterworth lowpass filter with the 3dB cut-off point at 1.5 times the data rate (i.e. 192kHz) was used in the receiver. Clock recovery was implemented using the modified early-late

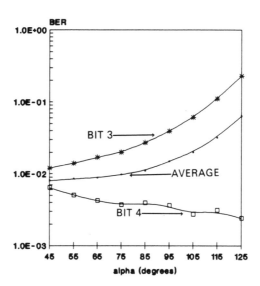

Figure 11.14: BER versus distortion angle α for bits 3 and 4 of
the Star 16-QAM constellation with $\theta = 45°$, at
30mph, 1.9GHz, 16ksymbols/s and SNR=30dB

recovery system discussed in Chapter 12, and 16 times oversampling
was implemented throughout the system. Unless stated otherwise,
these simulation parameters can be assumed to hold true for all subsequent simulations in this chapter.

The results show that at least 14 bits will be required if the receiver
is not to suffer a drop in terms of BER performance. In practice this
means that 16 bit A-D convertors will be necessary, since 14 bit
convertors are rare. Operation with only 12 bits would be feasible
but does entail a BER penalty at high SNRs.

Consideration of the waveforms into and out of the A-D convertor
showed that the full dynamic range of the convertor was not used
over a short time span, but it was necessary to accommodate the
peaks and troughs in the Rayleigh fading pattern. This suggested
that performance could be improved by the use of a simple AGC prior
to the A-D convertor. Because of the differential detection employed,
the absolute signal level is unimportant. However, it is critical that
the AGC must be sufficiently slow acting in order that its gain does

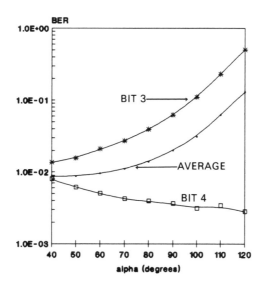

Figure 11.15: BER versus distortion angle α for bits 3 and 4 of the Star 16-QAM constellation with $\theta = 60°$, at 30mph, 1.9GHz, 16ksymbols/s and SNR=30dB

not change significantly from one symbol to the next, as this would make the differential detection more error prone. In practice this is not a problem because there are many symbols in each fade and so the AGC can be slow acting with respect to the symbol period and still track the envelope adequately. It is stressed that this AGC does not attempt to maintain a constant, or near constant input envelope, but merely to compress the fading range in order to reduce the A-D convertor's resolution requirements. Simulations suggested that a suitable system was a slow acting AGC, whose dynamic range could be suddenly increased if the input signal exceeded 95% of its allowed range. This tended to keep the fades within the input clipping range without unduly distorting the waveform when it was around the average value.

Results of simulations using this system are shown in Figure 11.18. Here it can be seen that adequate performance is obtained with only 12 bit conversion, and that with only 8 bits, the degradation is not unduly severe.

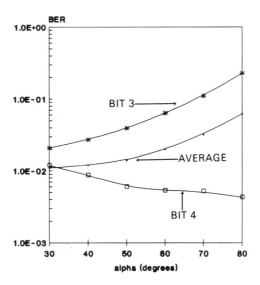

Figure 11.16: BER versus distortion angle α for bits 3 and 4 of the Star 16-QAM constellation with $\theta = 90^o$, at 30mph, 1.9GHz, 16ksymbols/s and SNR=30dB

11.9.2.2   I-Q Crosstalk

Another problem that is often encountered in the RF side of the modem is that of crosstalk between the quadrature branches. This problem can be reduced by balanced RF system design, but here an attempt is made to discover the maximum level of crosstalk which can be tolerated before unacceptable BER performance degradation occurs. No baseband counter-measures are proposed, merely adequate RF system design.

Results of simulations employing 8 A-D convertor quantisation levels and the same parameters as the previous section are shown in Figure 11.19. Here it can be seen that levels of I-Q crosstalk up to -40dB would seem acceptable, that is the leakage power from one quadrature branch to another should be 40dB less than the average power in that branch.

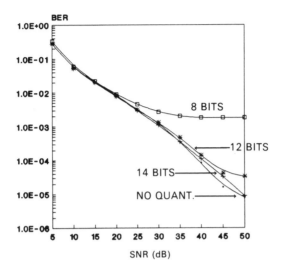

Figure 11.17: Star 16-QAM BER versus channel SNR performance using different input A-D resolutions at 128ksymbols/s, 30mph, 1.9GHz

11.9.2.3 Oversampling Ratio

In order for the clock recovery system to operate satisfactorily, it is necessary to sample the received waveform a number of times during each symbol period. This allows accurate location of waveform peaks. Ideally, the modem should work with as low an oversampling ratio as possible in order to keep internal clock speeds low. In this section the complete Star QAM system was simulated as the oversampling ratio was varied. For accuracy, a 16 times oversamping ratio was maintained in the simulations, but we only made a certain number of these samples available to the receiver.

The results for three different oversampling ratios are shown in Figure 11.20. Here it can be seen that the ratio can be satisfactorily reduced to 8 samples per symbol, but a reduction to only 4 causes a significant performance degradation.

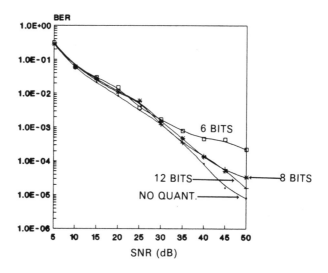

Figure 11.18: Star 16-QAM BER versus channel SNR per-
            formance using AGC and a variety of A-D
            convertor resolutions at 128ksymbols/s, 30mph,
            1.9GHz

11.9.2.4   AM-AM and AM-PM distortion

We have already touched upon the problems of amplitude modulation to both amplitude modulation (AM-AM) and to phase modulation (AM-PM) conversion, when discussing the characteristics of
power amplifiers in Section 5.6. A typical pair of AM-AM and AM-
PM conversion curves was given in Figure 5.27. In this subsection
we briefly attempt to quantify the effects of amplifier imperfections
on decoded BER. This impairment is difficult to model as it is not
known exactly what form the imperfections will take. In this section
a number of assumptions are made about possible forms of distortion in order to assess the effect they may have on a QAM system.
The AM-AM distortion is modelled by non-linear, compressed operation due to the limited dynamic range of the amplifier. This means
that whilst the maximum output is maintained, the pulseshape is
distorted. It was found that this had very little effect on the system,

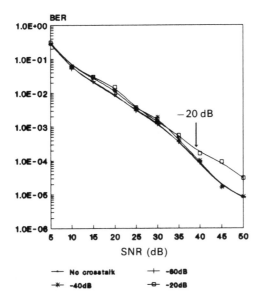

Figure 11.19: Star 16-QAM BER versus channel SNR performance using AGC and 8-bits A-D conversion when using different levels of I-Q crosstalk, at 128ksymbols/s, 30mph, 1.9GHz

causing a slight but acceptable degradation in the clock recovery system. The degradation could be completely removed by regenerating the original pulseshape. Since the pulseshape is typically derived from a look-up table, this does not increase the complexity of the design.

The AM-PM distortion is modelled by introducing a phase shift of P degrees when the received phasor is on the outer ring. So when moving from the inner to the outer ring an undesirable differential phase shift of $\theta_{enc} + P$ is experienced where θ_{enc} is the differentially encoded transmitted angle. When moving from the outer to the inner ring a detrimental phase shift of $\theta_{enc} - P$ is experienced.

In the first set of simulations, no corrective action was attempted at the receiver, and the maximum permissible distortion which did not unduly degrade the BER performance was found. BER versus channel SNR performance curves are shown in Figure 11.21 for various AM-PM distortion values, which suggest that a maximum

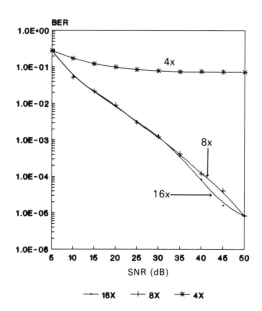

Figure 11.20: Star 16-QAM BER versus channel SNR performance using AGC, 8-bit A-D conversion, when oversampling at rates of 4, 8 and 16, 128ksymbols/s, 30mph, 1.9GHz

uncompensated phase shift of up to 10 degrees could be tolerated. However, since this phase shift is time invariant, it should be possible to take some sort of corrective action. In the differential decoder at the receiver, we can monitor the amplitude change. If there appears to have been a change from the inner to the outer ring then we subtract the known AM-PM distortion, and if there appears to have been a change from the outer to the inner ring then the known AM-PM distortion is added. This method is expected to remove most of the AM-PM distortion, but can precipitate errors if an error is made in decoding the amplitude change. BER versus channel SNR performance curves for this system are shown in Figure 11.22 for 0° and 40° conversion errors where we can see that satisfactory performance is achieved for large values of phase distortion.

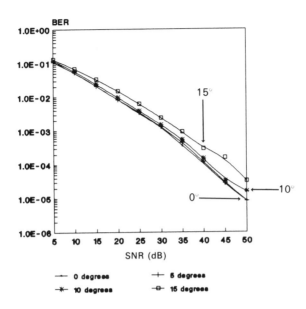

Figure 11.21: Star 16-QAM BER versus channel SNR performance at 128ksymbols/s, 30mph, 1.9GHz, for different values of AM-PM distortion without correction

11.10 Summary

In this chapter we have discussed various signal processing techniques to facilitate reliable QAM transmissions in Rayleigh fading environments. The well-known 16-level square constellation was found to be unsuitable for the mobile radio environment. The sub-optimal Star scheme with differential encoding and oversampling signal estimation dramatically improved the BER performance, rendering the channel appropriate for speech transmissions. The lower BERs essential for data transmissions were achieved by expanding the 16-level QAM signal set to 64 levels and using the extra channel capacity acquired for error correction coding. For SNRs in excess of 25dB the performance of the coded 64-level QAM was superior to that of the 16-level QAM and at values of SNR in excess of 30dB it was virtually error free. When the overall coding rate was lowered to allow the 16-level QAM scheme to incorporate a 3/4 rate RS code and the 64-level

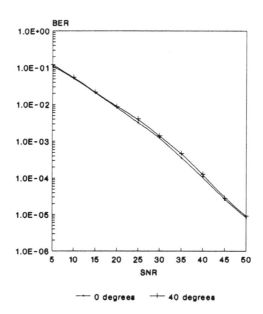

Figure 11.22: Star 16-QAM BER versus channel SNR performance at 128ksymbols/s, 30mph, 1.9GHz, for different values of AM-PM distortion with correction

QAM system had a 1/2 rate RS code, the 16-QAM arrangement out-performed the more complex 64-level scheme.

Unlike square QAM modems, Star QAM has an approximately equal BER for each of the bits in its symbols. This is normally advantageous, but there are some instances where a differing BER for each bit can be effectively used for unequal source-matched FEC coding of speech and video sources. Ways of rendering the BER of each bit different were considered. Unfortunately, in all cases, the average BER was increased, and large ratios between the BER performances of certain bits were not achieved for the scenarios considered. However, the BER ratios of approximately 6 were achieved when the average BER was degraded by a factor of 1.75.

The effects of hardware imperfections on Star 16-QAM modem performance was then considered. It was established that 8-bit A-D convertors could be employed if a slow-acting AGC was deployed prior to the convertor. Mild levels of IQ crosstalk were found acceptable and the minimum oversampling ratio was found to be 8. Finally, it was determined that small AM-AM and AM-PM distortions could be tolerated, especially if correction could be applied.

In the next chapter we investigate further the use of Star QAM transmission over mobile radio channels by considering the application of the clock and carrier recovery techniques introduced in Chapter 6. We show that a new clock recovery technique can be introduced which is advantagoeus for the particular combination of Star QAM and Rayleigh fading channels.

Bibliography

[1] **G.Ungerboeck**, "Trellis-coded modulation with redundant signal sets", *IEEE Communications magazine*, Feb 1987 pp5-21.

[2] **AT&T Information Services**, "A trellis coded modulation scheme that includes differential encoding for 9600 bit/sec full-duplex, two-wire modems", *CCITT SG XVII* No. D159 Aug 1983.

[3] **F.Edbauer**, "Performance of interleaved trellis-coded differential 8-PSK modulation over fading channels", *IEEE J-SAC* Vol 7. No 9. Dec 1989 pp1340-1346.

[4] **K.H.H.Wong and L.Hanzo** "Channel coding", Chapter 4, pp 347-488 in R.Steele (Ed.) "Mobile radio communications", *Pentech Press*, 1992.

[5] **R.A.Salami, L.Hanzo et al** "Speech coding", Chapter 3, pp 186-346 in R.Steele (Ed.) "Mobile radio communications", *Pentech Press*, 1992.

[6] **K.H.H.Wong, L.Hanzo and R.Steele**, "Channel coding for satellite mobile channels", *Int Jrnl of Satellite Comms*, Vol 7,pp143-163,1989.

[7] **K.J.Larsen**, "Short convolutional codes with maximal free distance for rates 1/2, 1/3 and 1/4", *IEEE Trans on Inf. Theory*, May 1973,pp371-372.

[8] **N.G.Kingsbury**, "Transmit and Receive Filters For QPSK Signals...", *IEE Proc. Vol 133 Pt. F* No. 4 July 1986 pp345-355.

[9] **P.Ho, J.Cavers and J.Varaldi**, "The effect of constellation density on trellis coded modulation in fading channels", *Proc. IEEE VTC'92*, Denver, USA, pp463-467.

[10] **M.L.Moher and J.H.Lodge**, "TCMP - A modulation and coding strategy for Rician fading channels", *IEEE J-SAC*, Vol.7, No.9, pp1347-1355, Dec 1989.

[11] **S.A.Fechtel and H.Meyer**, "Combined equalisation, decoding and antenna diversity combining for mobile personal digital radio transmission using feedforward synchronisation", *Proc. IEEE VTC'93*, NJ, USA, pp633-636.

[12] **L. Hanzo, R. Steele and P.M. Fortune**, "A Subband Coding, BCH Coding and 16-QAM System for Mobile Radio Speech Communications", *IEEE Trans. on Veh. Techn.*, Nov. 1990, Vol 39, No 4, pp 327-340

[13] **L. Hanzo, R. Salami, R. Steele and P.M. Fortune**, "Transmission of Digitally Encoded Speech at 1.2 KBd for PCN", *IEE Proceedings, Part I*, Vol. 139, No.4., Aug 1992, pp 437-447

[14] **R. Stedman, H. Gharavi, L. Hanzo and R. Steele**, "16-QAM Transmission of Sub-band Coded Images via Microcellular Mobile Channels", *IEEE Tr. on Circuits and Systems for Video Technology*, Vol.3, No.1, Feb 1993, pp15-27.

[15] **P.M.Fortune, L.Hanzo and R.Steele**, "On the computation of 16-QAM and 64-QAM performance in Rayleigh fading channels", *IEICE Trans. Comms.*, Vol.E75-B, No.6, June 1992, pp466-475.

[16] **Y.C.Chow, A.R.Nix and J.P.McGeehan**, "Analysis of 16-APSK modulation in AWGN and Rayleigh fading channels", *Electronics Letters*, Vol.28, No.17, Aug 1992, pp1608-1609.

Chapter 12

Timing Recovery for Mobile Radio

12.1 Introduction

Although the differential star QAM scheme proposed in Chapter 11 does not need carrier recovery, the characteristic 3dB penalty associated with non-coherent detection need not be incurred if low-complexity timing recovery can be implemented. Accurate clock recovery is always essential, irrespective of whether or not non-coherent detection is possible.

In this chapter clock and carrier recovery schemes for 16-level Star QAM transmitted over mobile radio channels are considered, and the effect of ISI is simulated. We commence our investigations by considering the two most pertinent classic clock recovery methods, namely, the times-two and the early-late timing recovery techniques. These two techniques were discussed in Chapter 6 in the context of AWGN channels, here their performance over mobile radio channels with star QAM is considered.

12.2 Times-two clock recovery for QAM

In order to implement times-two clock recovery in conjunction with QAM the received signal is split into Inphase (I) and Quadrature (Q) waveforms and each is processed separately, before being combined in the clock recovery system. In the case of QAM, however, the presence of high energy frequency components at half the data rate is less likely than with binary data schemes. This is because instead of changes in the baseband modulated signal about zero whenever we have a change of transmitted symbol, as with binary modulation, there can be swings between symbols on the positive side and to and from those on the negative side of the constellation resulting in fewer zero crossings. For example, in the case of 16-level QAM and transmitted levels of ± 1 and ± 3 on the I and Q channels, a data sequence of -1,-3,-1,1,3,1,-1,-3,-1....-1,-3 yields a component at 1/6 of the data rate. Simulations were performed using times-two clock recovery which showed the QAM performance to be unacceptably poor. For more details on times-two clock recovery the reader is referred to Chapter 6.

12.3 Basic Early-Late Clock Recovery for Star 16-QAM

The early-late (EL) clock recovery technique described in Chapter 6 was introduced into a star QAM receiver. The simulation results showed that the EL clock recovery performed better than the times-two system. Correct locking of the clock was eventually established, and maintained moderately well during fades. The locking time, however, was unacceptably long.

The major problem with EL clock recovery for QAM transmissions is that not all QAM sequences result in time-domain waveform peaks occurring every sampling period. An even more detrimental effect is that half the peaks are of the wrong polarity for the clock recovery technique. This problem is illustrated in Figure 12.1 where the polarity of the early signal minus the late signal is considered for three different received 16-QAM sequences, assuming in all cases that the sampling point is too early. Due to the squaring operation identical waveform segments having opposite polarity yield identical PLL control sequences. The early and late sampling points are shown by dashed vertical lines on the squared signal. The chosen sampling point is assumed to lie in the centre of these lines, whereas the correct sampling instant is seen to be nearer to the late sample, or the rightmost dashed line. When the sampling point is early, the early signal minus the late signal must be negative for conventional early-late schemes to function correctly, and this is represented in Figure 12.1 as "E-L Negative". In this example only the I channel is considered for simplicity. The practical implementation of this scheme could have independent EL recovery systems for both the I and Q channels, which would drive the same PLL using control logic.

In Figure 12.1(a) the QAM sequence 1,3,1 is shown where the first number in the sequences refers to the modulation level on the I channel transmitted in the symbol period prior to the one in which peak detection is to be performed. The second number in the sequences refers to the modulation level in the symbol period in which peak detection is attempted, while the third number refer to the modulation level in the symbol period after the one in which peak detection is attempted. Clearly not an oversampled waveform, but three independent symbols are considered. Also shown is the sequence -1,-3,-1 which leads to an identical waveform after squaring, where the squaring is an integral part of the EL process. Both of these sequences result in correct E-L polarity. In Figure 12.1(b) the received sequences 3,1,3 and -3,-1,-3 are shown, both of which lead to an identical waveform after squaring. It can be seen that despite sampling occurring early as in (a), the E-L value is of the opposite polarity to that in (a). Also problematic are sequences such as -1,1,3 and 1,-1,-3, both of which again lead to an identical waveform after squaring as shown in Figure 12.1(c). Observe that the monotonic waveform leads to negative early-late difference signals regardless of whether the sampling is early or late, although we only show it early.

The consequence is that the early-late difference signal, which should be negative for all the waveforms in Figure 12.1, is correct for only a fraction of the transmitted symbols. The dips of the type in Figure 12.1(b) will cause an incorrect symbol regeneration. Since the monotonic waveforms of Figure 12.1(c) always indicate that a timing retardation is required, they will cause an equal distribution of correct and incorrect PLL control signals. These problems render

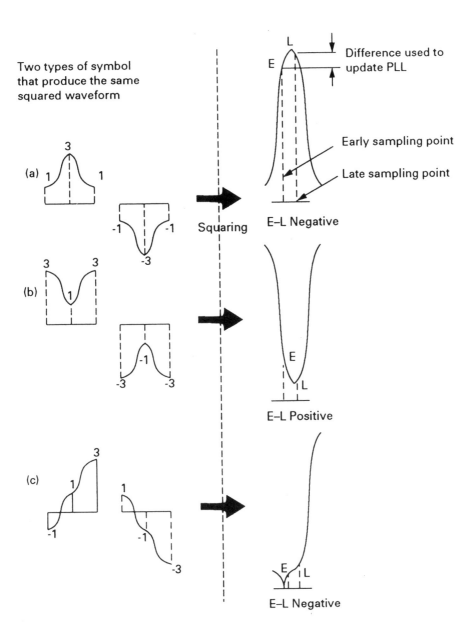

Figure 12.1: Problems with early-late clock recovery for QAM

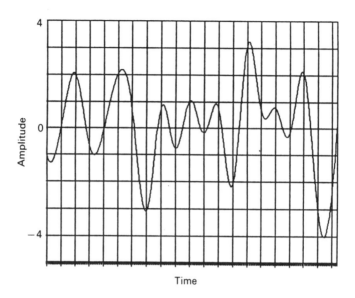

Figure 12.2: Raised cosine pulse shaping on the I channel

the system's operation unreliable.

The pulse shaping used at the transmitter can cause further problems. If raised cosine shaping is used, as suggested by Kingsbury [10], with matched filtering at the receiver, then a typical resulting transmitted star 16-QAM waveform I-component is shown in Figure 12.2. Note that for 16-level Star QAM the possible magnitudes of the I channel waveform are $0, \pm 0.707, \pm 1, \pm 2.12$ and ± 3 for the valid symbols.

As can be seen, the peaks do not always coincide with the equispaced sampling points shown by the vertical lines, rendering EL clock recovery inaccurate. This suggests the use of alternative pulse shaping schemes. One of the most suitable schemes would seem to be that of Non-Linear Filtering (NLF) discussed in Chapter 4, which guarantees that the peaks are at the correct sampling point. In addition, NLF has the virtue of implementational simplicity. A typical NLF waveforms is shown in Figure 12.3, where it can be seen that the peaks coincide with the optimal sampling points even though the zero-crossings are not equi-spaced. Again, the correct sampling

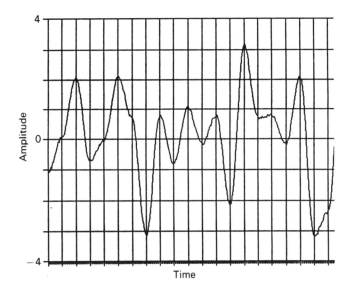

Figure 12.3: Non-linear filtered I channel waveform for star 16-QAM

times are given by the vertical grid lines. Based on the above arguments, it was decided to use NLF for our further investigations.

12.4 Modified Early-Late Clock Recovery for QAM

The basis of modified EL clock recovery is to search the current symbol period for a peak, and if one is found to assess its suitability for clock recovery. Only if a suitable peak is found is update information sent to the PLL. This improved system which is based on the use of oversampling, is now described in more detail with reference to Figure 12.4.

The clock recovery system waits until all n of the oversampled observations for a symbol period have been made, where the n observations are equi-spaced around the current sampling point. The maximum and the minimum samples during the observation period

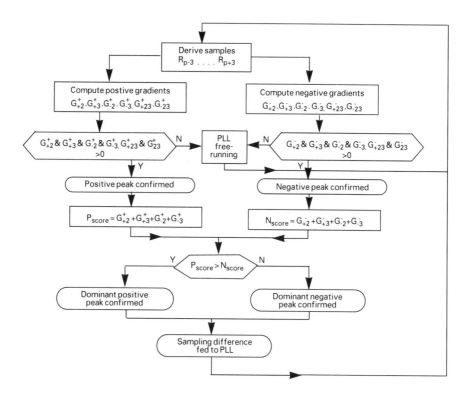

Figure 12.4: Modified early-late clock recovery flow chart

are then identified. If the maximum is at either end of the sampling period, the search for a positive pulse is discontinued since this implies that there cannot be a valid positive peak in the current sampling period. The same applies if the minimum is at either end of the sampling period.

If there is a valid maximum, sample gradients on both sides of the peak are calculated and the peak is rated depending on these gradients as described below. A similar rating is calculated for the negative pulse if there is still a valid minimum. The algorithm used for rating the positive peaks is based on evaluating the following gradients:-

$$
\begin{aligned}
G^+_{+2} &= R_p - R_{p+2} \\
G^+_{+3} &= R_p - R_{p+3} \\
G^+_{-2} &= R_p - R_{p-2} \\
G^+_{-3} &= R_p - R_{p-3} \\
G^+_{+23} &= R_{p+2} - R_{p+3} \\
G^+_{-23} &= R_{p-2} - R_{p-3}
\end{aligned}
\tag{12.1}
$$

where R_p is the amplitude of the incoming waveform at the peak p and R_{p+k} is the amplitude at the points k oversamples offset from p, where k takes the values $\pm 2, \pm 3$. The presence of a positive peak is only confirmed if all of these gradients are positive. This implies that moving away from the peak in both directions the waveform falls away, and that it does so with increasing steepness. The over-sampled values of R_{p+1} and R_{p-1} are not used as, due to the nature of the pulse shaping, these are very similar to R_p and so the gradient being small can be easily falsified by noise. If all these quantities are positive then the peak is rated according to

$$
P_{score} = G^+_{+2} + G^+_{+3} + G^+_{-2} + G^+_{-3}
\tag{12.2}
$$

where P_{score} is the positive peak score.

Similarly for the negative peaks

$$
\begin{aligned}
G^-_{+2} &= R_{p+2} - R_p \\
G^-_{+3} &= R_{p+3} - R_p \\
G^-_{-2} &= R_{p-2} - R_p \\
G^-_{-3} &= R_{p-3} - R_p \\
G^-_{+23} &= R_{p+3} - R_{p+2} \\
G^-_{-23} &= R_{p-3} - R_{p-2}
\end{aligned}
\tag{12.3}
$$

and if all these quantities are positive then the negative peak is rated as:-

$$
N_{score} = G^-_{+2} + G^-_{+3} + G^-_{-2} + G^-_{-3}
\tag{12.4}
$$

where N_{score} is the negative peak score. If $P_{score} > N_{score}$ then the positive peak is deemed more dominant and the negative peak is discarded, otherwise the negative peak is retained and the positive peak is discarded. If a valid peak is identified, the difference between the current sampling time and the peak just identified is used to update the variable internal clock, normally a phase locked loop (PLL)

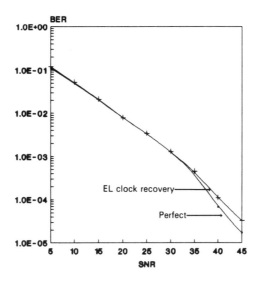

Figure 12.5: BER versus SNR performance of star 16-QAM using perfect and modified early-late clock recovery with no ISI, a mobile speed of 30mph, and a transmission frequency of 1.9GHz

system. Otherwise the PLL is allowed to continue running at its current level.

The BER performance of the star 16-QAM scheme using this clock recovery system operating without any ISI in Rayleigh fading is shown in Figure 12.5, compared to that of a system operating with perfect clock recovery. As can be seen in the figure the performance of the two systems is almost identical over a wide range of channel SNR values, indicating correct operation of the clock recovery system.

12.5 Clock Recovery in the Presence of ISI

12.5.1 Wideband Channel Models

In our earlier studies we used low signalling rates, which were significantly below the channel's coherence bandwidth, and hence no

ISI was introduced. When the signalling rate is increased to a few MSymbols/s, in most mobile radio environments distortion due to distant echos is introduced. In this section, unless stated, we use a vehicular speed of 30mph, a propagation frequency of 1.9GHz, and a signalling rate of 2MSymbols/s. Inter-symbol interference (ISI) distorts the received QAM pulse shape, complicating correct clock recovery. ISI can take many forms depending on the number of local radio scatterers and the terrain in the vicinity of the mobile station (MS). Let us consider two extreme cases.

The first extreme scenario is when the MS is in the presence of a single large reflector. Here there is a main path incident upon local scatterers leading to a flat Rayleigh fading path, and one single reflected path with a delay dependent on the position of the reflector, which is again incident upon the local scatterers, giving another independent Rayleigh distribution. This is the classic two-path dispersive channel with two delay bins. In our simulations we studied the effect of the delay τ between the direct path and the reflected path. In most practical cases τ will not be exactly equal to any multiple of the symbol period T, i.e. $\tau \neq nT$ where n represents an integer, hence the received signal peak due to the reflected path component arrives somewhere between two peaks spaced by T. There is the alternative, less likely two-path case where $\tau = nT$, that is the peak due to the reflected path component coincides with the peak of a different symbol which arrives at the receiver via the main path.

The second extreme scenario does not use the two-ray model. Instead a large number of indistinguishable incoming paths occur leading to a "peak smearing", or smoothing of the peak. We term this condition *smearing*. This situation was simulated using 16 delay bins, each one comprising 1/16 of a symbol period, and using 16-fold oversampling.

In our simulations Bultitude's wideband impulse response measurements [8] made in a street microcell in Canada were used. If the results presented graphically in his paper are divided into delay bins for a transmission rate of 2Msym/s with an oversample ratio of 16 then significant responses occur in bins 0, 12 and 32, each bin being 31.25ns wide. Each path was then subjected to independent

Rayleigh fading as seen in Figures 2.21 and 2.22 in Chapter 2. The approximate relative powers in these delay bins are 1, 0.28, and 0.01 respectively, i.e. if the first path is assumed to have a power of 1, then the path in delay bin 12 has a power of 0.28 times that of the first path. These results can be used directly for the $\tau \neq nT$ scenario. Furthermore, by altering the transmission rate to $16/12 \times 2MHz$, i.e. 2.66MHz, and ignoring the relatively insignificant path in delay bin 32, then the results can be used for the $\tau = nT$ scenario. For the smearing scenario an exponentially decaying impulse response over one symbol period was assumed. Based on measurements the smearing scenario seems less likely than the other scenarios considered here, nevertheless it is also included for the sake of completeness.

12.5.2 Clock Recovery in Two-Path Channels

12.5.2.1 Case of $\tau \neq nT$

A typical star 16-QAM NLF waveform for the ISI situation is shown in Figure 12.6. Let us compare this Figure with that for the ISI-free case shown in Figure 12.3. There is considerable distortion of the received waveform due to ISI, and although the peaks of the main pulses are still distinguishable, there are other peaks at different sampling points. Operation of the clock recovery system was closely monitored for this $\tau \neq nT$ scenario, and it was found that provided the interfering signal remained weaker than the wanted signal, the ISI did not hamper clock recovery as any additional peaks were either ignored, or given a lower peak score by the pulse rating system described previously. Once the delayed multipath signal became stronger than the main signal, which would be the case for when the main signal was in a fade, the clock recovery scheme switched to the delayed signal. The delayed signal had effectively become the main signal in that situation. The BER versus channel SNR performance of the star 16-QAM modified EL clock recovery system exposed to this form of ISI is shown in Figure 12.7. In this simulation no channel equalisation has been performed in order to keep the simulations tractable. A suitable equaliser for the star 16-QAM system is discussed in Chapter 14.

It can be seen from the figure that the performance of the system

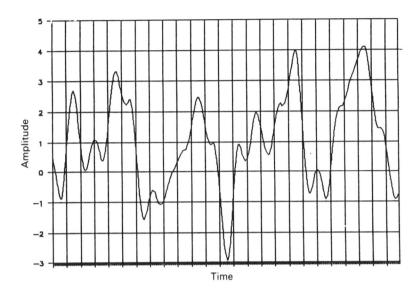

Figure 12.6: Typical star 16-QAM NLF I channel waveform
with $\tau \neq nT$

with the modified EL clock recovery scheme was almost identical to
that using perfect clock recovery, showing that the clock recovery
system worked adequately in this ISI-exposed scenario.

12.5.2.2 Case of $\tau = nT$

A typical star 16-QAM waveform for this ISI-impaired case is shown
in Figure 12.8. Again additional erroneous waveform peaks occur.
Although the waveform is considerably distorted compared to the
situation seen in Figure 12.3, the clock recovery system was not
unduly affected. Figure 12.9 shows the BER versus channel SNR
performance curves obtained with the modified EL clock recovery
system and when ideal clock recovery was used. The EL clock recovery is seen to operate almost perfectly in the presence of this form
of ISI.

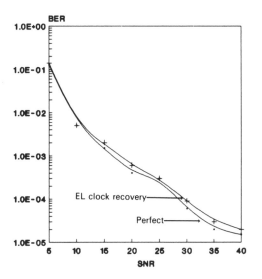

Figure 12.7: Clock recovery performance with $\tau \neq nT$, 30mph mobile speed, 1.9GHz carrier frequency, 2Msymbols/s data rate

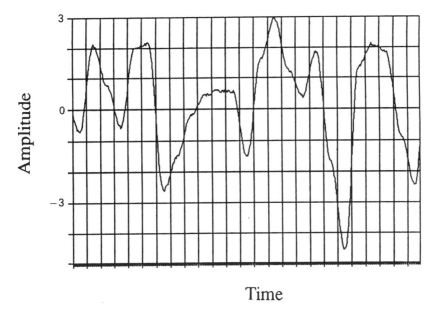

Time

Figure 12.8: Typical star 16-QAM NLF I channel waveform
with $\tau = nT$, 30mph mobile speed, 1.9GHz carrier frequency, 2Msymbols/s signalling rate

12.5.3   Clock Recovery Performance in Smeared ISI

A typical waveform for the star 16-QAM NLF smeared ISI condition is shown in Figure 12.10. Again, considerable distortion of the
original waveform was experienced, but interestingly the peaks became more distinguishable, although they were often shifted from
the sampling point. This shifting of peaks caused some problems to
the clock recovery system, the performance of which is shown in Figure 12.11. The performance of the system with clock recovery was
about 3dB worse in terms of channel SNR compared to ideal clock
recovery. This decrease in performance may be acceptable, especially
as measurements suggest that such channels are unlikely to be encountered in practice. The reason for the performance of the clock
recovery system diverging from that of perfect clock recovery as the
SNR increases is likely to be due to random phase jitter caused by
the ISI. This will tend to cause a certain number of errors regardless
of the SNR, and as the BER falls, the effect of jitter-induced errors

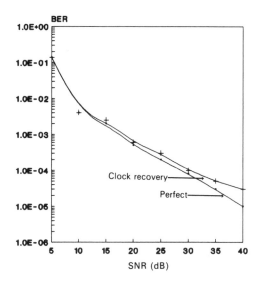

Figure 12.9: Star 16-QAM modified EL clock recovery performance with $\tau = nT$, 30mph, 1.9GHz, 2.66Msymbols/s data rate

will become more significant.

12.6 Early-Late Clock Recovery Implementation Details

A possible implementation arrangement of the modified EL clock recovery system is shown in Figure 12.12. The system is seen to consist of simple building blocks of comparators, adder/subtractors, selector switches and low capacity memory. In Figure 12.12 only the positive peak calculation system has been shown, a near-identical negative peak calculation system is also required. The received input signal passes to a comparator which compares it with the previous maximum value. If a new maximum has occurred then the value of this, along with its oversample address, is stored. The received input signal is also passed to a shift register which stores all the oversampled inputs occurring during the symbol period, typically eight. A bank

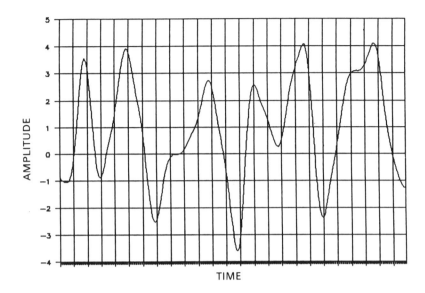

Figure 12.10: Star 16-QAM NLF I channel waveforms with smeared ISI

on n-way switches is then used to latch the appropriate values into the subtractors which perform the calculations of Equation 12.1. The results are then summed according to Equation 12.2, leading to the positive peak score P_{score}. This is then compared with the negative peak score N_{score} which has been derived in a near-identical system, and the larger of the two is passed to a switch. According to whether the score exceeds the threshold and whether it was a maximum or minimum, the switch is set appropriately to select the sample point and update the PLL.

Simplifications to the implementation can be made by reducing the number of gradient calculations in Equation 12.1 which reduces performance slightly but considerably simplifies the circuit's construction.

12.7 Carrier recovery

The problem of clock recovery is closely related to that of carrier recovery. In the case of simple modulation schemes such as BPSK, the

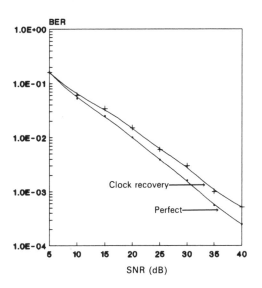

Figure 12.11: Star 16-QAM modified EL clock recovery performance with smeared ISI, 30mph, 1.9GHz, 2Msymbols/s

carrier recovery operation is straightforward as there is a transmitted component at the carrier frequency for the PLL to lock onto. QAM, however, is a suppressed carrier form of modulation. This means that we either have to deliberately insert a carrier as described in the TTIB section in Chapter 10, or we employ more sophisticated recovery schemes [7]. The problem with carrier insertion methods, such as Transparent Tone In Band (TTIB), is that they expand the required spectrum, and these defeat the underlying premise that spectral efficiency is the reason that QAM is employed. They also significantly increase the complexity. At low symbol rates, e.g. below 64Ksymbols/s, experience has shown that it is very difficult to resolve the phase ambiguities inherent in QAM resulting in false locking, especially during fades. This is because at low signalling rates the fading envelope and phase change more dramatically between signalling instances than in the case of high symbol rates. In this respect, doubling the symbol rate is equivalent to halving the vehicular speed since they both mitigate the rapid envelope fluctuations.

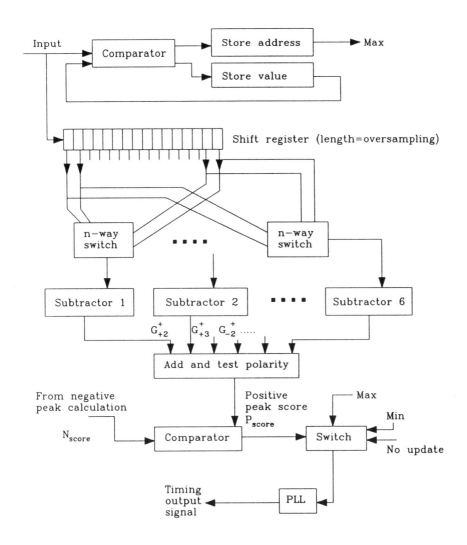

Figure 12.12: Implementation of the modified EL clock recovery system for star 16-QAM

At these low symbol rates differential detection is preferred which removes the need for carrier recovery. At high symbol rates, the inherent ability of an adaptive equaliser to remove phase ambiguity renders non-differential detection viable.

Simulations with decision directed methods showed little promise. The use of the circular Star constellation suggests an interesting and effective form of carrier recovery. One of the systems which has been used for QAM is *times four carrier recovery* [7]. In this system the complex received incoming signal is raised to the fourth power. This has the effect of raising the amplitude to the fourth power and multiplying the phase angle by four. In the case of the square QAM constellation this rotates the phase of half of the constellation points (those where the magnitude of I is equal to the magnitude of Q) to 180 degrees, and distributes the other half of the constellation points randomly in phase. This operation generates a carrier component at four times the carrier frequency which can be used to facilitate carrier recovery. This can be easily shown using simple trigonometrical equivalences and a QAM carrier. The accuracy of this recovery is limited by the constellation points which do not map onto 180 degrees. A long run of these can cause significant jitter and even loss of lock.

The circular QAM constellation offers the intriguing possibility of times eight carrier recovery. This would have the effect of rotating *all* the constellation point to 0 degrees, eliminating the jitter inherent in the previous system. This system, however, cannot resolve ambiguity between lock at any of the eight 45 degree positions and so it is necessary to periodically send a sounding sequence. The performance of this system compared to the differential system is shown in Figure 12.13. It is apparent that the system operating with carrier recovery performs slightly better than that without, but only by a small margin. The gains are lower than the expected 3dB because of operation in Rayleigh fading rather than Gaussian noise. Here the probability of the next symbol being in error is highly correlated with the probability of the current symbol being in error. There is also the problem of catastrophic failure during deep fades. It can be concluded that the extra complexity involved in adding carrier recovery

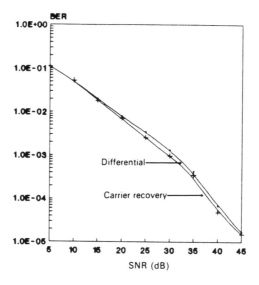

Figure 12.13: BER versus channel SNR performance of differential and coherent star 16-QAM at a mobile speed of 30mph, 1.9GHz carrier frequency and 64Ksymbols/s data rate

is not compensated by the gains in performance and so differential, non-coherent reception is generally preferred.

12.8 Summary

In this chapter clock and carrier recovery schemes for star 16-QAM transmissions over Rayleigh fading channels have been considered. It has been shown that a modified version of early-late clock recovery works well both in narrow and wideband channels. Consideration of carrier recovery schemes showed that differential detection was preferable for QAM transmission.

This now concludes the basic QAM schemes for mobile radio transmission. In the next section we will consider more advanced methods of transmission via QAM, which are generally concerned with mobile radio applications. We start the next section with an analysis of variable rate QAM whereby the number of levels are dynamically changed to reflect the changing channel.

Bibliography

[1] **D.Lyon**, "Envelope derived timing recovery in QAM and SQAM systems", *IEEE Trans Comms* Nov 1975 pp1327-1331.

[2] **M.Shafi and D.J.Moore**, "Further results on adaptive equalizer improvements for 16 QAM and 64 QAM digital radio", *IEEE Trans Comms*, COM-34 No 1, Jan 1986 pp59-66.

[3] **R.W.Chang and R.Srinivasagopalan**, "Carrier recovery for data communication systems with adaptive equalization", *IEEE Trans Comms* Vol COM-28 No 8 Aug 1980 pp1142-1153.

[4] **L.E.Franks**, "Carrier recovery and bit synchronisation in data communications - a tutorial review", *ibid pp1107-1120.*

[5] **R.D.Gitlin and J.Salz**, "Timing recovery in PAM systems", *BSTJ* Vol 50 No 5 May-June 1971 pp1645-1669.

[6] **M.H.Meyers and L.E.Franks**, "Joint carrier phase and symbol timing recovery for PAM systems", *IEEE Trans Comms* Vol COM-28 No 8 Aug 1980 pp1121-1129.

[7] **A.J.Rustako et al**, "Using times-four carrier recovery in M-QAM digital radio receivers", *IEEE J-SAC* No 3 April 1987 pp524-533.

[8] **R.J.C.Bultitude and G.K.Bedal**, "Propagation characteristics on microcellular urban mobile radio channels at 910MHz", *IEEE J-SAC* Vol 7 No.1, Jan 1989, pp31-39.

[9] **J.G.Proakis**, "Digital Communications", McGraw Hill 1983

[10] **N.G.Kingsbury**, "Transmit and receive filters for QPSK signals to optimise the performance on linear and hard-limited channels", *IEE Proc* Vol 133 Pt F No 4 July 1986 pp345-355.

[11] **K.Feher**, "Digital communications - Satellite/Earth station engineering", Prentice Hall 1983

[12] **L.C.Palmer and S.Lebowitz**, "Including synchronization in time-domain channel simulations", *Comsat Tech. Review* Vol 7 No 2 Fall 1977 pp475-525.

[13] **R.L.Cupo and R.D.Gitlin**, "Adaptive carrier recovery systems for digital data communications receivers", *IEE J-SAC* Vol 7 No 9 Dec 1989 pp1328-1339.

[14] **W.C.Lindsay and M.K.Simon**, "Carrier synchronization and detection of polyphase signals", *IEEE Trans Comms* June 1972 pp441-454.

Chapter 13

Variable Rate QAM [1]

13.1 Introduction

QAM transmissions over Rayleigh fading mobile radio channels are subjected to error bursts due to deep fades, even when the channel signal-to-noise (SNR) ratio is high, as was shown in Chapter 11. This leads to the notion of varying the number of modulation levels according to the integrity of the channel, so that when the receiver is not in a fade the number of constellation points is increased, and as the receiver enters a fade they are decreased to a value which provides an acceptable bit error rate (BER) [2]. If the required BER is specified and levels switched accordingly, a variable data throughput is obtained. Alternatively, if the throughput is held reasonably constant on average a variable BER results. Following Steele and Webb[1], in this chapter a variety of algorithms for an adaptive QAM modems are investigated to meet different criteria.

A variable rate system can only work with duplex transmission as some method of informing the transmitter of the quality of the link as perceived by the receiver is required. The transmitter can respond by changing the number of star QAM[1] levels according to the quality criteria adopted. Successful variable rate transmission requires that the fading channel changes slowly compared to a number of symbol periods. If this condition is not met, then the frequent transmission of quality control information will significantly increase the bandwidth requirements of the system. To avoid this problem the

384

data rate can be increased, allowing the transmission of more symbols before the channel changes significantly. The slower the mobile travels, the slower the fading rate and the lower the signalling rate required for adapting the modem to the channel.

Simulations suggest that for a mobile speed of 30mph and propagation frequency of 1.9GHz, the data rate should be a minimum of 512kSym/s. As the mobile speed decreased, and hence the fading rate fell, the minimum data rate reduced correspondingly, allowing a minimum of about 64kSym/sec at walking speed and 1.8GHz, and 32kSym/sec at 900MHz. For the high symbol rates associated with vehicular mobiles to occur without dispersion requires the use of microcells where the time delay spread is sufficiently small. This suggests cordless telecommunications (CT) in buildings or street microcells.

Varying the number of QAM levels in response to fading conditions results in a variable bit rate, which although nearly constant over long periods, could instantaneously vary by four times the average rate. This may be problematic for conventional speech codecs which typically generate a constant bit rate, although there do exist variable bit rate coders, but should not significantly affect computer data. Data transmissions often have the virtue that a variable throughput, and relatively large delays can be tolerated, provided the BER is sufficiently low. For computer file transfer the BER must be virtually zero.

The simplest duplex arrangement for variable rate modem operation is Time Division Duplex (TDD), where both Base Station (BS) and Mobile Station (MS) transmit over the *same* radio frequency channel, but at different times. In this case both BS and MS experience similar channel fading conditions as their transmissions are typically half a TDD frame apart. The transmission received by the MS is used to estimate the channel integrity which then dictates the number of QAM levels to be used by the MS transmitter. Similarly, the transmission received by the BS enables the number of QAM levels to be used in the subsequent BS transmission to be determined. It is critical that both the BS and MS inform the other of the number of QAM levels used by their transmitters and that this information is not corrupted by the channel, in order for the QAM demodulations to be properly performed.

Typically the data is divided into blocks, or packets that occupy a time slot, and the first few symbols in each block are reserved for signalling the side-information representing the number of QAM levels. The optimum size of the block is related to the mobile speed and propagation frequency as the channel should not change significantly over the block duration. In our simulations we have used signalling blocks of 100 symbols for transmissions at 512kSym/s, a mobile speed of 30mph and a carrier frequency of 1.9GHz. At the start of each block a signal was transmitted representing the number of QAM levels to be used in this block. This side information was encoded onto two symbols of a 4-level QAM, i.e. QPSK system, and each of these two symbols was transmitted three times. Majority voting was performed at the receiver in order to establish the number of QAM levels to demodulate in the current block. With larger block sizes, higher integrity codes based either on FEC codes or a higher number of repetitions can be used on the information containing the number of QAM levels without significantly reducing the effective information throughput.

Figure 13.1 shows the TDD framing arrangement for adaptive QAM transmissions using one carrier per channel. If N channels per carrier are used the QAM symbols shown in the Figure are transmitted N times faster, but the time over which the fading channel must remain essentially unchanged is the same.

Frequency Division Duplex (FDD) operation is used by GSM, DCS 1800 and IS-54. In FDD the uplink and the downlink use different propagation frequencies that are typically spaced by some 20 to 40MHz. Although the average path loss on the two channels is essentially the same, the fading on the two links may differ substantially. Both BS and MS must monitor their incoming channels and signal the required number of QAM levels to be used by the other in their transmissions on their outgoing channels. This results in twice the delay between estimating the number of levels required, and transmitting with this number of levels, when compared to TDD. Consequently the mobile speed in FDD must be half that in TDD for

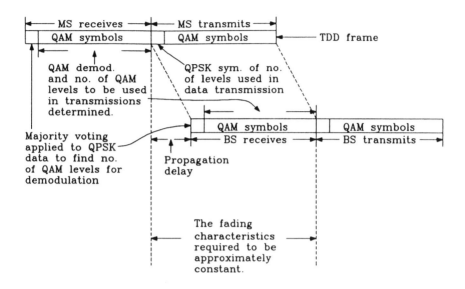

Figure 13.1: The framing structure used in the variable level scheme

equivalent performance. All the results in this chapter are reported for TDD.

13.2 Variable QAM Constellations

As proposed in the previous section, the QAM constellation changes as the number of levels is varied. The constellation system used is based upon Star QAM in conjunction with differential coding as described in Chapter 11. Constellations ranged from 1 bit/sym corresponding to BPSK through to 6 bits/sym star 64-QAM. The constellations for 2-level to 64-level Star QAM are shown in Figure 13.2. The actual distances between the rings, and the sizes of the rings are not drawn to scale. Each constellation has the same average energy, and the radii of the rings in the 8 and 16-level constellations are in the ratio of three-to-one.

Provided the receiver noise is sufficiently low, and implementation complexity is not an inhibiting factor, more than 6 bits/sym can be used. As the number of bits/sym is increased, the number of amplitude rings and the number of phase points are alternately doubled. Starting with BPSK, for 2 bits/sym the number of phase points is doubled to get QPSK. For 3 bits/sym the number of amplitude levels is doubled to get 2-level QPSK. For 4 bits/sym the number of phase points is doubled to get to the 16-level Star constellation, and so on until with 6 bits/sym there are 4 rings having 16 points per ring.

In the forthcoming two Sections we will be experimenting with two different systems, applying either the Received Signal Strength Indicator (RSSI) criterion or the prevailing bit error rate criterion in order to control the number of modulation levels employed.

13.3 The RSSI Switching System

The block diagram of the transceiver is shown in Figure 13.3. After recovering the baseband signal, demultiplexing is performed to separate the QPSK side information and star QAM primary information signals. QPSK demodulation is performed to obtain the number of QAM levels to be used in the QAM demodulation of the primary information. QPSK demodulation is followed by QAM demodulation to yield the recovered data. The average signal strength of the baseband signal over a signalling block provides an indication of the short-term path loss and fading envelope of the radio channel. If this average is very low the mobile is either in a deep fade or at the edge of the cell. In either case it is more appropriate for it to transmit using relatively few QAM levels. Conversely, if the average is high the channel is relatively good, enabling more QAM levels to be used in its next transmission. The average over a signalling block is computed using an exponential smoothing process which gives more weight to signal levels towards the end of the block associated with more recent samples. This average signal strength is then quantised, each quantised output signifying a particular number of QAM levels to be used in the forthcoming transmission. The transmitter seen in Figure 13.3 has the inverse structure to the receiver.

The baseband signal in Figure 13.3 is related to the received signal strength indicator (RSSI) at the RF stage. This system would function identically if the RF RSSI, instead of the baseband RSSI

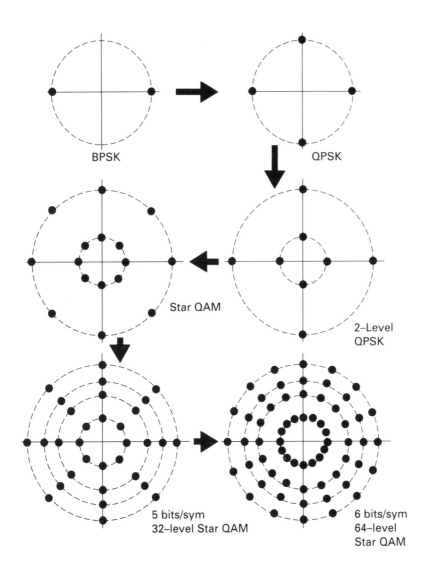

Figure 13.2: Star QAM constellations used in the variable level scheme

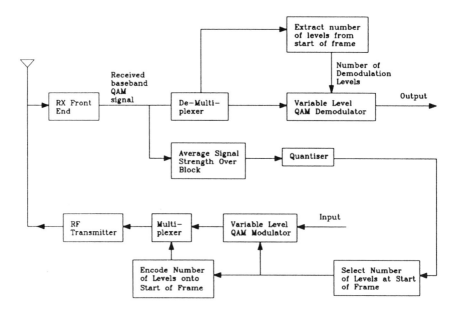

Figure 13.3: Transceiver block diagram for RSSI switching

indicator, was averaged over a signalling block. For ease of nomen-clature, this method of switching the QAM levels based on the base-band signals is called, baseband RSSI switching, or more simply, RSSI switching.

Two criteria can be used for the switching levels generated by the quantiser in Figure 13.3. One is to select the switching levels to achieve a specified BER, resulting in a variable data throughput. In order to establish the required threshold values simulations were conducted where graphs of BER as a function of channel SNR were plotted for the Star QAM modem having 2^n; $n = 1, 2, ...6$ fixed levels. In these simulations a Gaussian channel was used, as over any short period of time when switching is performed the channel essentially exhibits a constant RSSI level plus Gaussian noise. The channel SNR value corresponding to the BER of interest identifies the switching thresholds. The SNR is therefore quantised, with the quantisation zones corresponding to different number of QAM levels in the adaptive modem. Some hysteresis should be incorporated into the switching algorithm in order to prevent continual level changing.

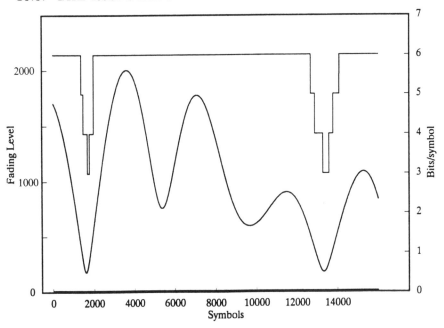

Figure 13.4: Stylized RSSI switching for variable bit rate

Figure 13.4 shows an arbitrary segment of the fading envelope of the received signal applied to the QAM demodulator, and the number of bits/sym selected during this period. The figure was produced from a simulation at a channel SNR of 30dB with other parameters as stated previously. Because of the relatively high SNR, much of the time the modem attained its maximum 6 bits/sym.

The second criterion for choosing the switching thresholds achieves a constant average bit rate whilst accepting a variable BER. Here the thresholds derived above for the constant BER system are multiplied by a factor at the start of each block. This factor is derived from the baseband signal averaged over a number of fades. This operation merely involves adding an extra averaging circuit with the averaging window increased over that used to average over a signalling block in Figure 13.3, so that it covered many blocks. Therefore as the average signal level rises, for example when moving closer to the base station, the switching thresholds increase accordingly maintaining a near constant average number of bits/symbol, but variable BER.

The average number of bits/sym can be set to any level within

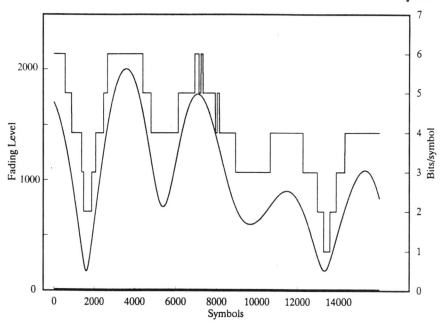

Figure 13.5: Stylized RSSI switching for constant bit rate

the maximum number of bits/sym by changing the scaling factor associated with the long term average of the received signal. Where the average bit rate was the same for both selection criteria, they both gave identical BERs, and can be viewed as equivalent systems. Figure 13.5 shows switching profiles for this constant throughput scheme over the same section of fading channel as for the previous profile. Again an SNR of 30dB is used. Here considerably more level changing took place in an effort to maintain an average number of bits/symbol close to the target value of 4 bits/sym. If a lower SNR had been chosen for both graphs then they would appear more similar as the former scheme would have had an average throughput closer to the 4 bits/symbol of the latter scheme.

In an effort to further improve the system's performance channel coding was added to both of above systems, in our case in the form of systematic binary BCH codes. The data was encoded and block diagonally interleaved over 15,600 bits before being passed to the input of the QAM modem in Figure 13.3. At the output of the modem de-interleaving was performed in an attempt to randomize the

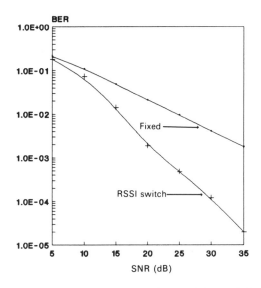

Figure 13.6: BER comparison of variable and fixed systems at 30mph, 1.9GHz, 512ksymbols/s

bursty channel errors before channel decoding took place. The variable QAM schemes had the advantage over the fixed QAM scheme that errors occurred in smaller blocks because of the use of fewer QAM levels in poor channels. This allowed the channel codecs to perform more efficiently. The performance of the RSSI switching system with channel coding will be presented in contrast to FEC coded results of another adaptive QAM modem in the next section.

13.3.1 Results

The performance of the RSSI switched variable level Star QAM system without FEC coding compared to a fixed 16-level (4 bits/sym) Star QAM system is shown in Figure 13.6. The adaptive QAM system has had its switching thresholds adjusted to also give an average number of bits/symbol close to 4. The necessary signalling information of the number of QAM levels used has been taken into account in calculating this throughput. The simulation was performed for a propagation frequency of 1.9GHz, a vehicular speed of

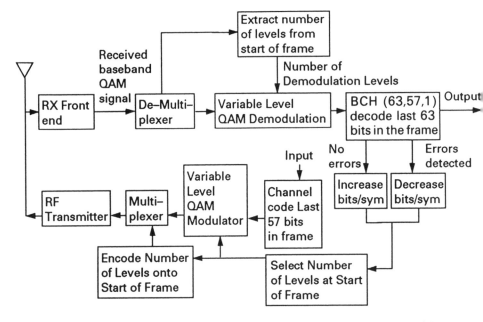

Figure 13.7: Block diagram of the adaptive BER switching
star QAM receiver

30mph, and a transmitted symbol rate of 512KSym/sec, providing a
bit rate of 2048Kbits/sec on average. The propagation environment
has been assumed to be microcellular so that ISI is insignificant.
There is a significant improvement in the performance of the adaptive scheme over the fixed modem at all SNRs. This improvement is
enhanced with increasing SNR. This suggests that the variable rate
system has advantages in certain applications.

13.4   The Error Detector Switching System

Rather than switching the number of QAM levels in harmony with
the RSSI they can be changed on the command of a channel codec,
in this case a systematic binary BCH codec. Figure 13.7 shows a
simplified block diagram of the BER switching transceiver. Observe
that its structure is similar to that of the RSSI switching system
of Figure 13.3, apart from the fact that the channel quality is now
monitored by a BCH coder. In order to obtain an estimate of the

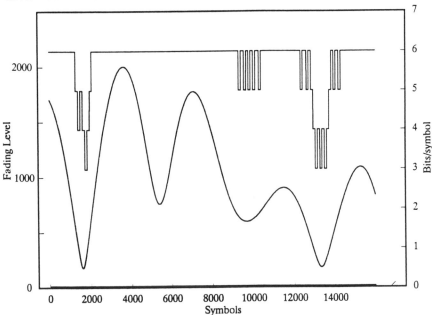

Figure 13.8: Stylized fading channel envelope and number of bits/symbol profiles for BER switching adaptive star QAM modem

channel during each received data packet, a BCH(63,57,1) code is overlaid onto the last 57 bits of input data in each block. The input data may already have been channel coded and interleaved using the same system as described in the previous section, the additional coding is overlaid onto whatever data was present. This codec is generally ineffective at correcting errors in the hostile fading environment as it is typically overwhelmed by the non-interleaved errors in a typical error burst, but it informs the receiver that channel conditions were poor. Such a coding system involves little overhead as it is only applied to the final 57 bits in a block which contains an average of 400 bits. The coded data is applied to the adaptive QAM modulator and the modulated output is up-converted and transmitted.

The QAM demodulation is performed using the number of QAM levels extracted from the QPSK header, as described in the section on the RSSI switched QAM system. Most of the data is passed to the output where it might be subjected to de-interleaving and channel

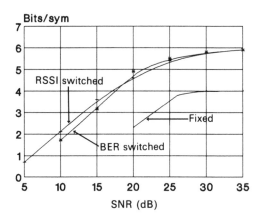

Figure 13.9: Comparison of variable and fixed star QAM systems at BER=10^{-2}, 30mph, 1.9GHz, 512ksym-
bols/s

decoding. However, the final 63 bits of the recovered bit stream
are passed through the BCH(63,57,1) codec before proceeding to the
output. If no errors are detected by this BCH codec then the number
of QAM levels used in the next block is doubled, otherwise they are
halved. Switching profiles for the same section of fading channel
envelope as used in Figures 13.4 and 13.5 are shown in Figure 13.8.
Again a channel SNR of 30dB was used. This figure shows that the
BER switched system had a similar level switching profile to the
variable throughput RSSI system, as might be expected. The lack
of hysteresis on level switching is evident but it does not cause any
additional signalling overhead, nor significantly alter the BER.

13.4.1   Results

A direct BER comparison between this adaptive system and the fixed
16-level QAM system cannot be made, since although the adaptive
modem maintains a constant symbol rate; the number of bits per

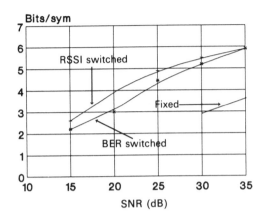

Figure 13.10: Comparison of variable and fixed star QAM systems at BER=10^{-3}, 30mph, 1.9GHz, 512ksymbols/s

symbol, or bit rate, is highly variable. Instead comparison curves of the average number of bits per symbol against SNR for a variety of different BERs can be drawn. This clearly shows the trade-off between the BER and the average number of bits/symbol that can be achieved using an adaptive QAM modem. The results are shown in Figures 13.9 to 13.12.

Observe from Figure 13.9 that the number of bits/sym of fixed Star QAM was four when the channel SNR was high, and then exhibited the same roll-off as the adaptive modems. Both the adaptive and fixed Star QAM modems decreased their number of bits/sym with falling SNR values at a rate of approximately 2 bits/sym per 10dB in SNR. As the SNR fell more powerful BCH codes were progressively invoked in order to maintain the fixed BER.

For all modems the BCH codes were composed of blocks of 63 bits, the number of data bits varying between 57 and 24 as the correction power increased from 1 to 7 bits/block. The corresponding BCH codes are: BCH(63,57,1), BCH(63,51,2), BCH(63,45,3),

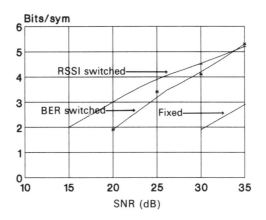

Figure 13.11: Comparison of variable and fixed star QAM systems at BER=10^{-4}, 30mph, 1.9GHz, 512ksym-
bols/s

BCH(63,39,4), BCH(63,36,5), BCH(63,30,6) and BCH(63,24,7).
Block diagonal interleavers of size 15,600 bits were used for all systems. Thus by having no BCH coding compared to when the maximum power BCH(63,24,7) code was used, the number of bits per
symbol decreased from 4 to approximately $R = 24/63 \approx 1.52$ for
the fixed system. For a given number of bits/symbol the adaptive
modems achieved an 8-10dB gain in SNR over the fixed system, due
to their ability to adjust the number of constellation points. As the
SNR increased above 25dB, the fixed modem settled to its 4 bits/sym
while both RSSI and BER switched adaptive systems were asymptotic towards the maximum of 6 bits/sym. This was because the
maximum number of bits/sym available to the modulator was six.
In general the BER versus channel SNR curves can be expected to
be asymptotic towards the maximum number of bits/sym available
in the system in use, given a sufficiently high SNR.

In all the curves, both the RSSI and BER switched adaptive star
QAM systems had similar performances, with the RSSI switching

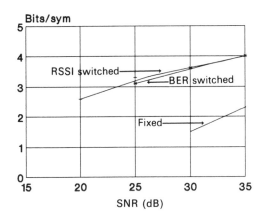

Figure 13.12: Comparison of variable and fixed star QAM systems at BER=10^{-5}, 30mph, 1.9GHz, 512ksymbols/s

system typically offering a slightly higher number of bits/sym at low SNRs for some BERs. These small gains were due to the RSSI switching system's ability to select a lower number of levels before any errors occurred. In terms of implementational complexity the RSSI-switched scheme is also slightly more attractive, since it can dispense with the additional BCH(63,57,1) codec.

The final comment on the curves in Figures 13.9 to 13.12 is that as the guaranteed minimum BER was increased from 10^{-5} to 10^{-3} the channel SNR required to achieve the same number of bits/sym for the variable systems was decreased by approximately 3dB per decade increase in BER.

13.5 Co-Channel Interference

Co-channel interference is nearly always present in mobile communications. Accordingly, it is necessary to ascertain whether improvements in performance can be obtained using variable level Star QAM

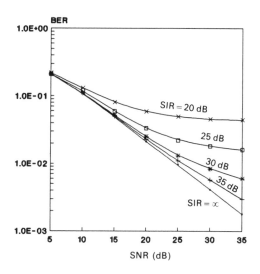

Figure 13.13: BER versus SNR performance of fixed star QAM with co-channel interference and 30mph, 1.9GHz, 512ksymbols/s

compared to fixed level Star QAM in the presence of a single Rayleigh faded co-channel interferer, this being the worst case interference since in the case of several co-channel interferers their effect tends towards that of AWGN of the same power due to the central limit theorem. The performance of 16-level Star QAM, i.e. a non-adaptive modem is shown in Figure 13.13 for different signal-to-co-channel interference ratios (SIR). The bench mark is the curve with no co-channel interference. These curves indicate that it is necessary to operate with both SNR and SIR values at approximately 30dB in order to achieve a BER performance better than 10^{-2}. No channel coding was used in the experiment.

When the Star-QAM modem with no channel coding was made adaptive using RSSI switching, this was based on the second RSSI switching criterion, where the switching thresholds were increased when encountering higher RSSI outputs, as described in the section on the RSSI switched system. This ensured that the average number of bits per symbol was four, as in the case of the fixed modem. Re-

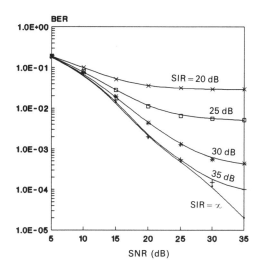

Figure 13.14: BER versus SNR performance of RSSI switched star QAM with co-channel interference and 30mph, 1.9GHz, 512ksymbols/s

call that this RSSI switching criterion was associated with a variable BER but near constant average number of bits/symbol. Performance curves using RSSI switching are presented in Figure 13.14. For all systems in this section the simulation parameters were the same as used in previous sections, namely 30mph, 1.9GHz and 512ksymbols/s. Comparing Figures 13.13 and 13.14 one can see that the residual BER (measured at a SNR of 35dB) was 2.2, 2 and 15 times lower compared to the fixed modem for SIR values of 20, 25 and 30dB respectively.

When BER switching was used it was not possible to ensure that the average number of bits per symbol was four. The BER and bits/sym vary in a complex manner and so BER and average number of bits/sym are plotted as a function of SIR for a fixed channel SNR. Figures 13.15 and 13.16 show plots for SNR values of 35 and 20dB, respectively, for both adaptive modems, and for the fixed 16-level Star QAM modem. From Figure 13.15 it is evident that the non-adaptive system had the worst performance. The BER switched

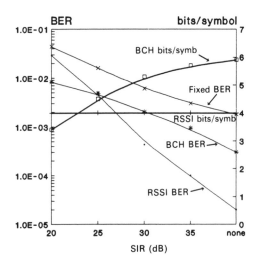

Figure 13.15: BER and bits/sym versus SIR performance of fixed and adaptive star QAM modems at SNR=35dB, 30mph, 1.9GHz, 512ksymbols/s

QAM gained in bits/sym at the expense of poorer BER performance when compared to the RSSI switched QAM as the SIR was increased. This was to be expected because in previous sections the BER switched system was shown to operate with a higher number of bits/sym and higher BER than the constant throughput RSSI system. Figure 13.16 shows the situation for a SNR of 20dB, where again both adaptive modems outperformed the fixed one.

13.6   Application to a DECT-Type System

The digital European cordless telecommunications (DECT) system uses TDD, supporting 12 channels per carrier. The 12 down-link and 12 up-link channels constitute a 24 slot frame lasting 10ms. Each time-slot containing a packet has a duration of 0.417ms. The data in the packet consists of 320 bits which are transmitted at 1152kSym/s. Each bit was replaced by a QAM symbol to increase

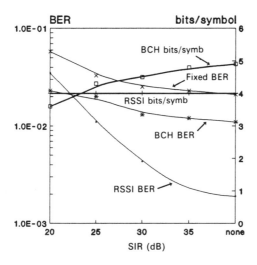

Figure 13.16: BER and bits/sym versus SIR performance of fixed and adaptive star QAM modems at SNR=20dB, 30mph, 1.9GHz, 512ksymbols/s

system capacity. The header informed the receiver of the number of constellation points. The RSSI switching system was employed.

Figure 13.17 shows the variation of BER as a function of channel SNR for this DECT-like system for MSs travelling at different speeds. No co-channel interference was present. The DECT framing meant that the transmission and reception were separated by 12 slots or 5ms, and consequently the channel could occasionally experience considerable changes between transmission and reception of data and therefore generate an inappropriate number of levels. Consequently all the curves for our twelve user QAM-based DECT system in Figure 13.17 demonstrate worse performance than for the single user bench mark scheme shown for no co-channel interference in Figure 13.14, i.e. when the transmit and receive packets were concatenated. When the MS travelled faster the BER deteriorated and when the mobile's speed was 20mph the adaptive and the fixed four-level QAM had similar performances. However, an order of

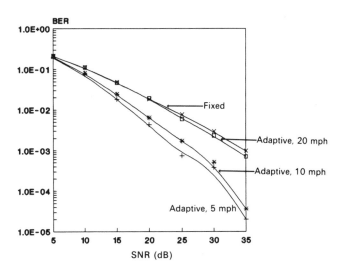

Figure 13.17: BER versus SNR performance of fixed and adaptive star QAM DECT-like modems with no co-channel interference for various vehicular speeds

magnitude improvement in BER was achieved for channel SNRs in excess of 20dB when the mobile's speed was decreased from 20 to 5mph. This was due to the slower fading rate making the channel estimation more accurate.

13.7 Summary

In this chapter we described an adaptive Star QAM modem for transmission of data over Rayleigh fading channels using a variable number of modulation levels. Criteria for deciding how to vary the number of modulation levels to give a required performance characteristic were discussed. The adaptive QAM modem can be arranged to provide a near constant BER over a wide range of channel SNRs, although the bit rate may vary considerably. This type of performance is suitable for data services that can tolerate some delay. In general, the adaptive modem provides the flexibility to vary both the BER and the bit rate in a prescribed manner to suit a particular application. The adaptive modems have a better performance than the fixed modems both with and without co-channel interference, but require a moderate increase in complexity. A DECT-type multi-user system was suggested and it was shown that at low mobile speeds the BER of a fixed 16-level QAM system can be reduced by an order of magnitude for SNR> 20dB by employing a variable rate modem.

In the next chapter we investigate some of the problems that transmitting at the high bit rates suggested in this chapter can cause with mobile radio channels, and suggest some possible equaliser structures to overcome these problems.

Bibliography

[1] **R. Steele, W.T. Webb**, "Variable rate QAM for data transmission over Rayleigh fading channels", Keynote Paper, Wireless'91, Calgary Alberta, July 1991

[2] **R.Steele**, "Deploying Personal Communications Networks", *IEEE Comms. Magazine*, Sept 1990, pp12-15.

[3] **W.T.Webb, L.Hanzo and R.Steele**, "Bandwidth-efficient QAM schemes for Rayleigh fading channels", *IEE Proceedings Part I*, Vol 138, No 3, June 1991, pp169-175.

Chapter 14

Wideband QAM Transmissions

14.1 Introduction

In current communications systems the majority of teletraffic is typically generated in office buildings, hence the capacity of mobile systems in these buildings must be very high. The high bit rates required to accommodate video, audio, computer data and other traffic may necessitate the symbol rate of the multilevel modulation systems being so high that the mobile radio channels exhibit dispersion. Performing equalisation of multilevel signals that are subjected to dispersion and fading is not an easy task. In this chapter methods whereby high bit rates can be conveyed via star 16-level QAM over wideband mobile radio channels are considered which we consider to be composed of three independent Rayleigh fading paths. This wideband channel response shown in Figure 14.1 is a derivative of Bultitude's indoor and outdoor measurements [1, 2] of impulse responses in microcells.

In Chapter 7 we gave a rudimentary introduction to various channel equalisers. Many of them are designed to operate with binary modulation, but can be modified to operate in conjunction with QAM with little, if any, modification. In this chapter we propose a novel channel equaliser scheme for star 16-QAM which is based on a combination of signal processing blocks, such as FEC codecs,

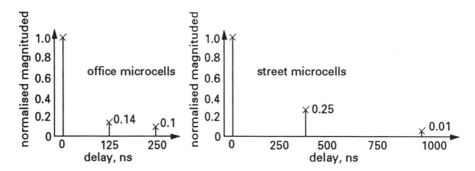

Figure 14.1: Microcellular impulse responses used in the simulations

the so-called RAKE diversity combiner to be described in the next section, and a linear equaliser (LE). We firstly detail the RAKE combiner.

14.2   The RAKE Combiner

The RAKE receiver is not an equaliser, but a combiner for diversity systems. The RAKE system inherits its name from the way it "rakes" in all the incoming pulses to form an equalised signal. A block diagram of the basic system is shown in Figure 14.2. The RAKE system is identical in structure to a maximum ratio combiner. It is designed to operate in a situation where the signal to be transmitted has a narrow bandwidth, but the bandwidth available is wide, and so the transmitted signal's bandwidth can be expanded in order to use the multipath diversity inherent in the wideband system. Multipath diversity exhibits itself in the fact that in wideband channels several echoes of the transmitted signal can be observed due to far-field reflections. The channel equaliser can remove the dispersion introduced by the channel, and by locking onto the echoes appearing in the impulse response, taps within the equaliser can exploit this so-called time-domain diversity effect. In order to achieve the required bandwidth expansion the baseband signal is transmitted as

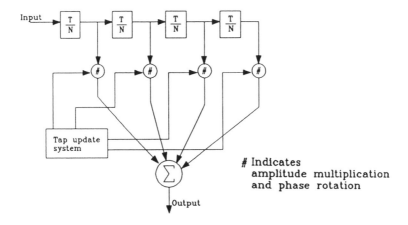

Figure 14.2: RAKE diversity combining system

a series of narrow pulses with a gap between each pulse as shown in Figure 14.3. Suppose, for example, that the signalling interval duration is T and the bandwidth required when these pulses are appropriately shaped is B, but the available system bandwidth is $N \times B$. In this case an N times narrower signalling pulse of duration T/N can be used to exploit the whole bandwidth. Accordingly the RAKE receiver of Figure 14.2 must be clocked at an N times higher rate.

Because of the delay spread, the receiver perceives each transmitted pulse as a series of received pulses. In order for the RAKE combiner to operate correctly it needs to know the expected attenuation and phase change suffered by each path. Each incoming pulse is then amplified and de-rotated by these expected factors, and then the resulting partially equalised pulses are superimposed to form the input to the symbol decision section. This is shown diagrammatically in Figure 14.3. Adaptive coefficient update systems can be used instead of channel sounding methods, but these tend to be less robust due to error propagation in the coefficient update section.

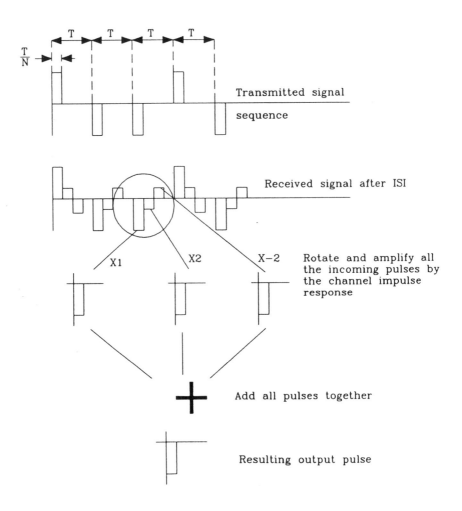

Figure 14.3: Time domain operation of the RAKE combiner

14.3 The Proposed Equaliser

14.3.1 Linear Equaliser

When transmitting in the Rayleigh fading environment, there are a number of counter-measures that are often employed against fading. Mobile subscribers may become stationary in a deep fade with consequent system failure. In order to combat this condition frequency hopping is often used. Accordingly, the data is divided into blocks, and at the end of each block a hop is made to a new frequency outside the coherence bandwidth of the channel. The channel is sounded at the start of the block in order to establish the impulse response of the channel at this new frequency. Sounding in the centre of the block will give better results because the impulse response of the channel cannot change so dramatically during half a block as during a whole block, and is often employed. The next block of data is then sent. The size of each block must be chosen so that the channel does not change significantly during the time the block is transmitted. However, the channel should be sounded as infrequently as possible in order to keep the data throughput high. The optimum block size is related to the mobile speed.

Simulations of adaptive linear and DFEs showed very poor performance due to catastrophic failure in fading environments. A similar problem was experienced with DFEs employing channel sounding. The linear equaliser with channel sounding offered the most promising performance.

A few slight changes are necessary as regards the channel sounding method used for binary modulation schemes in the case of QAM as the pseudo-random binary sequence (PRBS) used for sounding must be mapped onto the non-binary symbol set for transmission, and both the amplitude and phase shift of each of the propagation paths must be recovered. A logical 1 from the PRBS is mapped onto the outermost phasor of the star 16-QAM constellation at 0 degrees and a logical 0 from the PRBS onto the outermost symbol at 180 degrees. The use of the outermost symbol maximises the received SNR and by only transmitting on the I axis, measurement of the introduced phase shift is simplified. This principle is similar to those used in

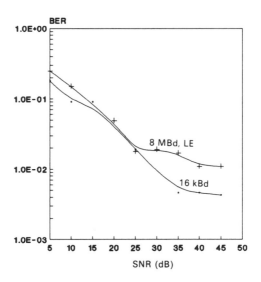

Figure 14.4: BER versus channel SNR performance of narrowband and wideband star 16-QAM at 30mph,
1.9GHz and 16kBd and 8MBd, respectively

the generation of equaliser training sequences in the CCITT V.series
modems discussed in Chapter 9. Separate correlation on both the
I and Q axes is performed, and the phase shift is found by taking
the arctan of the results. A comparison of the BER performance of
the differential 16-level star QAM modem operating at 16kBd over a
flat-fading, i.e. narrowband channel and the 8MBd (32Mbps) system
with a LE over a frequency selective wideband channel is presented
in Figure 14.4 where it can be seen that the performance of the
wideband system is inferior to the narrowband system, although the
difference is not substantial.

14.3.2 Iterative Equaliser System

Upon studying error events using the linear equaliser it was observed
in the simulations that the performance of the system would be considerably improved if it could be made more tolerant to fades which
prevented the LE coefficients from decaying, as was mentioned in

Chapter 7. Furthermore, the DFE is a potentially powerful equaliser if it can be prevented from failing catastrophically due to error propagation effects in the case of erroneous decisions, when incorrect information is fed back into the coefficient adjustment mechanism. A solution to this problem is to use an equaliser which exploited the advantages of both the LE and DFE but avoided their shortcomings.

The linear equaliser works satisfactorily most of the time, as previously described, except when the coefficients fail to decay. This failure to decay can be detected by comparing the values of the last few equaliser coefficients against an appropriate threshold value. If this threshold value is exceeded by the coefficient values, the decoded data from the linear equaliser will have a high error rate. A robust initial equaliser system is required which will not fail catastrophically during fades and whose output can then be further processed to reduce the BER.

In those situations where the LE failed to converge a DFE was therefore invoked which was constrained in order to prevent catastrophic failure, and a multi-stage equalisation algorithm was contrived. The first pass at equalising the channel was carried by a non-optimal equaliser based on the RAKE equaliser [3] that was described in the previous section. Although the RAKE combiner's operation is prone to errors, experience showed that these will be typically confined to neighbouring constellation points. The data regenerated by the RAKE has now a lower BER than the received data and can then be used to keep the DFE from failing catastrophically. We refer to this non-optimal equaliser as a one symbol window equaliser (OSWE). A block diagram of the complete system proposed is shown in Figure 14.5 and its operation is discussed in depth in the following sections.

14.3.2.1 The One Symbol Window Equaliser

This equaliser utilizes the principle that the ISI will generally exhibit itself as random noise and calculating an appropriately weighted average of the magnitude and phase of the incoming phasors over the duration of the channel impulse response will enable it to remove this ISI. Its principle of operation is discussed below and shown dia-

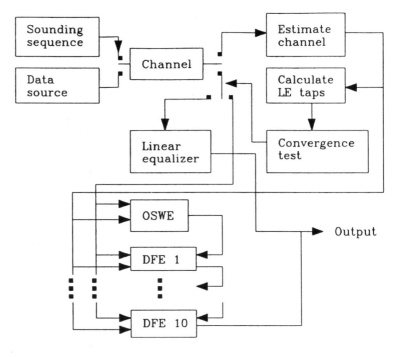

Figure 14.5: System Block Diagram

grammatically in Figure 14.6. First the channel impulse response is estimated from the received channel sounding sequence and in Figure 14.6 three significant paths are resolved, each having an associated magnitude and phase. Next the delay bin is determined, m symbol periods after the first significant received multipath component, in which the last significant path component was received. This informs the receiver about the duration of the channel's delay spread. For each of the m delay bins a copy of the locally stored transmitted constellation is rotated by the measured rotation of the impulse response for that particular bin and held in memory as portrayed in the figure. By this means any rotation of the constellation caused by the channel can be compensated. In order to make a decision as to the r-th received symbol all m received QAM phasors which include a contribution from the r-th symbol are taken into account. These phasors are mapped onto the appropriately rotated constellation. Thus the QAM phasor due to the first path signal is held with the constellation rotated by the phase shift of the first path. Similarly, all other paths up to path m generate a received phasor indicated by the arrows at the bottom of Figure 14.6 for $m = 3$ consecutive signalling periods. The QAM phasor comprising the first path from the $(r+1)$th transmitted symbol plus ISI contributions from the rth symbol would be held with the constellation rotated by the phase shift which the channel imposes on the second bin delay, and so on.

Then for each of the M possible transmitted phasors a distance summation is performed over all m rotated constellations. Specifically the distance between each rotated point of the m rotated constellations to which the mth phasor has been mapped and the received symbol are found. Each distance is scaled by the ratio of the path amplitude for that delay to the path amplitude of the main tap. This scaling has the effect of reducing the importance of significantly attenuated delayed signals when regenerating the symbol and is necessary as these delayed signals will be highly corrupted by noise and ISI from other symbols.

This distance calculation is demonstrated at the foot of Figure 14.6 for $M = 4$ and $m = 3$. The Euclidean distance between the received phasors in the $m = 3$ consecutive signalling intervals, and the appropriately rotated phasor 1 are computed, giving distances of a, b and c. Weighting them with their associated path magnitude introduces the required scaling based on their significance, giving a distance of $d_1 = a + 0.5b + 0.1c$. Similarly, for phasor 2 the distance becomes $d_2 = d + 0.5e + 0.1f$, etc., up to $d_M = d_4$. Then the rotated constellation point yielding the lowest distance d is deemed to be the most likely to have been transmitted. In general terms the distance d_n, $n = 1 \ldots M$ associated with any particular received symbol $S_n = x_t + jy_t$ at time t is given by

$$d_n = \sum_{i=1}^{m} \frac{a_i}{a_0} \sqrt{(x_{t+i} - u_i)^2 + (y_{t+i} - v_i)^2} \qquad (14.1)$$

where m is the last significant delay bin, x_t and y_t are the Cartesian values of the received signal at time t, a_i and a_0 are the amplitudes of the measured impulse response at tap i and the main tap respectively, and u and v are the Cartesian values of the rotated constellation

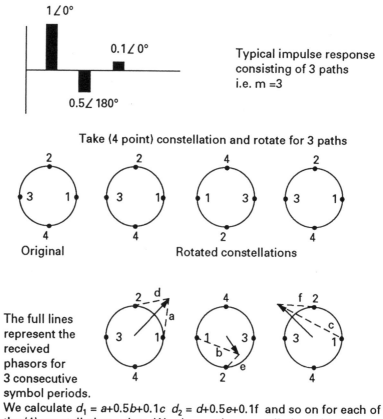

Figure 14.6: OWSE operation for $M = 4$ and $m = 3$

points and are given by

$$u_i = r_n \cos(\theta_n + \phi_i)$$
$$v_i = r_n \sin(\theta_n + \phi_i) \qquad (14.2)$$

r_n and θ_n are the polar amplitude and phase associated with symbol n at the transmitter, and ϕ_i is the phase shift of the ith component in the estimated channel impulse response.

Having found the total distance from between the m received phasors which include components of the r-th sample and each of the M constellation points, the constellation point associated with the lowest total distance according to Equation 14.1 is selected as the most likely one to have been transmitted. This symbol along with the actual received signal levels x_t and y_t is passed to the DFE. Observe the underlying similarity between the operation of the RAKE receiver described in Section 14.2 and that of the OSWE proposed.

14.3.2.2   The Limited Correction DFE

The power of the DFE can be used in order to significantly reduce the error rate from the OSWE. When the LE coefficients have failed to decay, and this is detected by the convergence test block of Figure 14.5, the DFE acts on the received signal level as per normal and decides on the transmitted symbol. If this decision concurs with that of the OSWE the symbol is input to the feedback taps of the DFE and is stored in a decision register maintained for the duration of the decoding of one block. If the DFE's decision represents a neighbouring symbol in the QAM constellation to the one decoded by the OSWE then again the symbol decoded by the DFE is passed back to the feedback taps and stored as the new decoded symbol. However, should the DFE's regenerated symbol *not* be a neighbour of the OWSE-estimated symbol the OSWE's estimated symbol is changed to one of its neighbours in such a way that it is moved nearer to the symbol position regenerated by the DFE, is input to the DFE feedback taps and stored as the new decoded symbol. This movement towards the DFE both tends to bring the DFE back towards lock and accounts for the likely inaccuracy of the OSWE during a fade.

This restriction on the symbols fed back by the DFE prevents it from failing catastrophically in all but the most severe fades. In order to improve the performance the DFE can be run iteratively a number of times using the same input signals but different feedback signals as the constraining output register changes slightly on each pass. Simulations revealed that when the LE failed completely, this iterative system typically produced a very low or zero symbol error rate. Using a knowledge of the transmitted symbol in the simulation showed that each iteration produced a lower or identical BER than the previous iteration. After approximately ten iterations a minimum BER was reached.

The OSWE will automatically lock onto and operate on the strongest multipath component in the channel impulse response. DFEs normally have a feedforward section to allow for the strongest component not being the first path. This feedforward section is essentially a LE and the tap coefficients are set by the inverse filter process as previously explained in Chapter 7. With the combination of equalisers proposed here, it is possible to remove most of the feedforward LE section of the DFE as the OSWE has already decoded the data that would normally be decoded in the feedforward part of the DFE. The DFE operates on the untampered OSWE output, the received signal itself and the feedback data derived as previously explained. This equaliser does not have as good iterative convergence properties as when the first path is the strongest, as it has to use data from the OSWE before it can modify it, but again it shows a significant improvement in performance over the LE.

The results for this system are shown in Figure 14.7 where the performance is significantly better than that of the LE alone, and shows also an improvement over the narrowband system. This improvement over the narrowband system is because this equaliser is successfully using the inherent multipath time-diversity present in the wideband channel.

14.3.3   Use of Error Correction Coding

The results shown in Figure 14.7 show the presence of a residual BER caused by impulse responses which cannot be equalised satisfactorily

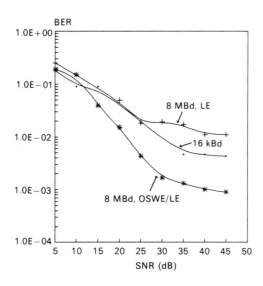

Figure 14.7: BER versus channel SNR comparison of star 16-QAM in the case of 16kBd and 8MBd transmission using the LE and OSWE at 30mph and 1.9GHz

by this system. For example, for the indoor environment, the system fails when the first component in the channel impulse response is in a fade of about 10dB, when its magnitude becomes approximately equal to that of the other multipath components.

In order to overcome the residual BER error correction coding can be used. Conventional FECs encode the bits, interleave and transmit them, perform equalisation, deinterleave the bits and then decode and correct them. The results of such an FEC strategy overlaid onto the system described in Section 14.3.2.2 are shown in Figure 14.8. The bracketed numbers in the caption indicate the bit correction ability for a block length of 63 bits when low-complexity binary BCH codecs are used. Explicitly, the codes employed are BCH(0) = No-FEC, BCH(1) = BCH(63,57,1), BCH(2) = BCH(63,51,2), BCH(3) = BCH(63,45,3), BCH(4) = BCH(63,39,4), BCH(5) = BCH(63,36,5) and BCH(6) = BCH(63,30,6).

As can be seen in the figure, even mild error correcting powers

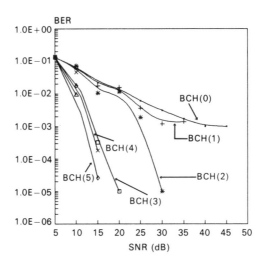

Figure 14.8: BER versus channel SNR performance of star 16-QAM at 8MBd using the LE, the OSWE and a range of BCH FEC codes at 30mph and 1.9GHz

proved to be effective, particularly with SNRs in excess of about 20dB. The residual BER is removed and the channel is rendered suitable for computer data transmission. Coding powers in excess of the BCH(63,45,3) offer little extra gain for the trade off in spectral efficiency. Note that coding reduces spectral efficiency but it has proved necessary to take this measure in most transmissions over Rayleigh fading channels.

With the system described in Section 14.3.2.2, error correction codes can be used in a more efficient manner than by merely decoding after the QAM symbol regeneration. In the same way that we use a number of passes through the DFE, we can pass the partially equalised data through the BCH decoder a number of times. If, as occurs most of the time, the LE has been used, the decoded data is stored in an array ready for deinterleaving. If the OSWE has been used then in addition to storing the decoded data in this array, both the received signal and a flag to identify that this block has been decoded by the OSWE are stored. The blocks of data, be they from the LE or the OSWE, are deinterleaved and BCH decoded.

Most deinterleaved blocks will have too many errors at this stage to allow their correction by the BCH decoder, but if any correction does occur a marker is placed beside the corrected bits. The non-interleaved blocks which were decoded by the OSWE are then passed through the DFE as previously described but with the small modification that any bits that were marked as correct are not permitted to be altered by the DFE. Notice that differential coding cannot be used because if we have corrected a differentially decoded symbol we would know the correct difference between the previous and current symbol, but not the absolute values of these symbols. This is not a severe limitation, since in high-integrity systems differential coding is often avoided because of the 3dB SNR penalty associated with its use.

After being passed through the DFE the data is again deinterleaved and another BCH decoding pass is attempted. This process continues for as many passes as are necessary. Since a good estimate of the number of errors can be gained from the overload detector of the BCH decoder, this iterative process can be continued until either there are no errors in the array, or no more errors have been removed since the previous pass. Convergence of the DFE is improved by the marking of the correct bits, helping to prevent it from making incorrect decisions. The performance of this system for the same BCH codes as before is shown in Figure 14.9. As can be seen the overall effect is very similar to the more conventional decoding method of Figure 14.8. Comparison of the two systems shows that there is a small gain of the order of 2-3dB for most coding powers and SNRs. This is not a particularly large reward for the considerable increase in receiver complexity. This system would only be worth implementing if SNR or BER was at an absolute premium.

The reason for the gain being small is probably that although the equaliser is now forced into a better convergence, the previous system was able to remove most of the errors from an unconverged equaliser, reducing the benefit of the more complex system.

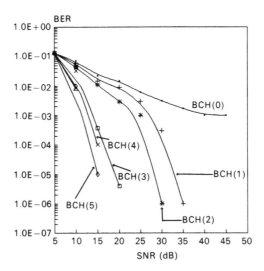

Figure 14.9: BER versus channel SNR performance of star 16-QAM at 8MBd using the LE, the OSWE and a range of iteratively decoded BCH FEC codes at 30mph and 1.9GHz

14.4   Diversity in the wideband system

In Chapter 11 it was shown that second order spatial diversity is beneficial in narrowband QAM. The selection or combination of the received signals from diversity receivers depends on their relative amplitudes. In the wideband system considered here, the scenario is different. Less benefit would be expected from space diversity because the time diversity inherent in a multipath environment is used to some extent in the equalisation process. If there are two channels with different impulse responses, then to implement switched diversity reception a decision must be made as to which channel has the most favourable response. This decision is governed by the equaliser's properties.

It is necessary to produce some figure of merit that relates to the likely number of errors for a given impulse response. With switched diversity the channel with the least likelihood of errors is chosen, and with maximal ratio combining the incoming channels are weighted by the likelihood of errors. In order to identify the types of impulse responses that are more likely to yield relatively low symbol error rates a series of simulations were performed using a channel whose impulse response has three coefficients but in contrast to Figure 14.1 the taps weights were now varied.

The magnitude of the strongest path is designated by a_0, that of the next strongest path by a_1 and that of the weakest path by a_2. The average power of the impulse response is arranged to be a constant, and the lowest error rate was achieved when there was a dominant path a_0, and a_1 was significantly larger than a_2. For the situation when two paths were approximately equal, fewer errors were incurred when the two smaller paths were equal compared to the two larger ones being equal. The highest error rate inflicted was when all the paths had the same magnitude.

Accordingly the diversity system was arranged to rate an impulse response according to the system parameter

$$r = ((a_0/a_1) + (a_0/a_2)) \cdot F + (a_1/a_2) \qquad (14.3)$$

where F is another system parameter which must exceed unity. The first term in r weighted by the factor F provides a measure of the dominance of the strongest path a_0, while the second unweighted term, (a_1/a_2) represents the dominance of a_1 over a_2. For different channels, the one having the largest r parameter will have the most favourably shaped impulse response, and if all impulse responses have the same average power, will give the lowest BER. In general, the impulse responses will have differing average powers and so the channel rating is modified to

$$R = a_0 r \qquad (14.4)$$

as r deals in ratios and is only concerned with the shape of the impulse response. Due to multiplying r by the dominant coefficient a_0 r is scaled appropriately. The BER was examined as the parameter F varied from 1 to 10, and was found to be relatively insensitive to the value selected.

Armed with an algorithm R to rate the quality of a channel's impulse response, second-order diversity simulations can be performed.

The two diversity channels had impulse responses with three coefficients each. All three coefficients had magnitudes and phases which conformed to independent Rayleigh fading statistics. The PRBS sounding sequence was transmitted over both channels for each block of data, and the channel impulse responses were estimated. The diversity branch whose impulse response had the larger R parameter was used in our switch diversity arrangements.

The variation of BER as a function of channel SNR is displayed in Figure 14.10 for this diversity system with a data rate of 8MBd, i.e., 32Mb/s. A bench-marker for the non-diversity condition is also shown. For a BER of 10^{-2} (no FEC is used here) the diversity yielded a reduction in SNR of approximately 6dB. For comparison the performance of the system which selects the incoming channel not by using R of Equation 14.4, but merely by selecting the impulse response with the strongest average power, i.e. rating the impulse responses on the basis of

$$\hat{R} = a_0^2 + a_1^2 + a_2^2 \qquad (14.5)$$

is shown.

The curves in Figure 14.10 show that despite the inherent diversity in the multipath signal which was exploited by the equaliser system of Figure 14.5, there were further significant gains to be made by introducing second-order spatial diversity. The method of selecting the impulse response using Equation 14.4 yielded the profile switch curve. This performed better than the conventional method of selecting the signal with the highest average power using $\hat{R}$ of Equation 14.5, the performance of which is labelled as the power switch curve in Figure 14.10.

14.5 Summary

At a transmission frequency of 1.9GHz, data at a rate of 8Msymbols/s, corresponding to 32Mbits/s, can be sent via star 16-level QAM over wideband dispersive channels at an integrity acceptable in many applications. In most instances a linear equaliser worked satisfactorily, but when the main component of the impulse response was

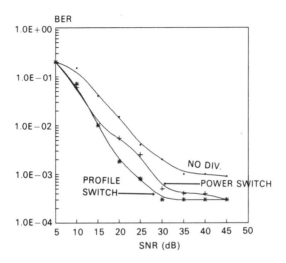

Figure 14.10: BER versus channel SNR performance of star
16-QAM at 8MBd using the LE, the OSWE
and a range of diversity combining techniques
at 30mph and 1.9GHz

in a deep fade it was advantageous to carry out a first pass equalisation with a non-optimal equaliser and then use the partially equalised
signal to prevent a DFE from failing catastrophically. When this system was used in an iterative fashion, considerable improvements in
BER were achieved. The system discussed incorporates three types
of equalisers in a concatenated arrangement with switching between
them as conditions in the fading channel change. Improvements in
BER of an order of magnitude over a linear equaliser system were
obtained for SNRs in excess of 15dB.

Second order spatial diversity gave about 5-7dB gain in terms of
channel SNR over an equivalent uncoded system using no diversity
providing that it was implemented in an intelligent way, leading to
a BER of 3×10^{-4} at a SNR of 30dB with no channel coding.

The use of channel coding provided very significant reductions
in BER. With an approximately 2/3 rate BCH code, BERs as low
as 1×10^{-5} were achieved for SNRs as low as 20dB, and when an

iterative channel decoding approach was adopted BERs of 1×10^{-6} were realised for the same coding power and SNR, but at the cost of a considerable increase in complexity.

In the next chapter we consider an alternative means of transmitting at high bit rates over mobile radio channels. This involves dividing the message to be transmitted into a number of streams and sending each of these streams simultaneously. It is known as orthogonal multiplexing.

Bibliography

[1] **R.Bultitude and G.Bedal**, "Propagation characteristics on microcellular urban mobile radio channels at 910MHz", *IEEE J-SAC* Vol 7 No 1 Jan 89 pp31-39.

[2] **R.Bultitude, S.Mahmoud and W.Sullivan**, "A comparison of indoor radio propagation characteristics at 910MHz and 1.75GHz", *ibid* pp20-30.

[3] **J.G.Proakis**, "Digital communications", McGraw-Hill 1983.

Chapter 15

Orthogonal Multiplex Systems

15.1 Introduction

In this chapter we examine Frequency Division Multiplexing (FDM), also referred to as Orthogonal Multiplexing (OMPX), as a means of dealing with the problems encountered when transmitting over a radio channel. The fundamental principle of orthogonal multiplexing originates from Chang [1], and over the years a number of researchers have investigated this technique [2]–[13]. Despite its conceptual elegance, until recently its deployment has been mostly limited to military applications due to implementational difficulties. However, it has recently been adopted as the new European digital audio broadcasting (DAB) standard, and this consumer electronics application underlines its significance as a broadcasting technique [14]–[18].

In the FDM scheme of Figure 15.1 the serial data stream of a traffic channel is passed through a serial-to-parallel convertor which splits the data into a number of parallel channels. The data in each channel are applied to a modulator, such that for N channels there are N modulators whose carrier frequencies are f_0, f_1, ...f_{N-1}. The difference between adjacent channels is Δf and the overall bandwidth W of the N modulated carriers is $N\Delta f$, as shown in Figure 15.2.

These N modulated carriers are then combined to give an FDM signal. We may view the serial-to-parallel convertor as applying

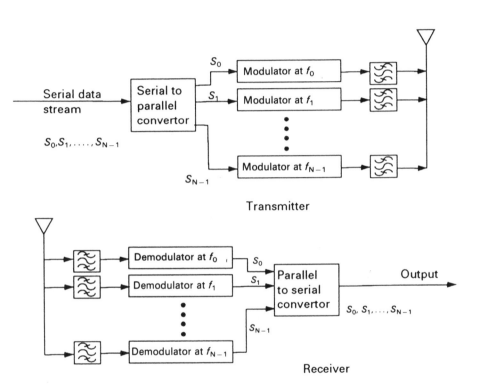

Figure 15.1: Basic FDM System

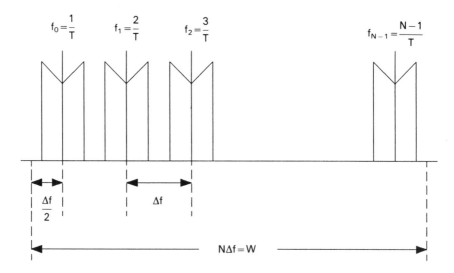

Figure 15.2: FDM frequency assignment

every Nth symbol to a modulator. This has the effect of interleaving the symbols into each modulator, e.g., symbols S_0, S_N, S_{2N},.... are applied to the modulator whose carrier frequency is f_1. At the receiver the received FDM signal is demultiplexed into N frequency bands, and the N modulated signals are demodulated. The baseband signals are then recombined using a parallel-to-serial convertor.

In the more conventional approach the traffic data is applied directly to the modulator operating with a carrier frequency at the centre of the transmission band $f_0 \ldots f_{N-1}$, ie at $(f_{N-1} + f_0)/2$, and the modulated signal occupies the entire bandwidth W. When the data is applied sequentially the effect of a deep fade in a mobile channel is to cause burst errors. Figure 15.3 shows the serial transmission of symbols S_0, S_1, ...S_{N-1}, while the solid shaded block indicates the position of the error burst which affects $k < N$ symbols. By contrast, during the N symbol period of the conventional serial system, each FDM modulator carries only one symbol, and the error burst causes severe signal degradation for the duration of k serial symbols. This degradation is shown cross-hatched. However, if the error burst is only a small fraction of the symbol period then each of the FDM symbols may only be slightly affected by the fade and they can still

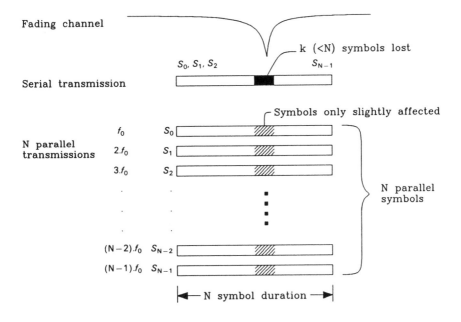

Figure 15.3: Effect of a fade on serial and parallel systems

be correctly demodulated. Thus while the serial system exhibits an error burst, no or few errors may occur using the FDM approach. A further advantage of FDM is that because the symbol period has been increased, the channel delay spread is a significantly shorter fraction of a symbol period than in the serial system, potentially rendering the system less sensitive to ISI than the conventional serial system.

A disadvantage of the FDM approach shown in Figure 15.1 is the increased complexity over the conventional system caused by employing N modulators and filters at the transmitter and N demodulators and filters at the receiver. This complexity can be reduced by the use of the discrete Fourier transform (DFT), typically implemented as a Fast Fourier Transform (FFT). This will be shown in a subsequent section.

15.2 Principles of QAM-FDM

The simplest version of the basic FDM system has N subbands, each separated from its neighbour by a sufficiently large guard band in order to prevent interference between signals in adjacent bands. However, the available spectrum can be used much more efficiently if the spectra of the individual subbands are allowed to overlap. By using coherent detection and orthogonal subband tones the original data can be correctly recovered.

In the system shown in Figure 15.4, the input serial data stream is rearranged into a sequence $\{d_n\}$ of N QAM symbols at baseband. Each serial QAM symbol is spaced by $\Delta t = 1/f_s$ where f_s is the serial signalling or symbol rate. At the nth symbol instant, the QAM symbol $d(n) = a(n) + jb(n)$ is represented by an inphase component $a(n)$ and a quadrature component $b(n)$. A block of N QAM symbols are applied to a serial-to-parallel convertor and the resulting inphase symbols $a(0)$, $a(1)$,...$a(N-1)$, and quadrature symbols $b(0)$, $b(1)$,...$b(N-1)$ are applied to N pairs of balanced modulators. The quadrature components $a(n)$ and $b(n)$, $n = 0, 1, ...N-1$, modulate the quadrature carriers $\cos w_n t$ and $\sin w_n t$, respectively. Notice that the signalling interval of the subbands in the parallel system is N times longer than that of the serial system giving $T = N \Delta t$, which corresponds to an N-times lower signalling rate. The subband carrier frequencies $w_n = 2\pi n f_0$ are spaced apart by $w_0 = 2\pi/T$.

The modulated carriers $a(n) \cos w_n t$ and $b(n) \sin w_n t$ when added together constitute a QAM signal, and as $n = 0, 1, ..N-1$ we have N QAM symbols at RF, where the nth QAM signal is given by:

$$X_n(t) = a(n) \cos w_n t + b(n) \sin w_n t \qquad (15.1)$$
$$= \gamma(n) \cos(w_n t + \psi_n)$$

where

$$\gamma(n) = \sqrt{a^2(n) + b^2(n)} \qquad (15.2)$$

and

$$\psi_n = \tan^{-1} \left(\frac{b(n)}{a(n)} \right) \qquad (15.3)$$
$$n = 0, 1, ...N-1.$$

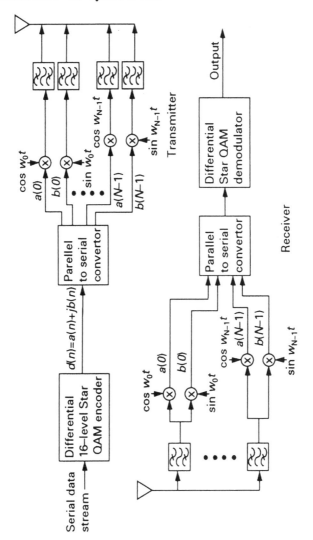

Figure 15.4: Detailed FDM System

By adding the outputs of each subchannel signal $X_n(t)$ whose carriers are offset by $\omega_0 = 2\pi/T$ we obtain the FDM/QAM signal

$$D(t) = \sum_{n=0}^{N-1} X_n(t). \tag{15.4}$$

This set of N FDM/QAM signals is transmitted over the mobile radio channel. At the receiver this FDM signal is demultiplexed using a bank of N filters to regenerate the N QAM signals. The QAM baseband signals $a(n)$ and $b(n)$ are recovered and turned into serial form $\{d_n\}$. Recovery of the data ensues using the QAM baseband demodulator and differential decoding.

In theory, such a system is capable of achieving the maximum transmission rate of $log_2 Q$ $bits/s/Hz$, where Q is the number of QAM levels. In practice, there is some spectral spillage due to adjacent frequency subbands which reduces this efficiency. Spectral spillage due to the subbands at the top and bottom of the overall frequency band requires a certain amount of guard space between adjacent users. Furthermore, spectral spillage between FDM subbands due to the imperfections of each of the subband filters requires that the subbands be spaced further apart than the theoretically required minimum amount, decreasing spectral efficiency. In order to obtain the highest efficiency, the block size should be kept high and the subband filters made to meet stringent specifications.

One of the most attractive features of this scheme is that the bandwidth of the subchannels is very narrow when compared to the communications channel's coherence bandwidth. Therefore, flat-fading narrowband propagation conditions apply. The subchannel modems can use almost any modulation scheme, and QAM is an attractive choice in some situations.

15.3 Modulation by Discrete Fourier Transform

A fundamental problem associated with the FDM scheme described is that in order to achieve high resilience against fades in the channels we consider, the block size, N, has to be of the order of 100, requiring a large number of subchannel modems. Fortunately, it can be shown mathematically that taking the discrete Fourier transform (DFT) of the original block of N QAM symbols and then transmitting the DFT coefficients serially is exactly equivalent to the operations required by the FDM transmitter of Figure 15.4. Substantial hardware simplifications can be made with FDM transmissions if the bank of subchannel modulators/demodulators is implemented using the computationally efficient pair of inverse fast Fourier transform and fast Fourier transform (IFFT/FFT).

The modulated signal $m(t)$ is given by

$$m(t) = \Re\left\{b(t)e^{j2\pi f_0 t}\right\}, \tag{15.5}$$

where $b(t)$ is the equivalent baseband information signal and f_0 is the carrier frequency, as introduced in Equations 2.6, 2.9 and 2.10 in Chapter 2. Using the rectangular full-response modulation elements $m_T(t - kT) = rect\frac{(t-kT)}{T}$ "weighted" by the complex QAM information symbols $X(k) = I(k) + jQ(k)$ to be transmitted, where $I(k)$ and $Q(k)$ are the quadrature components, the equivalent baseband information signal is given by:

$$b(t) = \sum_{k=-\infty}^{\infty} X(k)m_T(t - kT), \tag{15.6}$$

where k is the signalling interval index and T is its duration. On substituting Equation 15.6 into Equation 15.5 we have:

$$m(t) = \Re\left\{\sum_{k=-\infty}^{\infty} X(k)m_T(t - kT)e^{j2\pi f_0 t}\right\}. \tag{15.7}$$

Without loss of generality let us consider the signalling interval $k = 0$:

$$m_0(t) = m(t)rect\frac{t}{T}, \tag{15.8}$$

where adding the modulated signals of the subchannel modulators yields

$$m_0(t) = \sum_{n=0}^{N-1} m_{0n}(t). \tag{15.9}$$

Observe that the stream of complex baseband symbols $X(k)$ to

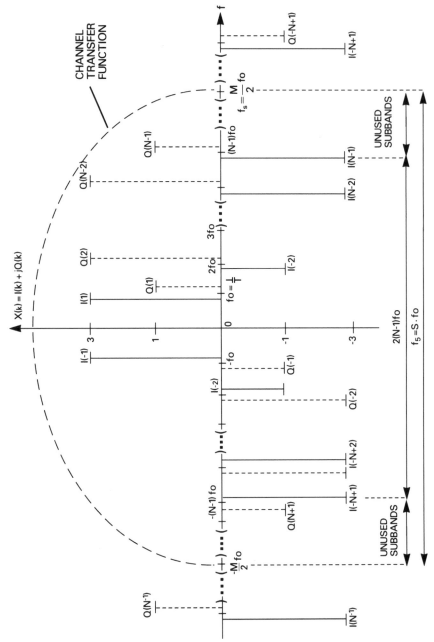

Figure 15.5: Conjugate complex symmetric square 16-QAM transmitted sequence $X(k) = I(k) + jQ(k)$

be transmitted can be described both in terms of inphase $I(k)$ and quadrature phase $Q(k)$ components, as well as by magnitude and phase. In case of a square-shaped constellation which was used in Chapter 10 $X(k) = I(k) + jQ(k)$ might be a more convenient formalism, while for the star-QAM constellation introduced in Chapter 11 $X(k) = |X(k)|e^{j\Phi(k)}$ appears to be more attractive.

If $X_n = X_{n,k=0}$ is the complex baseband QAM symbol to be transmitted via subchannel n in signalling interval $k = 0$, then

$$m_0(t) = \begin{cases} \sum_{n=0}^{N-1} \Re\left\{X_{n,0}e^{j2\pi f_{0,n}t}\right\} & \text{for } |t| < \frac{T}{2}, \\ 0 & \text{otherwise.} \end{cases} \qquad (15.10)$$

Bearing in mind that $m_0(t)$ is confined to the interval $|t| < \frac{T}{2}$ we drop the sampling interval index $k = 0$ and simplify our formalism to

$$m_0(t) = \sum_{n=0}^{N-1} \Re\left\{X_n e^{j2\pi f_{0n}t}\right\}. \qquad (15.11)$$

When computing the $\Re$ part using the complex conjugate we have:

$$\begin{aligned} m_0(t) &= \sum_{n=0}^{N-1} \frac{1}{2}\left\{X_n e^{j2\pi f_{0n}t} + X_n^* e^{-j2\pi f_{0n}t}\right\} \\ &= \sum_{n=-(N-1)}^{N-1} \frac{1}{2}X_n e^{j2\pi f_{0n}t}, \end{aligned} \qquad (15.12)$$

where for $n = 0 \ldots N - 1$ we have:

$$X_{-n} = X_n^*, \quad X_0 = 0, \quad f_{0(-n)} = -f_{0n}, \quad f_{00} = 0.$$

This conjugate complex symmetric sequence is shown in Figure 15.5 in case of the square 16-QAM constellation of Figure 3.3, where both the I and Q components can assume values of ± 1 and ± 3.

We streamline our formalism in Equation 15.12 by introducing the Fourier coefficients F_n given by

$$F_n = \begin{cases} \frac{1}{2}X_n & if & 1 \le n \le N - 1 \\ \frac{1}{2}X_n^* & if & -(N-1) \le n \le -1 \\ 0 & if & n = 0 \end{cases} \qquad (15.13)$$

emphasising that the Fourier coefficients of a real signal are conjugate
complex symmetric. Then Equation 15.12 can be rewritten as:

$$m_0(t) = \sum_{n=-(N-1)}^{N-1} F_n \cdot e^{j2\pi f_{0n}t}. \tag{15.14}$$

Observe that Equation 15.14 already bears close resemblance to the
DFT. Assuming that the subchannel carriers take values of $f_{0n} = nf_0$, $n = 0 \ldots N - 1$, where again $f_0 = 1/T$ represents the subcarrier spacing chosen to be the reciprocal of the subchannel signalling interval, then the total one-sided bandwidth is $B = (N - 1)f_0$.

So far the subchannel modulated signals $m_{0n}(t)$ have been assumed
to be continuous functions of time within the parallel signalling interval $k = 0$. In order to assist sampled, time-discrete processing by the
DFT within the signalling interval $k = 0$ we introduce the discretised time $t = i\Delta t$, where $\Delta t = 1/f_s$ is the reciprocal of the sampling
frequency f_s which must be chosen in accordance with Nyquist's
sampling theorem to adequately represent $m_0(t)$. Recall furthermore from the previous Section that $\Delta t = 1/f_s$ is the original serial
QAM symbol spacing and f_s is the serial QAM symbol rate. Then
we have:

$$m_0(i\Delta t) = \sum_{n=-(N-1)}^{N-1} F_n e^{j2\pi n f_0 i\Delta t}. \tag{15.15}$$

The Nyquist-criterion is met if

$$f_s > 2(N - 1)f_0, \tag{15.16}$$

where for practical reasons $f_s = M f_0$ is assumed, implying that the
sampling frequency f_s is an integer multiple of the subcarrier spacing f_0, with $M > 2(N - 1)$ being a positive integer, implying also
that $f_s = 1/\Delta t = M f_0$, i.e., $f_0 \Delta t = 1/M$. Again, these frequencies
are portrayed in Figure 15.5. Bearing in mind that the spectrum
of a sampled signal repeats itself at multiples of the sampling frequency f_s with a periodicity of $M = f_s/f_0$ samples, and exploiting
the conjugate complex symmetry of the spectrum, for the Fourier
coefficients F_n we have:

$$F_n = \begin{cases} F_{n-M} = F_{M-n}^* & if \ (\frac{M}{2} + 1) \le n \le M - 1 \\ 0 & if \ N - 1 < n \le \frac{M}{2}. \end{cases} \tag{15.17}$$

Observe that the frequency region $(N-1)f_0 < f_n \leq \frac{M}{2}f_0$ represents the typical unused transition band of the communications channel, where it exhibits significant amplitude and group-delay distortion as suggested by Figure 15.5. However, in the narrow subbands the originally wide-band frequency selective fading channel can be rendered flat upon using a high number of subchannels.

The set of QAM symbols can be interpreted as a spectral domain sequence, which due to its conjugate complex symmetricity will have a real IDFT pair in the time domain, representing the real modulated signal, which can be written as:

$$m_0(i\Delta t) = \sum_{n=0}^{M-1} F_n e^{j\frac{2\pi}{M}ni}, \quad i = 0\ldots M-1. \tag{15.18}$$

This is the standard IDFT that can be computed by the IFFT if the transform-length M is an integer power of two. The rectangular modulation elements $m_T(t) = rect\frac{t}{T}$ introduced in Equation 15.6 have an infinite bandwidth requirement since in effect they rectangularly window the set of orthogonal basis functions constituted by the carriers $rect\frac{t}{T} \cdot \cos w_{0l}t$ and $rect\frac{t}{T} \cdot \sin w_{0l}t$. It is possible to use a time-domain raised cosine pulse instead of the $rect\frac{t}{T}$ function [6], but this will impose further impairments on the time-domain modulated signal which is also exposed to the hostile communications channel. These problems will be briefly revisited in Section 15.10.

Observe that the representation of $m_0(t)$ by its $\Delta t = 1/f_s$-spaced samples is only correct if $m_0(t)$ is assumed to be periodic and bandlimited to $2(N-1)f_0$. This is equivalent to saying that $m_0(t)$ can only have a bandlimited frequency domain representation, if in time domain it expands from $-\infty$ to ∞. Due to sampling at a rate of $f_s = 1/\Delta t$ the spectral lobes become periodic at the multiples of f_s, but if the Nyquist sampling theorem is observed, no aliasing occurs. In order to fulfil these requirements, the modulating signal $m_0(t)$ derived by IFFT from the conjugate complex symmetric baseband information signal X_l has to be quasi-periodically extended before transmission via the channel at least for the duration of the channel's memory. The effects of bandlimited transmission media will be discussed in the following section.

15.4   Transmission via Bandlimited Channels

The DFT/IDFT operations assume that the input signal is periodic in both time and frequency domain with a periodicity of M samples. If the modulated sample sequence of Equation 15.18 is periodically repeated and transmitted via the low pass filter (LPF) preceding the channel, the channel is excited with a continuous, periodic signal. However, in order not to waste precious transmission time and hence channel capacity we would like to transmit only one period of $m_0(t)$ constituted by M samples. Assuming a LPF with a cut-off frequency of $f_c = 1/2\Delta t = f_s/2$ and transmitting only one period of $m_0(i\Delta t)$ the channel's input signal becomes:

$$
\begin{aligned}
m_{0,LPF}(t) &= m_0(i\Delta t) * \frac{1}{\Delta t}\frac{\sin(\pi t/\Delta t)}{\pi t/\Delta t} \\
&= m_0(i\Delta t) * \frac{1}{\Delta t}sinc\frac{\pi t}{\Delta t},
\end{aligned}
\tag{15.19}
$$

where the LPF's impulse response is given by the *sinc* function and hence $m_{0,LPF}(t)$ has an infinite time-domain duration. One period of the periodic modulated signal $m_{0,p}(i\Delta t)$, is given by

$$
m_0(i\Delta t) = m_{0,p}(i\Delta t)rect\frac{t}{T}.
\tag{15.20}
$$

The convolution in Equation 15.19 can be written as:

$$
m_{0,LPF}(t) = \sum_{i=0}^{M-1} m_0(i\Delta t)\frac{1}{\Delta t}sinc\frac{\pi(t-i\Delta t)}{\Delta t}.
\tag{15.21}
$$

In spectral domain this is equivalent to writing

$$
M_{0,LPF}(f) = M_0(f)rect\frac{f}{f_c},
\tag{15.22}
$$

where $M_0(f) = FFT\{m_0(i\Delta t)\}$ and $H_{LPF}(f) = rect\frac{f}{f_c}$ is the LPF's frequency domain transfer function. Transforming Equation 15.20 into the frequency domain yields:

$$
\begin{aligned}
M_0(f) &= FFT\{m_{0,p}(i\Delta t)rect\frac{t}{T}\} \\
&= M_{0,p}(f) * \frac{1}{f_0}sinc\frac{\pi f}{f_0},
\end{aligned}
\tag{15.23}
$$

where $M_{0,p}(f)$ is the frequency domain representation of $m_{0,p}(i\Delta t)$, which is convolved with the Fourier transform of the $rect\frac{t}{T}$ function. Now $M_0(f)$ of Equation 15.23 is low pass filtered according to Equation 15.22, giving:

$$M_{0,LPF}(f) = M_0(f)rect\frac{f}{f_c}$$
$$= \left[M_{0,p}(f) * \frac{1}{f_0}sinc\frac{\pi f}{f_0}\right] rect\frac{f}{f_c}. \quad (15.24)$$

So the effect of the time domain truncation of the periodic modulated signal $m_{0,p}(i\Delta t)$ to a single period as in Equation 15.20 manifests itself in frequency domain as the convolution of Equation 15.23, generating the infinite bandwidth signal $M_0(f)$. When $M_0(f)$ is LP filtered according to Equation 15.24, it becomes band limited to f_c, and its Fourier transform pair $m_{0,LPF}(t)$ in Equation 15.19 has an infinite time domain support due to the convolution with $sinc(\pi t/\Delta t)$. This phenomenon results in interference due to time-domain overlapping between consecutive transmission blocks, which can be mitigated by quasi-periodically extending $m_0(i\Delta t)$ for the duration of the memory of the channel before transmission. At the receiver only the un-impaired central section is used for signal detection.

In order to portray a practical OMPX scheme and to aid the exposition of this and the previous Section, in Figure 15.6 we plotted a few characteristic signals. Figure 15.6a shows the transmitted spectrum using $M = 128$ and rectangular 16-QAM having $I, Q = \pm 1; \pm 3$.

In contrast to Figure 15.5, where the I and Q components were portrayed next to each other in order to emphasise that they belong to the same frequency, here the I and Q components associated with the same frequency are plotted with the same spacing as adjacent subbands. In Figure 15.6a there are 64 legitimate frequencies between 0 and 4 kHz, corresponding to 128 lines. Observe however that for frequencies between 0-300 HZ and 3.4-4.0 kHz we have allocated no QAM symbols. This is because this signal was transmitted after conjugate complex extension and IFFT over the M1020 CCITT telephone channel simulator, which has a high attenuation in these frequency slots. The real modulated signal after IFFT is plotted in Figure 15.6b, which is constituted by 128 real samples. At the

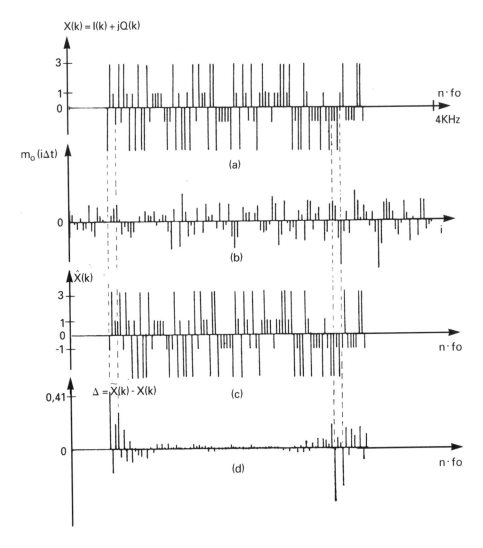

Figure 15.6: Characteristic OMPX signals for $M = 128$ and 16-QAM

receiver this signal is demodulated by FFT in order to derive the received signal $\tilde{X}(k)$, which is then subjected to hard decision delivering the sequence $\hat{X}(k)$ seen in Figure 15.6c. Lastly, Figure 15.6d portrays the error signal $\Delta(k) = X(k) - \tilde{X}(k)$, where large errors can be observed towards the transmission band edges due to the M1020 channel's attenuation. The interpretation of these characteristic signals will be further augmented in Section 15.6, as further details of the OMPX system are unravelled.

15.5   Generalised Nyquist Criterion

Using frequency division or orthogonal multiplexing (OMPX) two different sources of interferences can be identified [20]–[24]. Inter-symbol interference (ISI) is defined as the cross-talk between signals within the same subchannel of consecutive FFT-frames, which are separated in time by the signalling interval T. Inter-channel interference (ICI) is the cross-talk between adjacent subchannels or frequency slots of the same FFT-frame. Since the effects of these interference sources and their mitigation methods are similar, it is convenient to introduce the term multi-dimensional interference (MDI) [22].

In order to describe MDI we assume the linear system model depicted in Figure 15.7, which is the concatenation of the M-subchannel multiplex transmission medium to the M-subchannel receiver filter-bank. The channel's impulse response between its input j and output i is denoted by $h_{ij}(t)$, while that of the receiver filter-bank is $g_{ni}(t)$. With the assumption of this linear system model the output signal of the receiver filter is the superposition of the system responses due to all input signals $1 \ldots M$. Our objective is to optimise the linear receiver in order to minimise the effects of AWGN and MDI, which will reduce the BER of the receiver.

Assuming a subchannel noise spectral density of N_i and receiver filter transfer functions of $G_{ni}(f)$ between the input i and output n, the noise variance at output n becomes:

$$\sigma_n{}^2 = \sum_{i=1}^{M} N_i \int_0^\infty G_{ni}^2(f) df, \qquad (15.25)$$

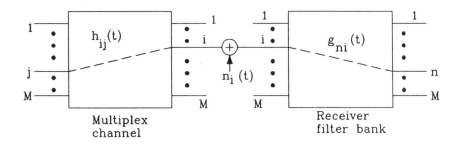

Figure 15.7: Multidimensional   interference   model [21]©IEEE, 1975, Van Etten

which can also be expressed in terms of $g_{ni}(t)$ using Parseval's theorem:

$$\sigma_n^2 = \sum_{i=1}^{M} N_i \int_0^\infty g_{ni}^2(\tau)d\tau. \tag{15.26}$$

Following the approaches in [22]–[24] the noise variance can be minimised as a function of the receiver filter impulse response $g_{ni}(t)$. Supposing that the subchannel input signals a_j $j = 1\ldots M$ can take any value from the mutually independent, equiprobable set of L-ary alphabet, then the channel's input vector in the kth signalling interval is given by:

$$u^T(k) = [a_1^k, a_2^k, \ldots, a_M^k]. \tag{15.27}$$

Observe that the number of possible input vectors is L^M.

From Figure 15.7 we can see that the system's response at the receiver output can be computed by the help of the convolution of the channel and receiver filter impulse responses. The input signal of subchannel j generates an output at every receiver filter input $i = 1\ldots M$, each of which gives rise to a response at the nth receiver filter output. In order to derive the nth output, the contributions must be summed first fixing the jth subchannel input over the receiver filter input index i. Then, since the input signal vector $u^T(k)$ excites all subchannel inputs $j = 1 \ldots M$, summing over the index j gives the output signal of the nth receiver filter, as seen below:

$$s_n{}^k(t) = \sum_{j=1}^{M} a_j{}^k \sum_{i=1}^{M} \int_0^\infty g_{ni}(\tau)h_{ij}(t - \tau)d\tau. \qquad (15.28)$$

At the received sampling instants $(t_s + lT)$ we have

$$s_n{}^k(t_s + lT) = \sum_{j=1}^{M} a_j{}^k \sum_{i=1}^{M} \int_0^\infty g_{ni}(\tau)h_{ij}(t_s + lT - \tau)d\tau. \qquad (15.29)$$

The optimisation problem now is to find the system transfer functions, which minimise the noise variance at the output of the nth receiver filter under the constraint of constant $s_n{}^k(t_s + lT)$, for all l and k. Using the technique of variational calculus, the following functional must be minimised [21]:

$$F_n = \sigma_n^2 - 2\sum_{k=1}^{LM}\sum_{l} \lambda_{nkl} s_n{}^k(t_s + lT), \qquad (15.30)$$

where λ_{nkl} is the so-called Lagrange multiplier. On substituting Equation 15.26 and 15.29 in Equation 15.30 we have:

$$\begin{aligned} F_n &= \sum_{i=1}^{M} N_i \int_0^\infty g_{ni}{}^2(\tau)d\tau \\ &\quad - 2\sum_{k=1}^{LM}\sum_{l} \lambda_{nkl} \sum_{j=1}^{M} a_j{}^k \sum_{i=1}^{M} \int_0^\infty g_{ni}(\tau)h_{ij}(t_s + lT - \tau)d\tau. \end{aligned} \qquad (15.31)$$

The minimisation of F_n in Equation 15.31 yields [21]:

$$g_{ni}(t) = \frac{1}{N_i}\sum_{k=1}^{LM}\sum_{l} \lambda_{nkl} \sum_{j=1}^{M} a_j{}^k h_{ij}(t_s + lT - t). \qquad (15.32)$$

Assuming identical noise spectral density in all subchannels, i.e., that $N_i = N$ for all i and introducing the short-hand given below:

$$c_{njl} = \frac{1}{N}\sum_{k=1}^{LM} a_j{}^k \lambda_{nkl}, \qquad (15.33)$$

then Equation 15.32 can be simplified to:

$$g_{ni}(t) = \sum_{j=1}^{M} \sum_{l} c_{njl} h_{ij}(t_s + lT - t). \qquad (15.34)$$

As seen from Equation 15.34, the set of optimum receiver filters $g_{ni}(t)$ depends on the subchannel impulse responses $h_{ij}(t)$. The receiver filter impulse responses $g_{ni}(t)$ from the ith filter input to all filter outputs have to be matched to the responses $h_{ij}(t)$ from all subchannel inputs $j = 1 \ldots M$ to the ith subchannel output or received filter input, as detailed in Subsection 4.5.2.

In order to derive the matched receiver filter response $g_{ni}(t)$ according to Equation 15.34, we have to superimpose the responses of all receiver filters that are matched to the OMPX subchannel outputs due to the jth OMPX subchannel input. The summation over the index l weighted by the coefficients c_{njl} in Equation 15.34 represents the ISI due to the T-spaced h_{ij} contributions from previous sampling instants.

In order to augment our exposition of Equation 15.34 and the MDI-minimisation concept a simple three-channel receiver ($M = 3$) is depicted in Figure 15.8 using $t_s = 0$, where at each receiver filter input i, $i = 1 \ldots 3$ a bank of filters h_{ij}, $j = 1 \ldots 3$ is matched to the OMPX subchannel responses h_{ij}, $j = 1 \ldots 3$ due to the individual inputs. Now all the matched filter output signals due to the same subchannel input j, $j = 1 \ldots 3$ are added up to generate the signals a, b and c, respectively, seen in Figure 15.8. These contributions are delayed by lT, $l = 0, 1, \ldots R$ and weighted by the coefficients c_{njl}, $n = 1 \ldots 3$, $j = 1 \ldots 3$, $l = 1, 2, \ldots R$, as in conventional R^{th}-order FIR transversal filters, before summing them over $j = 1 \ldots 3$ and $l = 1, 2, \ldots R$ in order to generate the nth receiver filter output. The set of filter coefficients c_{njl} must be appropriately chosen to satisfy the optimisation criterion.

According to Van Etten [21] there is no analytical solution for the set c_{njl} under the optimisation constraint of minimum error probability, instead one has to opt for using the numeric steepest descent algorithm [25]. However, he proposes an approach to determine the optimum coefficients c_{njl} under the constraint of minimum MDI and demonstrates the effects of optimum coefficients with the aid of the

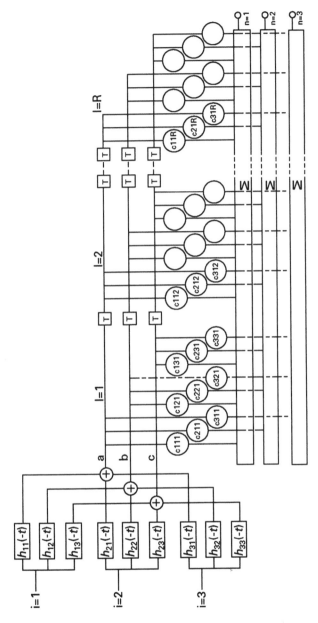

Figure 15.8: Three-Channel Matched OMPX Receiver with Impulse Responses g_{ni} [21]©IEEE, 1975, Van Etten

eye-pattern. He also shows that the error probability achieved under the minimum MDI constraint is similar to that achieved under the assumption of minimum error probability.

Using our general MDI model in Figure 15.7 the overall impulse response at the sampling instant (lT) between the jth OMPX subchannel input and the nth receiver filter output can be denoted by $f_{nj}(lT)$, $n, j = 1 \dots M$ or in matrix form:

$$F_l = \begin{bmatrix} f_{11}(lT) & f_{12}(lT) & \dots & f_{1M}(lT) \\ f_{21}(lT) & f_{22}(lT) & \dots & f_{2M}(lT) \\ \vdots & & & \\ f_{M1}(lT) & f_{M2}(lT) & \dots & f_{MM}(lT) \end{bmatrix}. \tag{15.35}$$

The total accumulated MDI at the nth receiver filter output due to both ISI and ICI can be defined as [21]:

$$MDI_n = \frac{|f_{nn}(0)| - \sum_l \sum_{i=1}^{M} |f_{ni}(l)|}{f_{nn}(0)}. \tag{15.36}$$

It is quite plausible that the condition of MDI-free transmission is met if there is no cross-talk amongst the subchannels, i.e., the matrix of Equation 15.35 is the diagonal identity matrix for any arbitrary sampling instant (lT). In formal terms this means that for $n, j = 1, 2, \dots M$, $l = 0, \pm 1, \pm 2, \dots \pm \infty$ the generalised Nyquist criterion proposed by Schnidman [20] given below must be satisfied:

$$\sum_l f_{nj}(lT) = \begin{cases} 1 & \text{if } n = j \\ 0 & \text{otherwise.} \end{cases} \tag{15.37}$$

If Equation 15.37 is satisfied, the MDI term in Equation 15.36 becomes zero and the generalised Nyquist criterion can be fulfilled by the appropriate choice of the coefficients c_{njl}.

Quite clearly, the generalised Nyquist criterion in Equation 15.37 requires not only that the conventional Nyquist criterion shall be met, i.e., $f_{nn}(lT) = \delta_l$, $l = 0, 1, \dots \infty$, where δ_l is the Kronecker delta, in order to render the ISI from other signalling intervals zero. It also requires that all the other $M(M-1)$ number of subchannels with their matched receiver filters shall have a zero crossing in their impulse responses, i.e. for $n, j = 1, 2, \dots M$ and $l = 0, \pm 1, \dots \pm \infty$

$$F_{nj}(lT) = \delta_{nj}\delta_l \tag{15.38}$$

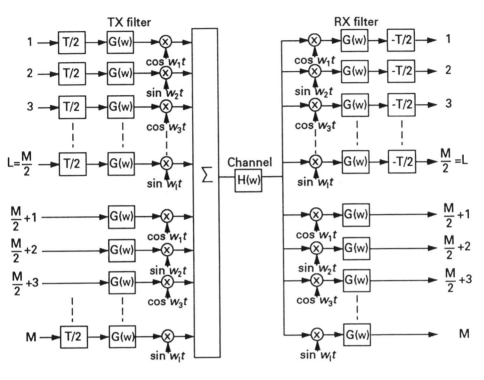

Figure 15.9: Filter-Bank Implementation of the FDM Modem [8]©IEEE, 1981, Hirosaki

shall be satisfied, where

$$\delta_{nj} = \begin{cases} 1 & \text{if } n = j \\ 0 & \text{otherwise.} \end{cases} \tag{15.39}$$

Therefore, the generalised Nyquist criterion requires the equivalent folded-in baseband transfer characteristic introduced in Chapter 4 to be an ideal low-pass characteristic for $n = j$ and zero otherwise.

15.6 OMPX Modem Implementations

A specific OMPX modem implementation was proposed by Hirosaki in reference [8] and is shown in Figure 15.9. This implementation is based on staggered QAM (SQAM) or offset QAM (OQAM), where the quadrature components are delayed by half a signalling interval with respect to each other in order to reduce the signal envelope fluctuation (see Chapter 4). The system is constituted by M synchronised baseband channels operating with a Baud-rate of $f_0 = 1/T$. The baseband modulating signals of subchannels i and $(i+M/2)$ are amplitude modulated onto the carriers $f_i = [f_0 + (i-1)f_0]$, $i = 1 \ldots M/2$, with the carrier suppressed. This implies that the subchannels are spaced according to the Baud-rate of $f_0 = 1/T$. Then the sum of the subchannel signals i and $(i+M/2)$, $i = 1 \ldots M/2$ form the ith SQAM subchannel, where the inphase and quadrature-phase modulating signals are shifted by $T/2$ with respect to each other. The transmit and receive filters $G(\omega)$ are identical square-root raised-cosine Nyquist filters and an equaliser implementation is also proposed in [8].

The FFT-based QAM/FDM modem's schematic diagram is shown in Figure 15.10. The bits provided by the source are serial/parallel converted in order to form the n-level Gray coded symbols, M of which are collected in TX buffer 1, while the contents of TX buffer 2 are being transformed by the IFFT in order to form the time-domain modulated signal. Observe that the conjugate-complex symmetric extension takes place in the IFFT block. The digital-to-analogue (D-A) converted, low-pass filtered modulated signal is then transmitted via the channel and its received samples are collected in RX buffer 1, while the contents of RX buffer 2 are being transformed to derive the demodulated signal. The twin buffers are alternately filled with data to allow for the finite FFT demodulation time. Before the data is Gray coded and passed to the data sink, it is equalised by a low complexity method to be outlined in Section 15.9 and then hard decisions are performed.

Exposition is further aided by Figure 15.11 where characteristic waveforms at points (1), (2) and (3) of Figure 15.10 are seen in parts (a), (b) and (c), respectively, of Figure 15.11. According to the phasor diagram of the star 16-QAM constellation shown in Figure 11.1 there are four positive and four negative real and imaginary values besides zero in the transmitted "spectrum" depicted in Figure 15.11(a). This signal is complex-conjugate symmetrically extended in the negative frequency domain before IFFT ensues in order

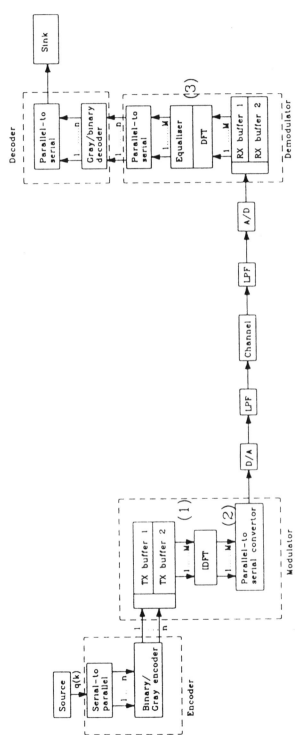

Figure 15.10: FFT based QAM modem

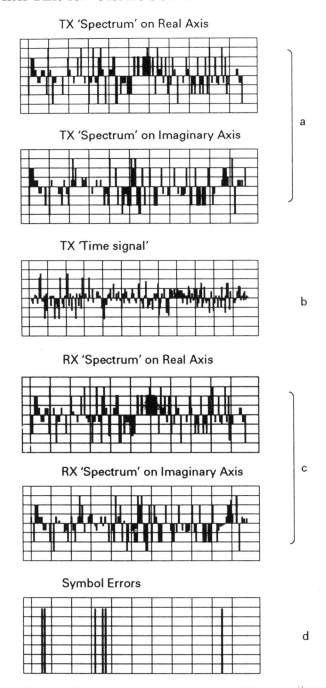

Figure 15.11: Characteristic waveforms within the FFT modem

to generate the real time-domain signal of Figure 15.11(b), which is transmitted and eventually corrupted by fading. The real and imaginary received spectra are different from the transmitted spectra and are shown in Figure 15.11(c). Rigorous comparison shows up the errors indicated in Figure 15.11(d). The corresponding square 16-QAM signals were plotted in Figure 15.6.

15.7 Reducing MDI by Block Extension

As we have seen in Section 15.4, the response of the low-pass filtered OMPX channels to a block of modulated signal is theoretically infinite. In Section 15.5 we introduced the generalised Nyquist criterion, which allowed infinite-length system responses, as long as their periodic zero-crossings yielded no MDI. If however the zero-crossings or the sampling instants fluctuate, the MDI soon becomes prohibitively high.

An alternative method of combating MDI is to transmit quasi-periodically extended time domain blocks after modulation by IFFT [9]. The length of the added quasi-periodic extension depends on the memory-length of the channel, in other words, on the length of the transient response of the channel to the quasi-periodic excitation constituted by the modulated signal. The method is best explained with reference to Figure 15.12. Every block of length-T modulated signal-segment is quasi-periodically extended by a length of T_T transient duration simply repeating N_T samples of the useful information block. Then the total sequence length becomes $(M + N_T)$ samples, corresponding to a duration of $(T + T_T)$. Trailing and leading samples of this extended block are corrupted by the channel's transient response, hence the receiver is instructed to ignore the first j number of samples of the received block and also disregard $(M + N_T - j)$ trailing samples. Only the central M number of samples are demodulated by FFT at the receiver, which are essentially unaffected by the channel's transient response, as seen in Figure 15.12.

The number of extension samples N_T required depends on the length of the channel's transient response and the number of modulation levels. If the number of modulation levels is high, the max-

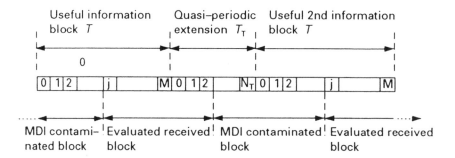

Figure 15.12: Reducing MDI by quasi-periodic block extension

imum acceptable MDI due to channel transients must be kept low in order to maintain sufficient noise margins before the data is corrupted. This then requires a longer quasi-periodic extension, i.e., N_T must be also higher. It must also be appreciated that this MDI-corrupted extension actually wastes channel capacity as well as transmitted power. However, if the useful information blocks are long, i.e., $M \geq 128$, the extension length can be kept as low as 10 % of the useful information block-length.

15.8 Reducing MDI by Compensation[9]

15.8.1 Transient System Analysis

Following Kolb's [9] and Schüssler's [10] approach, we can describe the OMPX transmission system by using input and output vectors $u(k)$ and $y(k)$, respectively, that are related by

$$y(k) = Su(k), \qquad (15.40)$$

where the convolution matrix S is given by [29]:

$$S = \begin{bmatrix} h_0 & 0 & \dots & \dots & 0 \\ h_1 & h_0 & \dots & \dots & 0 \\ h_2 & h_1 & h_0 & \dots & 0 \\ \vdots & \vdots & \vdots & & \vdots \end{bmatrix}. \qquad (15.41)$$

Due to causality the vectors $u(k)$ and $y(k)$ are of infinite length for positive sample indices only. Let us assume furthermore that the input vector $u(k)$ represents $L \geq 2$ periods of an M-sample periodic sequence and that the channel's impulse response is shorter than M samples. Then, for example, for $L = 3$ periods and a channel impulse response length of $n = M - 1$ samples the convolution in Equation 15.40 can be written as:

$$\begin{bmatrix} y_1 \\ y_2 \\ y_3 \\ y_4 \end{bmatrix} = \begin{bmatrix} S_0 & 0 & 0 \\ S_1 & S_0 & 0 \\ 0 & S_1 & S_0 \\ 0 & 0 & S_1 \end{bmatrix} \begin{bmatrix} u \\ u \\ u \end{bmatrix}, \tag{15.42}$$

where

$$S_0 = \begin{bmatrix} h_0 & 0 & \cdots & \cdots & 0 \\ h_1 & h_0 & \cdots & \cdots & 0 \\ h_2 & h_1 & h_0 & \cdots & 0 \\ \vdots & \vdots & \vdots & & \vdots \\ h_n & h_{n-1} & h_{n-2} & \cdots & h_0 \end{bmatrix} \tag{15.43}$$

and

$$S_1 = \begin{bmatrix} 0 & h_n & h_{n-1} & \cdots & h_1 \\ 0 & 0 & h_n & \cdots & h_2 \\ \vdots & \vdots & \vdots & & \vdots \\ 0 & 0 & 0 & \cdots & h_n \\ 0 & 0 & 0 & \cdots & 0 \end{bmatrix}. \tag{15.44}$$

Upon exciting our transmission channel with a periodic signal, its response is constituted by a transient response $y_{in}(k)$ plus a stationary periodic response $y_{st}(k)$. The stationary response has the periodicity M of the excitation, while the channel's transient response dies down after $n = M - 1$ samples.

The system's response during the first period of M samples is then given by:

$$\begin{aligned} y_1 &= y_{in} + y_{st} = S_0 u \tag{15.45} \\ &= [h_0 u_0; (h_1 u_0 + h_0 u_1); (h_2 u_0 + h_1 u_1 + h_0 u_2); \\ &\quad \ldots; (h_n u_0 + h_{n-1} u_1 + h_{n-2} u_2 + \ldots + h_0 u_n)]^T, \end{aligned}$$

where we also exploited Equation 15.42 and $[\ ]^T$ means the transpose of $[\ ]$. During the second cycle of the excitation the transient does not affect the system's response since $u < M$, and hence by the help of Equation 15.42 we get:

$$
\begin{aligned}
y_2 &= y_{st} = [S_1 S_0][uu]^T \\
&= [S_1 + S_0]u = H u,
\end{aligned} \tag{15.46}
$$

where the matrix $H = [S_1 + S_0]$ is computed from Equations 15.43 and 15.44 as follows:

$$
H = S_1 + S_0 = \begin{bmatrix}
h_0 & h_n & h_{n-1} & \cdots & h_1 \\
h_1 & h_0 & h_n & \cdots & h_2 \\
\vdots & & & & \\
h_n & h_{n-1} & h_{n-2} & \cdots & h_0
\end{bmatrix}. \tag{15.47}
$$

Then the system's response for the second cycle from Equation 15.46 can be written as:

$$
y_2 = \begin{bmatrix}
h_0 u_0 + h_n u_1 + \ldots + h_1 u_n \\
h_1 u_0 + h_0 u_1 + \ldots + h_2 u_n \\
\vdots \\
h_n u_0 + h_{n-1} u_1 + \ldots + h_0 u_n
\end{bmatrix}. \tag{15.48}
$$

Similarly, the system's response during the third period of the excitation is unaffected by transients, and hence given by:

$$
y_3 = H u. \tag{15.49}
$$

The switch-off transient $y_4 = y_{out}$ of the system describes the output signal after the excitation died down. From Equation 15.42 we get:

$$
\begin{aligned}
y_{out} = y_4 &= S_1 u = S_1 u + S_0 u - S_0 u \\
&= (S_1 + S_0)u - S_0 u.
\end{aligned} \tag{15.50}
$$

Combining Equations 15.46 and 15.47 gives:

$$
y_{out} = y_4 = y_{st} - (y_{in} + y_{st}) = -y_{in}, \tag{15.51}
$$

which implies that the trailing transient is the "inverse" of the leading transient.

Based on the previous analysis our aim is to transmit each information block only once ($L = 1$) and remove the effects of MDI by cancellation, rather than reduce the system's effective transmission rate by the factor $M/(M + N_T)$, where N_T is the number of samples used for the quasi-periodic transmission block expansion. The kth received signal vector y^k is constituted by an initial transient due to the trailing transient y_{out}^{k-1} of the $(k-1)^{th}$ transmitted vector, a stationary response y_{st}^k due to the kth transmitted vector plus the initial transient y_{in}^{k-1} due to the kth transmitted vector, as given below:

$$y^k = y_{out}^{k-1} + y_{st}^k + y_{in}^k. \tag{15.52}$$

Equation 15.51, for the trailing transient from block $(k-1)$, gives us:

$$y_{out}^{k-1} = -y_{in}^{k-1}, \tag{15.53}$$

which can be substituted in Equation 15.52 to yield:

$$y^k = y_{in}^k + y_{st}^k - y_{in}^{k-1}. \tag{15.54}$$

15.8.2 Recursive MDI Compensation

Our objective is now to determine the transmitted vector u^k, which can be inferred if y^k is known. Hence the compensation of MDI ensues as follows.

(1) Initially a known preamble sequence u_0 is transmitted, sending $L \geq 2$ repetitions to determine the channel's impulse response, i.e., the matrix H. This is possible using Equation 15.46 and 15.47, where the system's response is in its stationary phase during the second cycle of the periodic preamble. The system's impulse response can be conveniently measured by transmitting a specific preamble u_0, which is constituted by a "white" spectrum with the real part set to one, and imaginary part set to zero. This input signal modulates the subchannel modulators, where the modulated signal after IFFT becomes the Kronecker delta. When this preamble signal excites the transmission system, its response is the impulse response itself. Once the impulse response is known, the matrices H, S_0 and S_1 are also known.

(2) Since the system responses y_1^0 and y_2^0 due to the preamble u_0 during the first two periods are now known, the system's initial

transient can be computed from Equations 15.45 and 15.46 using:

$$y_1^0 = y_{in}^0 + y_{st}^0 = S_0 u \tag{15.55}$$

and

$$y_2^0 = y_{st}^0 = [S_1 + S_0]u \tag{15.56}$$

as follows:

$$y_{in}^0 = y_1^0 - y_{st}^0 = y_1^0 - y_2^0 = -S_1 u. \tag{15.57}$$

With the knowledge of this initial transient response the trailing effects corrupting the consecutive blocks can be recursively compensated.

(3) The preamble u_0 is followed by the useful information blocks y^k, $k = 1, 2, \ldots \infty$, transmitted only once ($L = 1$). Upon receiving the system's response y^k due to u^k, $k = 1, 2, \ldots \infty$, the trailing transient of the previous block can be subtracted as follows:

$$y^k - y_{out}^{k-1} = y^k + y_{in}^{k-1}. \tag{15.58}$$

When considering Equations 15.52 and 15.46 we get:

$$y^k - y_{out}^{k-1} = y_{st}^k + y_{in}^k = S_0 \tilde{u}^k, \tag{15.59}$$

where we used $\tilde{u}^k$ which is different from u^k due to channel effects. The estimated transmitted signal $\tilde{u}^k$ can be recovered using Equations 15.58 and 15.59:

$$\tilde{u}^k = S_0^{-1}(y^k - y_{out}^{k-1}) = S_0^{-1}(y^k + y_{in}^{k-1}). \tag{15.60}$$

From Equation 15.50 we have $y_{out}^{k-1} = S_1 u^{k-1}$ that can be substituted in Equation 15.60, giving

$$\tilde{u}^k = S_0^{-1}(y^k - S_1 u^{k-1}), \tag{15.61}$$

which is an explicit formula for the estimated transmitted vector $\tilde{u}^k$ in terms of the received vector y^k, the previously recovered transmitted vector u^{k-1} and the matrices S_0 and S_1, which depend only on the system's impulse response.

(4) Now the compensated vector $\tilde{u}^k$ in Equation 15.61 can be demodulated by FFT and the demodulated signal $\tilde{U}^k$ is subjected to

hard-decisions, which are represented as $D\{\ \}$, giving the recovered information signal in the following form:

$$U^k = D\{\tilde{u}^k\} = D\{FFT[\tilde{u}^k]\}. \qquad (15.62)$$

(5) Since u^k is needed in Equation 15.61 for the next recursive compensation step,

$$u^k = IFFT[U^k] \qquad (15.63)$$

is computed to conclude the compensation process.

This method bears a strong resemblance to the conventional partial response technique, allowing signals belonging to adjacent signalling intervals to overlap. The controlled ISI can then be recursively compensated, if the channel can be considered slowly changing.

15.9 Adaptive Channel Equalisation

In this section it will be assumed that the MDI was removed by compensation, quasi-periodic block extension or by obeying the generalised Nyquist criterion. The linear distortions introduced by the unequalised channel transfer function $H(f)$ can be removed by estimating $H(if_0)$ and then dividing the received signal spectrum by $H(if_0)$, before hard-decision decoding is performed using the function $D\{\ \}$.

In the previous section we mentioned how $H(if_0)$ can be measured using a preamble having a real-valued "white" spectrum. By setting all real spectral lines to unity and all imaginary lines to zero in the preamble data frame, after modulation by the IFFT the transmitted signal is the Kronecker delta. Therefore the received signal is the channel's impulse response, which after demodulation by FFT gives the channel's frequency domain transfer function $H(if_0)$. The received signal's spectrum after demodulation by FFT becomes:

$$\tilde{X}_i = H(if_0)X_i, \quad i = 1, \ldots M, \qquad (15.64)$$

where X_i is the i-th transmitted spectral line at frequency if_0. After equalisation by dividing the received spectral line $\tilde{X}_i$ with the estimated channel transfer function $H(if_0)$ and taking hard-decisions we obtain the recovered sequence:

$$\hat{X}_i = D\left\{\frac{\tilde{X}_i}{H(if_0)}\right\}, \ i = 1,\ldots M. \qquad (15.65)$$

If the recovered sequence $\hat{X}_i$ is error-free, it lends itself to the recursive re-computation of the channel's frequency response in order to cope with slowly time-varying transmission media [9]. The up-dated transfer function is given by:

$$H_a(if_0) = \frac{\tilde{X}_i}{\hat{X}_i} = \frac{\tilde{X}_i}{D\left\{\frac{\tilde{X}_i}{H(if_0)}\right\}}, \ i = 1,\ldots M. \qquad (15.66)$$

In order to retain robustness for transmissions over channels having high bit error rate a leaky algorithm can be introduced to generate a weighted average of the previous and current transfer function using the leakage factor β in the following fashion:

$$H_{\text{adaptive}}(if_0) = \beta H_a^k(if_0) + (1-\beta)H_a^{k-1}(if_0). \qquad (15.67)$$

The leakage factor β is a parameter determined by the prevailing channel bit error rate.

An interesting aspect of our OMPX scheme is that if the channel varies slowly, then using differential coding between corresponding subchannels of consecutive OMPX transmission frames removes the requirement for a channel equaliser as long as the difference is computed before hard-decision takes place [6]. This is due to the fact that spectral lines of the same subchannel or same frequency will suffer the same attenuation due to the channel's linear distortion. Hence the effect of channel attenuation and phase shift drops out, before hard-decision takes place. Similar arguments can be exploited between adjacent lines of the same OMPX transmission frame as well, if the channel's transfer characteristic is sufficiently smooth.

If the frequency domain transfer function $H(if_0)$ is more erratic as a function of frequency or time, a number of known pilot tones can be included in the transmitted spectrum. These pilots facilitate the more accurate estimation and equalisation of the channel transfer function. This technique was proposed by Cimini for wide-band, frequency-selective multi-path mobile channels in reference [11]. In case of narrow-band Rayleigh-fading mobile radio channels the fading is flat, each transmitted frequency component suffers the same attenuation and phase shift. In this case time domain pilot symbols deployed as in the PSAM schemes of Chapter 10 are useful to allow the tracking of the Rayleigh-fading envelope [31].

15.10 Wide-Sense Orthogonality

Following Luke's approach [30] signalling in subchannel l is carried out by transmitting the carrier or basis function $u_l(t)$ weighted by the information sample $y_l(0)$ to be transmitted, where the basis function must be selected so that the linear channel appears transparent to $u_l(t)$. Then the received signal $r(t)$ is given by:

$$r(t) = y_l(0)u_l(t) + n(t), \qquad (15.68)$$

where $n(t)$ is the AWGN. Under the minimum mean squared error (mmse) criterion the received signal can be recovered by the help of the following cross-correlation:

$$
\begin{aligned}
r(t) \otimes u_l(t) &= [y_l(0)u_l(t) + n(t)] \otimes u_l(t)|_{\tau=0} \\
&= y_l(0)\phi_{ll}(0) + \phi_{ln}(0), \qquad (15.69)
\end{aligned}
$$

where $\otimes$ means correlation, $\phi_{ll}(\tau)$ is the autocorrelation of the basis function $u_l(t)$ and $\phi_{ln}(\tau)$ is the cross-correlation of $u_l(t)$ and $n(t)$.

In our OMPX system shifted versions of the subchannel carrier $u_l(t - kT)$, $k = 1 \ldots \infty$, $l = 1 \ldots M$ are modulated by the subchannel information sequences $y_l(k)$, yielding the modulated signal

$$m(t) = \sum_{l=1}^{M} \sum_{k=-\infty}^{\infty} y_l(k)u_l(t - kT), \qquad (15.70)$$

where M is the number of subchannels and T is the signalling interval duration. A bank of M correlation receivers demodulates the multiplex signal of Equation 15.70, and the output signal of the l-th subchannel's correlation receiver becomes:

$$[m(t) + n(t)] \otimes u_l(t)|_{\tau=0} = y_l(0)\phi_{ll}(0) + \phi_{ln}(0) + \sum_{j=1}^{M} \sum_{k=-\infty}^{\infty} y_{jk}\phi_{lj}(kT),$$

$$(15.71)$$

where $y_{jk} = y_j(k)$ is the information to be transmitted in the kth signalling interval in subchannel j. The first term at the right hand side of Equation 15.71 represents the useful information signal $y_l(0)$, the second term the effect of noise, while the third represents the effect of subchannel cross-talk. The cross-talk term can be eliminated if

$$\phi_{lj}(kT) = 0 \text{ for all } |l - j| + |k| \neq 0. \tag{15.72}$$

More explicitly, the subchannel carrier waveforms have to satisfy

$$\int_{-\infty}^{\infty} u_l(t)u_j(t - kT)dt = \begin{cases} E_u & \text{if } |l - j| + |k| = 0 \\ 0 & \text{if } |l - j| + |k| \neq 0 \end{cases}, \tag{15.73}$$

where

$$E_u = \int_{-\infty}^{\infty} u_l^2(t)dt$$

is the identical energy of the carriers or basis functions.

Clearly, Equation 15.73 represents the conventional orthogonality criterion for $k = 0$. In case of $k \neq 0$ Equation 15.73 defines a wide-sense orthogonality criterion for our OMPX system, requiring the conventional orthogonality of all carriers shifted by kT. If the M subchannel carriers satisfy the wide-sense orthogonality criterion of Equation 15.73 and we take into account the following relationship of convolution ($*$) and correlation ($\otimes$):

$$\phi_{lj}(t) = u_l(-t) * u_j(t), \tag{15.74}$$

then demodulation can be carried out with the aid of

$$\begin{aligned} y_l(k) &= \frac{1}{E_u}[m(t) * u_l(-t)|_{t=kT}] \\ &= \frac{1}{E_u}\int_{-\infty}^{\infty} m(t)u_l(t - kT)dt \end{aligned} \tag{15.75}$$

For the sake of illustration let us consider the wide-sense orthogonal carrier functions

$$\begin{aligned} u_1(t) &= rect\frac{t}{T}\cos(\omega_0 t) \\ -u_2(t) &= rect\frac{t}{T}\sin(\omega_0 t), \end{aligned} \tag{15.76}$$

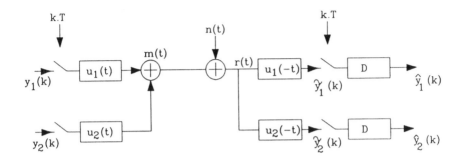

Figure 15.13: Twin-channel OMPX System

which obey Equation 15.73. The corresponding two-channel OMPX
system using the correlation receiver of Equation 15.75 is displayed in
Figure 15.13. The information symbols $y_1(k)$ and $y_2(k)$ weight the
wide-sense orthogonal carriers $u_1(t)$ and $u_2(t)$ and they are multiplexed in order to generate the modulated signal $m(t)$. The received
signal $r(t)$ is correlated with all wide-sense orthogonal subchannel
carriers using the matched filters $u_1(-t)$ and $u_2(-t)$, as it was explained in Subsection 4.5.2, before decisions are made on the correlator's outputs in the D blocks. Only one correlator output will be
non-zero since due to orthogonality the basis function cross-correlations
are zero, which allows recovery of the symbol transmitted via the
particular subchannel carrier. Then the modulated signal can be
written using Equations 15.5–15.7 as follows:

$$m(t) = \Re \left\{ a(t)e^{j\omega_o t} \right\}, \tag{15.77}$$

where $b(t)$ is the baseband equivalent information signal given by:

$$b(t) = \sum_{k=-\infty}^{\infty} X(k)m_T(t - kT) = \sum_{k=-\infty}^{\infty} X(k)rect\frac{(t - kT)}{T} \tag{15.78}$$

and $m(t)$ represents the full response modulation pulse. Substituting

Equation 15.78 into Equation 15.77 yields:

$$m(t) = \Re\left\{\sum_{k=-\infty}^{\infty} X(k) rect\frac{(t-kT)}{T} e^{j\omega_0 t}\right\}, \qquad (15.79)$$

and multiplying with both $e^{j\omega_0 kT}$ and $e^{-j\omega_0 kT}$ gives:

$$m(t) = \Re\left\{\sum_{k=-\infty}^{\infty} X(k) e^{j\omega_0 kT} rect\frac{(t-kT)}{T} e^{j\omega_0(t-kT)}\right\}. \qquad (15.80)$$

Upon rewriting the complex terms in Equation 15.80 in real and imaginary terms we arrive at:

$$m(t) = \Re\left\{\sum_{k=-\infty}^{\infty} [\Re\{X(k)e^{j\omega_0 kT}\} + j\Im\{X(k)e^{j\omega_0 kT}\}] \quad (15.81)\right.$$
$$\left. rect\frac{(t-kT)}{T}[\cos(\omega_0(t-kT)) + j\sin(\omega_0(t-kT))]\right\}.$$

Using Equation 15.76 and assigning

$$y_1(k) = \Re\{X(k)e^{j\omega_0 kT}\}$$
$$y_2(k) = \Im\{X(k)e^{j\omega_0 kT}\}$$
$$(15.82)$$

which constitute the information sequences modulating the in-phase and quadrature carriers $u_1(t)$ and $u_2(t)$ respectively, as seen in Figure 15.13, we get:

$$m(t) = \Re\left\{\sum_{k=-\infty}^{\infty} [y_1(k) + jy_2(k)][u_1(t-kT) - ju_2(t-kT)]\right\}.$$
$$(15.83)$$

Rearranging Equation 15.83 yields:

$$m(t) = \Re\left\{\sum_{k=-\infty}^{\infty} y_1(k)u_1(t-kT) + y_2(k)u_2(t-kT)\right.$$
$$\left. + j[y_2(k)u_1(t-kT) - y_1(k)u_2(t-kT)]\right\}, \qquad (15.84)$$

and finally taking the real part gives:

$$m(t) = \sum_{k=-\infty}^{\infty} y_1(k)u_1(t-kT) + y_2(k)u_2(t-kT)$$
$$= \sum_{l=1}^{2}\sum_{k=-\infty}^{\infty} y_l(k)u_l(t-kT). \qquad (15.85)$$

Observe that when using M subchannels, Equation 15.85 becomes identical to Equation 15.70. In order to allow the transmission of new information in each new modulated block, the wide-sense orthogonal carriers u_l, $l = 1 \ldots M$ are typically windowed to a finite duration of $M \cdot \Delta t$. The effects of using a rectangular window of $m_T(t) = rect\frac{t}{T}$ were considered in Section 15.4.

If the subchannel carriers $\cos(\omega_n t)$ and $\sin(\omega_n t)$ were not rectangularly windowed to the IFFT block-length of $M\Delta t$, passing these infinite duration tones through the channel transfer function $H(f)$ would give rise to another tone of the same frequency, but different amplitude and phase; namely to

$$|H(f_n)| \cos(2\pi f_n t + \phi_n) \tag{15.86}$$

and

$$|H(f_n)| \sin(2\pi f_n t + \phi_n) \tag{15.87}$$

where

$$\phi_n = \tan^{-1} \left\{ \frac{\Im H(f_n)}{\Re H(f_n)} \right\}.$$

However, the rectangular windowing introduced by truncating transmissions to a block-length of $M\Delta t$ results in frequency domain Gibbs oscillation, requiring the subchannels to accommodate a frequency domain $sinc$ function instead of a pure tonal impulse at f_n. This phenomenon results in subchannel overlap. Weinstein and Ebert [6] proposed raised cosine time domain windowing, rather than rectangular, to mitigate this effect.

In closing we emphasize that we have been using the physical interpretation of a conjugate complex symmetric spectrum for the information data frame to be transmitted, in order to arrive at a real time domain modulated signal after IFFT. However, one could also interpret the input data as a time domain sequence and use FFT for generating the modulated signal, which would be associated with a hypothetical spectrum. This duality leads to the concept of orthogonal multiplexing as a generalisation of time and frequency multiplexing, which was introduced by Harmuth in references [32], [33] and [34]. This duality allows us to select our basis functions used as carriers from a wider family of orthogonal functions, which might be more suitable for our specific requirements.

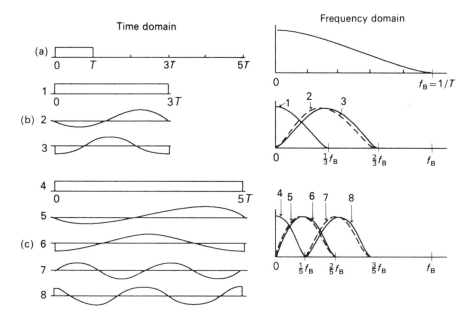

Figure 15.14: OMPX carriers, their stylized spectra and band-width requirement a.   One-carrier System, b. Three-carrier System, c. Five-carrier System [32]©Springer, 1969, Harmuth

15.11 OMPX Bandwidth Efficiency

In the OMPX system each symbol to be transmitted modulates an assigned carrier of a set of wide-sense orthogonal basis functions and these modulated subchannel signals are superimposed for transmission via the communications channel. The received signal can be demodulated for example by the correlation receiver described in the previous section or by FFT.

A set of suitable wide-sense orthogonal basis functions of gradually increased length of T, $3T$ and $5T$, similar to those used in our OMPX schemes, is depicted in Figure 15.14 a, b and c for a one-carrier, three-carrier and five-carrier system, respectively [32], [33]. Both their time domain waveforms and stylized spectra are shown in Figure 15.14. In a simplistic approach here we assume that the signal spectra can be band-limited to the bandwidth of its main spectral lobe, as suggested by the figure.

Using an essentially serial system with one carrier, as seen in Figure 15.14a, the minimum bandwidth required is $f_B = 1/T$ and the bandwidth efficiency is $\eta = 1\,Bd/Hz$ because the spectrum of this pulse is represented by the sinc function whose first zero is at $f_B = 1/T$. The three-carrier system of Figure 15.14b expands the length of the basis functions to $3T$, thereby reduces the bandwidth requirement to $B = \frac{2}{3}f_B$, giving $\eta = 1.5\,Bd/Hz$. This is because the rectangularly windows sin and cos spectra are represented by the convolution of a tonal spectral line and a frequency domain sinc function describing the spectrum of the rectangular time-domain window. The five-carrier scheme using basis functions of $5T$ length further reduces the bandwidth to $B = \frac{3}{5}f_B$ and increases the spectral efficiency to $1.67\,Bd/Hz$.

Similarly, the approximate bandwidth of a $(2M+1)$-carrier system using an impulse as well as M sine-wave and M cosine-wave carriers of length $(2M + 1)T$ becomes

$$B = \frac{M+1}{2M+1}\frac{1}{T},\tag{15.88}$$

yielding a bandwidth efficiency of

$$\eta = \frac{2M+1}{M+1}\ Bd/Hz.\tag{15.89}$$

When $M \to \infty$, we have $\lim_{M\to\infty} \eta = 2\,Bd/Hz$, which for a typical value of $M = 64$ gives $\eta = 129/65 = 1.98\,Bd/Hz$. The interferences caused by the above-mentioned band-limitation are given in closed form in reference [33] for a variety of carriers, but for the more attractive scenarios using a higher number of carriers it can only be estimated by simulation studies.

15.12 Performance of an OMPX Scheme

As mentioned in Section 15.1, the OMPX scheme has been proposed for the European digital audio broadcasting (DAB) standard [15]–[17], which underlines the importance of this arrangement. Some performance figures have been quoted in Reference [35] using the trellis coded orthogonal FDM (TCOFDM) scheme of Figure 15.15.

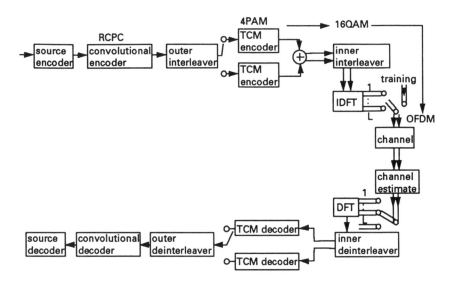

Figure 15.15: Model of the TCOFDM system [35]©Elsevier, 1992, Hoeher

In Hoeher's proposed scheme the source encoded audio bits are rate compatible punctured convolutionally (RCPC) encoded [38] by an outer FEC encoder and interleaved by the outer interleaver. The 1/2 rate RCPC codec provides unequal source matched protection for the audio bits. Observe on the figure that there is also an inner trellis coding and interleaving layer. Such double layer concatenated FEC arrangements have been found to be powerful in fading environments [38]. The typically soft-decoded internal layer removes most channel errors, while the FEC/interleaver layer is provided to combat residual burst errors, which are dispersed by the outer interleaver.

The inner TCM encoder proposed by Hoeher outputs 16-QAM symbols, which are interleaved by the inner interleaver and IDFT modulated before transmission. Frequency hopping was combined with both time- and frequency-domain pilot insertion, complying with Nyquist's sampling theorem at a wide range of vehicular speeds. These pilot-based techniques were discussed in Chapter 10. No equaliser was proposed since the sophisticated multi-tone pilot schemes associated with narrowband TCOFDM subchannels produce effectively flat-fading conditions. MDI is combatted using time-domain guard periods, as explained in Section 15.7. The half-rate RCPC-coded audio bits are input to two independent quadrature TCM-schemes which expand the uniform symmetrical four-level pulse amplitude modulation (4-PAM) to 16-QAM. This TCM scheme was originally proposed by Moher and Lodge [36], and was used by other authors [37], with some performance figures being included in the TCM section of Chapter 11.

Further parameters of Hoeher's proposed scheme are a TCOFDM symbol duration of $T = 320\mu s$, corresponding to a subchannel Baud rate of 3.125kBd, a stereo audio input bit rate of $2 \cdot 128$ kbits/s, and a guard interval length of $G = 64\mu s$. The DAB system proposal specifies a set of standard multipath delay profiles similar to those of the pan-European GSM. However, the impulse response extends to $48\mu s$ in the DAB hilly terrain (HT) model. The proposed guard band period is sufficiently long to remove the multipath effects, but wastes 20% of the signalling interval. The number of carriers was $M = 75$ and the outer RCPC code used punctured audio coding

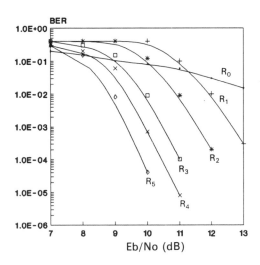

Figure 15.16: BER versus channel SNR performance of the TCOFDM system over the DAB HT model [35]©Elsevier, 1992, Hoeher

rates of $R_0 = 1$, $R_1 = 8/9$, $R_2 = 8/10$, $R_3 = 8/12$, $R_4 = 8/14$ and $R_5 = 8/16$.

The BER versus channel SNR performance of Hoeher's proposed TCOFDM scheme over the DAB HT model is shown in Figure 15.16. Observe in the figure that while the RCPC schemes increase the BER for very low SNR values due to error precipitation effects, the $R_5 = 1/2$-rate code ensures a BER of about 3×10^{-5} at an SNR of 10dB. Overall, the TCOFDM scheme proposed by Hoeher offers excellent performance over the hostile wideband mobile channels, and demonstrates the efficiency of the OMPX principle.

15.13   Summary

In this chapter we have investigated orthogonal multiplexing as an alternative means of transmission, particularly over mobile radio channels. The essential premise of orthogonal multiplexing is to divide the serial input data stream into a number of parallel streams and to transmit these simultaneously. This offered two main advantages. Firstly, by increasing the time over which a symbol was transmitted, the probability of it being completely destroyed in a fade were reduced. Secondly, by decreasing the bandwidth of each channel, the need for an equaliser was diminished. Modulation on each of these orthogonal channels could be either binary or multi-level, and both were considered.

However, orthogonal multiplexing also has a number of disadvantages. It requires a significant increase in the complexity of the transmitting and receiving equipment, and may also engender an increased transmission delay. It will typically also require pilot symbols or some other similar redundancy such that the receiver can be informed of how each individual channel has been modified by the mobile radio channel.

A number of sections were concerned with the issue of multi-dimensional interference, whereby interference might occur not only within symbols on the same channel, but also from one channel to adjacent channels, and methods to ameliorate this were suggested.

Simulation of orthogonal multiplexing schemes was reported at the end of the chapter which seemed to suggest that orthogonal multiplexing offered clear advantages in certain situations.

In the next chapter a different method of attempting to split the input data into a number of schemes and transmit them simultaneously is detailed. However, in this scheme an attempt is made to send two streams simultaneously over the same channel using a technique known as quadrature-quadrature modulation.

Bibliography

[1] **R.W. Chang**, "Synthesis of Band-Limited Orthogonal Signals for Multichannel Data Transmission", *BSTJ*, Dec. 1966

[2] **M.S. Zimmermann and A.L. Kirsch**, "The AN/GSC-10 /KATH-RYN/ Variable Rate Data Modem for HF Radio", *IEEE Trans. Commun. Techn.*, vol. CCM–15, no. 2, April 1967

[3] **E.N. Powers and M.S. Zimmermann**, "A Digital Implementation of a Multichannel Data Modem", *Proc. of the IEEE Int. Conf. on Commun.*, Philadelphia, 1968

[4] **B.R. Saltzberg**, "Performance of an Efficient Parallel Data Transmission System", *IEEE Trans. Commun. Techn.*, December 1967

[5] **R.W. Chang and R.A. Gibby** "A Theoretical Study of Performance of an Orthogonal Multiplexing Data Transmission Scheme", *IEEE Trans. Commun. Techn.*, vol. COM–16, no. 4, August 1968

[6] **S.B. Weinstein and P.M. Ebert**, "Data Transmission by Frequency Division Multiplexing Using the Discrete Fourier Transform", *IEEE Trans. Commun. Techn.*, vol. COM–19, no. 5, October 1971

[7] **A. Peled and A. Ruiz**, "Frequency Domain Data Transmission Using Reduced Computational Complexity Algorithms", *Proc. of the ICASSP*, pp. 964–967, 1980

[8] **B. Hirosaki**, "An Orthogonally Multiplexed QAM System Using the Discrete Fourier Transform", *IEEE Trans. Commun.*, vol. COM–29, no. 7, July 1981

[9] **H.J. Kolb**, "Untersuchungen über ein digitales Mehrfrequenzver-fahren zur Datenübertragung", *Ausgewählte Arbeiten über Nachrichtensysteme, Universität Erlangen-Nürnberg, no. 50*

[10] **H.W. Schüssler** "Ein digitales Mehrfrequenzverfahren zur Datenüber-tragung", *Professoren-Konferenz, Stand und Entwicklungsaussichten der Daten und Telekommunikation, Darmstadt, Germany*, pp. 179–196, 1983

[11] **J. Cimini**, "Analysis and Simulation of a Digital Mobile Channel Using Orthogonal Frequency Division Multiplexing", *IEEE Trans. Commun.*, vol. COM–33, no. 7, pp. 665–675, July 1985

[12] **K. Preuss**, "Ein Parallelverfahren zur schnellen Datenübertragung Im Ortsnetz", *Ausgewählte Arbeiten über Nachrichtensysteme, Universität Erlangen-Nürnberg, no. 56*

[13] **R. Rückriem**, "Realisierung und messtechnische Untersuchung an einem digitalen Parallelverfahren zur Datenübertragung im Fernsprech-kanal", *Ausgewählte Arbeiten über Nachrichtensysteme, Universität Erlangen-Nürnberg, no. 59*

[14] **F.Mueller-Roemer**, "Directions in audio broadcasting", *Jnl Audio Eng. Soc.*, Vol.41, No.3, March 1993, pp158-173.

[15] **G.Plenge**, "DAB - A new radio broadcasting system - state of develop-ment and ways for its introduction", *Rundfunktech. Mitt*, Vol.35, No.2, 1991, pp45ff.

[16] **M.Alard and R.Lassalle**, "Principles of modulation and channel cod-ing for digital broadcasting for mobile receivers", *EBU Review*, Tech-nical No. 224, Aug 1987, pp47-69.

[17] **Proc. 1st Int. Symp.**, "DAB", Montreux, Switzerland, June 1992.

[18] **I.Kalet**, "The multitone channel", *IEEE Tran. on Comms*, Vol.37, No.2, Feb 1989, pp119-124.

[19] **D. Esteban and C. Galand**, "Application of Quadrature Mirror Fil-ters to Split Band Voice Coding Scheme", *Proc. of ICASSP'77*, pp. 191–195, May 1977

474 BIBLIOGRAPHY

[20] **D.A. Schnidman**, "A Generalized Nyquist Criterion and an Optimum Linear Receiver for a Pulse Modulation System", *BSTJ*, pp. 2163-2177, November 1967

[21] **W. Van Etten**, "An Optimum Linear Receiver for Multiple Channel Digital Transmission Systems", *IEEE Trans. Comm.*, vol. COM-23, pp. 828-834, August 1975

[22] **A.R. Kaye and D.A. George**, "Transmission of Multiplexed PAM Signals over Multiple Channel and Diversity Systems", *IEEE Trans. Comm. Techn.*, vol. COM-18, pp. 520-525, October 1970

[23] **M.R. Aaron and D.W. Tufts**, "Intersymbol Interference and Error Probability", *IEEE Trans. Inform. Theory*, vol. IT-12, pp. 26-34, January 1966

[24] **D.W. Tufts**, "Nyquist's Problem: The Joint Optimization of Transmitter and Receiver in Pulse Amplitude Modulation", *Proc. IEEE*, vol. 53, pp. 248-259, March 1965

[25] **B.D. Bunday**, "Basic Optimisation Methods", Edward Arnold Publishers Ltd., London, 1984

[26] **M.C. Austin, M.V. Chang**, "Quadrature Overlapped Raised Cosine Modulation", *IEEE Trans. Comm.*, vol. COM-29, March 1981

[27] **R.D. Gitlin and E.Y. Ho**, "The Performance of Staggered Quadrature Amplitude Modulation in the Presence of Phase Jitter", *IEEE Trans. Comm.*, vol. COM-23, no. 3, pp. 348–352, March 1975

[28] **B. Hirosaki**, "An Analysis of Automatic Equalizers for Orthogonally Multiplexed QAM Systems", *IEEE Trans. Comm.*, vol. COM-28, no. 1, January 1980

[29] **H.W. Schüssler**, "Digitale Systeme zur Signalverarbeitung", *Springer Verlag, Berlin, Heidelberg, New York*, 1974

[30] **H.D. Lüke**, "Multiplexsysteme mit orthogonalen Traägerfunktionen", NTZ Heft 11, 1968, pp 672-682

[31] **J.K. Cavers**, "An Analysis of Pilot Symbol Assisted Modulation for Rayleigh-Fading Channels", *IEEE Tr. on VT.*, vol. 40, no. 4, pp. 686-693, Nov. 1991

[32] **H.F. Harmuth**, "Transmission of Information by Orthogonal Time Functions", Springer Verlag, Berlin, 1969

[33] **H.F. Harmuth**, "On the Transmission of Information by Orthogonal Time Functions", *AIEE*, July 1960

[34] **H.F. Harmuth**, "Die Orthogonalteilung als Verallgemeinerung der Zeit- und Frequenzteilung", *AEÜ 18.*, pp. 43-50, 1964

[35] **P.Hoeher**, "TCM on frequency selective land mobile fading channels", *in E.Biglieri and M.Luise (Eds.) "Coded modulation and bandwidth efficient transmission"*, 1992 Elsevier, pp317-328.

[36] **M.L.Moher and J.H.Lodge**, "TCMP - A modulation and coding strategy for Rician fading channels", *IEEE J-SAC*, Vol.7, No.9, pp1347-1355, Dec 1989.

[37] **P.Ho, J.Cavers and J.Varaldi**, "The effect of constellation density on trellis coded modulation in fading channels", *Proc. IEEE VTC'92*, Denver, USA, pp463-467.

[38] **R.Steele (Ed.)**, "Mobile radio communications", *Pentech Press*, 1992.

Chapter 16

Quadrature-Quadrature AM

16.1 Introduction

In Section 15.11 we showed that by extending the signalling interval from T to $(2M + 1)T$ the asymptotic bandwidth efficiency reached 2Bd/Hz, which is the theoretical transmission limit. In order to reach this limit $(2M + 1)$ orthogonal basis functions representing $(2M + 1)$ separable dimensions were used. In Chapter 15, the set of wide-sense orthogonal basis functions was constrained to the sinusoidal and co-sinusoidal functions by the implementational convenience of using IFFT/FFT for modulation. A variety of other orthogonal functions were proposed in References [1]–[3].

One of the simplest manifestations of orthogonal multiplexing is conventional QAM, where information is transmitted using two or-thogonal carriers, the in-phase and quadrature channels. These con-stitute two dimensions of an orthogonal space. There is a pleth-ora of methods to generate *orthogonal dimensions* that can be used for uniquely recoverable telecommunications signalling. Using a set of orthogonal modulation elements or signalling pulses $m_T(t)$ can create a further dimension for bandwidth efficient orthogonal sig-nalling. In Sections 15.3 and 15.11 we used a rectangular pulse $m_T(t) = rect(t/T)$ in order to avoid distortion of the IFFT mod-ulated signal, although this required a theoretically infinite bandwidth. In conventional modulation schemes bandlimited pulses are used, but there is considerable freedom in the choice of the pulse shape. These issues will form the topic of this chapter in the context of Quadrature-Quadrature Amplitude Modulation (Q^2AM). As an introduction to of these systems, Q^2PSK [4] is examined first.

16.2 Quadrature-Quadrature Phase Shift Keying

We have seen in previous chapters that by moving from BPSK to QPSK, spectral compactness is increased. This is achieved by transmitting two bits per modulation symbol, which allows us to expand the BPSK signalling interval of T to $2T$, thereby halving the bandwidth requirement whilst maintaining the same bit rate. Alternatively, one could double the bit rate in the same bandwidth. This is because the number of signalling dimensions used in the modulation scheme is increased. BPSK can be considered to only have a single dimension - the in-phase or I channel. QPSK then has two dimensions, the in-phase and quadrature channels, or I and Q. A signal space limited in time to an interval τ and to a one-sided bandwidth W has $2\tau W$ possible dimensions [4]. For example, in QPSK the symbol duration τ is 2T, where T is the period of the bits in the incoming data stream, i.e. the signalling interval duration in BPSK. If the channel is bandlimited to 1/2T on each side of the carrier then the one sided bandwidth occupancy is W=1/T. The number of dimensions available within this bandwidth is $2\tau W = 4T(1/T) = 4$. Only two of these dimensions are utilized in QPSK. In theory, this bound on the number of dimensions can be reached by using the so-called prolate spheroidal wave functions but these have been shown to be unrealisable [5]. There may be other ways to approach this bound, ways which can be realised. By moving from QPSK to Q^2PSK it becomes possible to exploit all four possible dimensions.

For unshaped infinite bandwidth QPSK the input data consists of pulses $a(t)$ having period T and amplitude ± 1 which is equivalent to using the rectangular modulation elements $m_T(t) = rect(t/T)$ of the previous chapter. The incoming data stream of pulse-duration T is

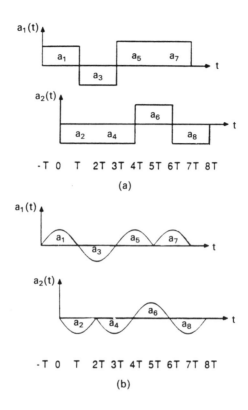

Figure 16.1: Pulse-shaping: a. Rectangular, b. Sinusoidal and cosinusoidal [4] ©IEEE, 1989, Saha

demultiplexed into two parallel streams, $a_1(t)$ and $a_2(t)$, consisting of alternative pulses of duration $2T$. These streams are multiplied by sine and cosine carriers and summed to form the QPSK signal

$$S_{QPSK}(t) = \frac{1}{2T}a_1(t)cos\,(2\pi f_c t) \qquad (16.1)$$
$$+\frac{1}{2T}a_2(t)sin\,(2\pi f_c t)\,.$$

In Offset QPSK (OQPSK) the bit stream $a_2(t)$ is delayed by a fraction of the symbol period $2T$, normally half, i.e. by T, in order to mitigate instantaneous changes in the carrier phase, as portrayed by Figure 16.1a. Although the power spectral density of QPSK and OQPSK are identical, they react to band limiting and non-linear amplification differently. As opposed to QPSK, OQPSK cannot have a 180° phase-shift, which could be caused by the coincident changes in $a_1(t)$ and $a_2(t)$. Thus OQPSK has a lower envelope fluctuation than QPSK and hence non-linear amplification will not regenerate the high frequency side-lobes removed by filtering. Avoiding the above rectangular transition completely, the data streams $a_1(t)$ and $a_2(t)$ can be shaped by cosine and sine functions, respectively, which modulate the quadrature carriers, yielding:-

$$S(t) = \frac{1}{T} a_1(t) cos \left(\frac{\pi t}{2T} \right) cos(2\pi f_c t) \qquad (16.2)$$
$$+ \frac{1}{T} a_2(t) sin \left(\frac{\pi t}{2T} \right) sin(2\pi f_c t).$$

Note, however, that the modulation pulses $cos(\frac{\pi t}{2T})$ and $sin(\frac{\pi t}{2T})$ shown in Figure 16.1b are different from the more conventional raised cosine pulse introduced as non-linear filtering in the time-domain (NLF) in Chapter 4.

Observe in Equation 16.3 that we have introduced two orthogonal pulse shaping functions, namely:

$$p_1(t) = sin(\pi t/2T) \qquad (16.3)$$

and

$$p_2(t) = cos(\pi t/2T) \qquad (16.4)$$

respectively. Armed with these functions the following set of orthogonal basis functions can be formulated

$$\begin{aligned} s_1(t) &= p_1(t) sin 2\pi f_c t \\ s_2(t) &= p_2(t) sin 2\pi f_c t \\ s_3(t) &= p_1(t) cos 2\pi f_c t \\ s_4(t) &= p_2(t) cos 2\pi f_c t. \end{aligned} \qquad (16.5)$$

It can be seen that between any two signals in the above set there is a common factor which is either a data shaping pulse or a carrier component. The remaining factor in one is orthogonal to, or in quadrature with respect to the remaining factor in the other. The modulated Q²PSK signal is formulated as

$$S_{Q^2PSK} = \sum_{i=1}^{4} a_i(t) s_i(t) \qquad (16.6)$$

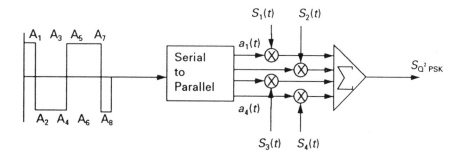

Figure 16.2: Structure of a Quadrature-Quadrature Phase Shift Keying Modulator

and the block diagram of the modulator is shown in Figure 16.2. The waveforms of the components $a_i(t)s_i(t)$, i=1,2,3,4, are displayed in Figure 16.3 for the input pulses $A_1,A_2...A_8$, where A_n is the nth binary input pulse with value -1 or 1, and whose polarities are shown in Figure 16.2.

The waveforms are displayed for two symbol periods, remembering that this modulation scheme encodes four bits per symbol. For the first symbol period the output from the serial-to-parallel convertor $a_1(t)$ is A_1. In the second symbol interval $a_1(t)$ is A_5, and in general $a_1(t) = A_{4i+1}, i = 0, 1....$ Considering the waveform at the top of Figure 16.3, that for $a_1(t)p_1(t)$, it is composed of two positive sine half cycles, corresponding to positive pulses A_1 and A_5. The second waveform, that for $a_2(t)p_2(t)$, is composed of a negative cosine half cycle as A_2 is -1, followed by a positive cosine half cycle as A_6 is +1. Since the serial-to-parallel convertor processes four bits at a time, compared to two for QPSK, twice the amount of data per modulation interval is accommodated. Indeed, without any bandlimiting, Q²PSK can obtain twice the throughput of QPSK at the same SNR and BER [4]. However, due to the sudden changes in the modulating signal as for example $a_4(t)p_2(t)$ in Figure 16.3, when the signal is bandlimited this statement is invalid. Bandlimit-

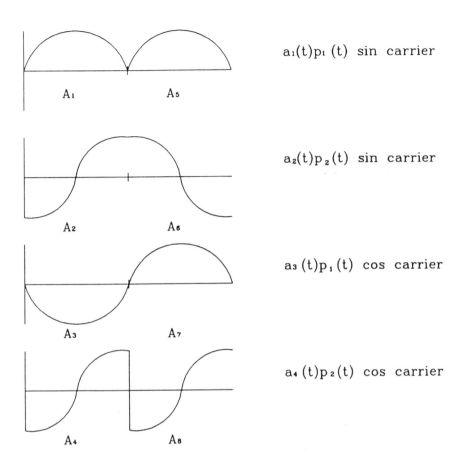

$a_1(t)p_1(t)$ sin carrier

$a_2(t)p_2(t)$ sin carrier

$a_3(t)p_1(t)$ cos carrier

$a_4(t)p_2(t)$ cos carrier

Figure 16.3: Pulse Shapes for the $Q^2 PSK$ Modulator

ing Q^2PSK transmissions over AWGN channels requires an increase of 1.6dB transmitted power in order to provide an identical BER performance to that of QPSK for the same channel bandwidth [4].

a_n	a_{n+1}	Output
0	0	-1
0	1	-3
1	0	+1
1	1	+3

Table 16.1: Encoding scheme for Figure 16.4

16.3   Quadrature-Quadrature Amplitude Modulation

16.3.1   Square 16-QAM

In this section the modifications necessary to include orthogonal data shaping pulses in square and star QAM are discussed.

In our approach, which is a direct expansion of Q^2PSK, we take four data bits for each of the I and Q channels. The structure of the modulator for this scheme is shown in Figure 16.4 and the corresponding waveforms in Figure 16.5. The four bits for the I channel, which are A_1 to A_4 for the first symbol and A_9 to A_{12} for the second symbol in Figure 16.4 are split into two groups. The first group consists of $a_1(t) + a_2(t)$ where $a_1(t) = A_1$ and $a_2(t) = A_2$, representing the first two bits of an eight bit symbol. Each group of two adjacent input bits passes in parallel through a block labelled EN-CODE in Figure 16.4 which takes the two binary bits and encodes them onto one of four levels, ± 1 or ± 3, corresponding to the valid amplitude levels in a square 16-QAM constellation. The mapping is Gray encoded and shown in Table 16.1 where $n = 1, 3, 5, 7$.

Extending the assignments for $s_i(t)$ in Equation 16.5 to 16-QAM by allowing not only the sign but also the magnitude of the modulation pulses to change, the amplitude derived from $a_1(t)$ and $a_2(t)$ can be encoded onto the sinusoidal pulse shape on the sinusoidal, i.e., I carrier, while that derived from $a_3(t)$ and $a_4(t)$ can be encoded onto the cosinusoidal pulse shape on the I carrier as suggested by the waveforms of Figure 16.5. The same procedure applies to the Q channel. Namely, the amplitude derived from bits $a_5(t)$ and $a_6(t)$ is

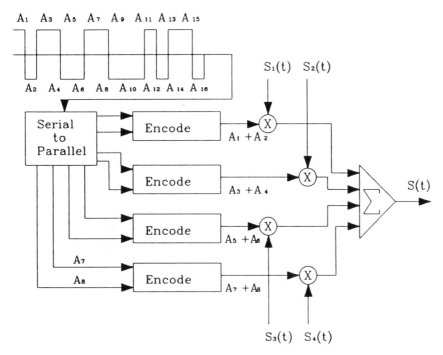

Figure 16.4: Structure of a Quadrature-Quadrature Amplitude Modulator

encoded onto the sinusoidal pulse shape on the cosinusoidal i.e. Q
carrier, and that derived from bits $a_7(t)$ and $a_8(t)$ is encoded onto
the cosinusoidal pulse shape on the Q carrier.

In Figure 16.5 the same principle has been used as for Figure 16.3.
Here $A_1 + A_2$ has been used to signify the amplitude derived by the
mapping described previously from the bits A_1 and A_2, etc. Therefore, considering the uppermost waveform, from Figure 16.4 it can be
seen that $A_1 = 1$ and $A_2 = 0$, where negative pulses are considered to
have a logical value of 0. Consulting Table 16.1 shows that the output of the encoder has an amplitude of +1, consequently a positive
half cycle of a sin wave with amplitude 1 results. In the next symbol
period A_9 and A_{10} which are both logical zeros are used, which from
Table 16.1 is represented by -1, and accordingly a sin half wave of
amplitude -1 is observed. This allows eight bits per symbol to be
encoded onto a 16-level QAM constellation.

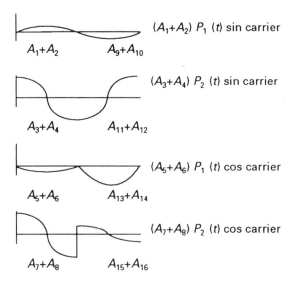

$(A_1+A_2)\ P_1\ (t)$ sin carrier

A_1+A_2 A_9+A_{10}

$(A_3+A_4)\ P_2\ (t)$ sin carrier

A_3+A_4 $A_{11}+A_{12}$

$(A_5+A_6)\ P_1\ (t)$ cos carrier

A_5+A_6 $A_{13}+A_{14}$

$(A_7+A_8)\ P_2\ (t)$ cos carrier

A_7+A_8 $A_{15}+A_{16}$

Figure 16.5: Pulse Shapes for the Q^2AM Modulator

16.3.2   Star 16-QAM

The square constellation Q^2AM with 8 bits/symbol maps almost directly onto the star 16-QAM system. Instead of considering the I and
Q channels separately, the system is considered to have two separate
differential encoders. This is shown diagrammatically in Figure 16.6.
The incoming pulse stream is split into two streams, each of which
has four bits per symbol. Both streams are fed to identical differential encoders which both internally derive an amplitude and phase
angle representing their differentially encoded data. The amplitude
is designated $Z_1(t)$ and $Z_2(t)$ for differential coders 1 and 2, respectively, while the corresponding phases are $\theta_1(t)$ and $\theta_2(t)$.

The encoding scheme differentially encodes the first bit onto the
amplitude and differentially Gray encodes the remaining 3 bits onto
the phase. This information is then converted into two pairs of values representing I and Q magnitude for each differential coder. Thus
$I_1(t) = Z_1(t)\sin\theta_1(t)$, $Q_1(t) = Z_1(t)\cos\theta_1(t)$ and so on. Note that
the star 16-QAM system allows nine possible values of $I(t)$ and $Q(t)$.
$I_1(t)$ is then encoded onto a sinusoidal pulse while $I_2(t)$ from differ-

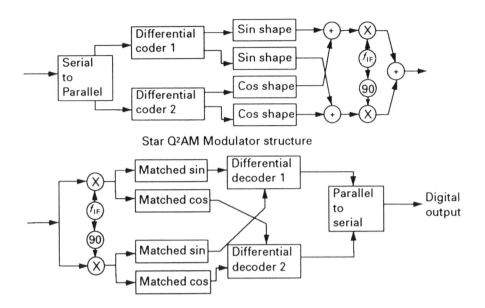

Star Q²AM Modulator structure

Star Q²AM Demodulator Structure

Figure 16.6: Star Q^2AM Modulator and Demodulator Structure

ential encoder 2 is encoded onto a cosinusoidal pulse. These are then added and multiplied by $\cos w_c t$ to give the I carrier. A similar procedure is carried out for the Q channel.

At the receiver there are four matched filters, two with sinusoidal impulse responses and two with cosinusoidal impulse responses. These form two pairs used for the I and Q channels, each pair consisting of a sin and cosine filter. After the I and Q channels are separated by the quadrature mixers, each is simultaneously applied to the matched sin and cosine filter pairs for the appropriate quadrature arms. Because the encoding consisted of a sin and cosine pulse on each channel, by this matched filtering the pulses with their appropriate magnitude and polarity can be separated. The outputs of these matched filters are fed to the appropriate differential decoders which are configured so as to reconstruct the original data stream.

Simulations using this 16-Q^2AM system based on different ortho-

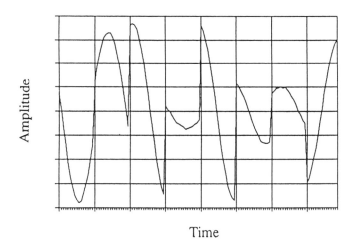

Figure 16.7: Q^{2}AM I Channel Time Domain Waveforms

gonal modulation pulses in an infinite bandwidth channel gave an identical BER to a 16-QAM system using a specific sinusoidal pulse shaping over one symbol alone. It should be noted that such sinusoidal pulse shaping would not normally be used, we would employ some form of raised cosine pulse shaping [7]. Conventional pulse shaping techniques have been considered in Chapter 4.

16.4 Spectral efficiency

As expected, there is a penalty to pay for the doubling of the data throughput. The sharp changes caused mainly by the step change in the cosinusoidal pulse, as can be seen in a typical time domain waveform shown in Figure 16.7, cause considerable spectral spreading.

The spectral efficiency of Q^{2}AM can be improved by using different orthogonal pulse shapes, and then independently filtering these pulse shapes in order to reduce the sharp changes at modulation instants necessary in order to achieve pulse shape orthogonality. In

Reference [4] a number of transmit and receiver filter pairs are suggested for this purpose. It is easy to smooth the sinusoidal pulse, but there are severe difficulties with the cosinusoidal pulse due to the sharp changes that occur at the end of some symbol periods. When bandlimiting filtering is carried out it "smears" these changes significantly, considerably distorting the modulated signal waveform and increasing the BER. Essentially this filtering reduces the orthogonality between the data pulses. QAM is more sensitive than QPSK as more information has been encoded onto each pulse, and severe bandlimiting renders this information inaccurate.

16.5 Bandlimiting 16-Q²AM

In order to make an accurate comparison between previous 16-QAM systems and 16-Q²AM systems we need to compare their bandlimited performance.

Three bandlimited filtering systems are examined. The first system was the raised cosine pulse shaping of the data bits over five symbols prior to modulation as suggested in [7]. This makes use of a generalised equation for the filter impulse response given as

$$g(t) = 1 - A\cos(wt) + B\cos(2wt) - C\cos(3wt)$$

$$0 < t < LT \qquad (16.7)$$

where $w = 2\pi/LT$ and LT is the duration of the impulse response. The recommended coefficients for the transmit filter are given in Reference [7] as $A = 2.0$, $B = 1.823$, $C = 0.823$ and $L = 5$. The receiver filter is the corresponding matched filter for this response, but as the response is symmetrical about $t = 0$ it has an identical impulse response. Also considered was the Non-Linear Filtering (NLF) system as suggested by Feher [8] and discussed in Chapter 4. This system fits a raised cosine segment between adjacent symbols if they have differing amplitudes, and a fixed level if they are of the same magnitude. Finally Q²AM with the previously described simple unsmoothed sinusoidal and cosinusoidal pulse shapes was also included as a benchmark.

Since Q²AM has twice the throughput of QAM, it can be considered a superior system if it can operate with the same BER as

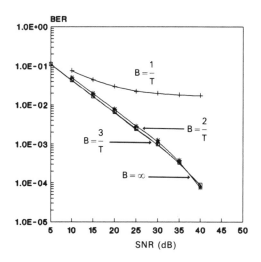

Figure 16.8: BER versus channel SNR performance of star 16-QAM at 30mph, 1.9GHz, 2Msymbols/s using raised cosine filtering and various lowpass bandwidths

QAM but in less than *twice* the bandwidth. Indeed, it could be argued, especially at high bit rates, that Q^2AM is superior if it can operate with the same BER in just over twice the bandwidth, as the lower symbol rate will tend to reduce the effects of Inter-Symbol Interference (ISI) and thus dispense with equalisation or render it simpler and more accurate.

16.6   Performance of Bandlimited 16-QAM and 16-Q^{2}AM

Initial simulations using our star QAM modem were performed at a transmission rate of 2MSym/sec over a flat-fading channel where Inter-Symbol Interference (ISI) did not occur. This situation would correspond to a microcellular or indoor environment. Lower transmission rates than 2MSym/s merely had the effect of increasing the residual BER as shown in previous chapters due to the inability of

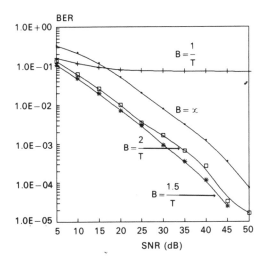

Figure 16.9: BER versus channel SNR performance of star 16-QAM at 30mph, 1.9GHz, 2Msymbols/s using raised NLF filtering and various lowpass bandwidths

the differential detector to track the rapidly changing fading envelope. The vehicular speed of the mobile station (MS) was assumed to be 30mph. Higher MS speeds increased the residual BER, while lower speeds reduced it. The MS speed could also be directly traded off against transmission rate, so if we were to reduce our MS speed by half to 15mph, we would be able to reduce our transmission rate by half to 1MSym/sec, and get identical results (assuming no ISI). The carrier frequency was 1.9GHz.

The performance of the raised cosine filtering is shown in Figure 16.8. In Reference [7] the bandwidth of QPSK with this pulse-shaping is quoted as being $1.2/T$, where T is the symbol rate. That this bandwidth is approximately true for star 16-QAM is substantiated by the results shown. When the bandwidth of the equipment filters was 3dB down at $B = 1/T$, the performance decreased dramatically from the infinite bandwidth case. When the 3dB point was moved to $B = 2/T$, the performance was only about 1dB worse

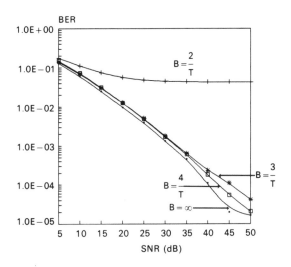

Figure 16.10: BER versus channel SNR performance of star
16-Q^{2}AM at 30mph, 1.9GHz, 2Msymbols/s using various lowpass bandwidths

than the infinite bandwidth case, and by increasing the 3dB point
to $B = 3/T$, the performance of the infinite bandwidth system was
essentially achieved, as shown in Figure 16.8.

Figure 16.9 shows the performance of the NLF 16-QAM system
under the previous propagation conditions with various amounts of
bandlimiting. Note that the BER of the non-linearly filtered but
otherwise un-bandlimited 16-QAM scheme was significantly higher
than the case of raised cosine (RC) pulse shaping. This was because
of the use of a matched filter in the raised cosine filtered receiver
compared to simple sampling in the NLF 16-QAM scheme. NLF
schemes cannot employ matched filtering, instead it must rely on
lowpass filtering of the noise at the receiver. In our simulations we
used the same receive filter as transmit filter. There was an optimum
filter bandwidth for the case where the lowpass filter removes most
of the noise without smearing the pulses significantly. It can be seen
from the figure that this occurred at a 3dB down cutoff frequency of
about $B = 1.5/T$. When the 3dB point was decreased to $B = 1/T$,

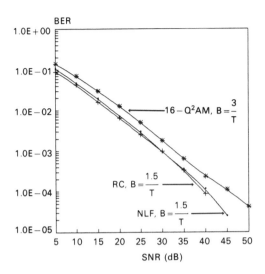

Figure 16.11: BER versus channel SNR comparison of star 16-QAM and 16-Q^{2}AM at 30mph, 1.9GHz, 2Msymbols/s using filtering at $B = 1.5/T$ and $B = 3/T$

significant performance degradation occurred.

Figure 16.10 shows the performance of the 16-Q^{2}AM system with various amounts of bandlimiting. The performance was approximately that of the infinite bandwidth channel for the 3dB point above $B = 2/T$, while when this point was reduced below $B = 2/T$ the BER became unacceptable.

In Figures 16.11 and 16.12 we compare the performance of the three different filtering systems all operating at *identical bit rates*. This means that the symbol rate of Q^{2}AM is half that of the other two systems. Hence, in Figure 16.11 we compare the performance of Raised Cosine and NLF with the 3dB point at $B = 1.5/T$ to Q^{2}AM with the 3dB point at $B = 3/T$. This comparison is carried out in order to show how Q^{2}AM performs relative to a near-optimally filtered 16-QAM modem using raised cosine pulse shaping and a practically filtered QAM modem using the NLF system. The same format is adhered to in Figure 16.12 where we consider 3dB bandwidths of $B = 2/T$ and $B = 4/T$ for the various systems. When bandlimited

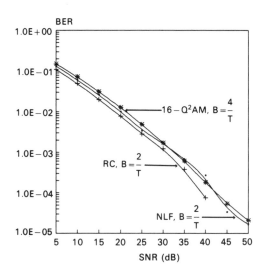

Figure 16.12: BER versus channel SNR comparison of star 16-QAM and 16-Q²AM at 30mph, 1.9GHz, 2Msymbols/s using filtering at $B = 2/T$ and $B = 4/T$

to $B = 2/T$ and $B = 4/T$ the performance of all three systems is virtually identical, although the Q²AM scheme is slightly down on the other two. When the bandlimiting is tightened to $B = 1.5/T$ and $B = 3/T$, a level at which our preferred NLF scheme performs best, the performance of the Q²AM scheme deteriorates to some 3dB below that of the other two schemes. This is more significant, and suggests that Q²AM is only worth implementing if ISI is causing serious problems.

16.7 Summary

This chapter considered how Quadrature-Quadrature amplitude modulation can be successfully applied for transmissions over Rayleigh fading channels. This scheme is termed Q²AM, and for a given symbol rate Q²AM requires approximately twice the channel bandwidth of QAM but operates at twice the bit rate. Alternatively, for the same channel bandwidth, Q²AM operates at half the transmission rate compared to QAM, causing any ISI to be spread over fewer symbols. Decreasing the symbol rate by a factor of two may result in Q^2AM not needing equalization when QAM does. In this case Q^2AM is advantageous. Otherwise it can be concluded that the necessary increase in complexity and decrease in performance is not warranted.

In the next chapter we go on to further examine the issue of spectral efficiency which was touched upon in this chapter when the need to compare different schemes within the same bandwidth was described. The next chapter considers the spectral efficiency of QAM when employed in cellular communications and compares it to other modulation schemes.

Bibliography

[1] **H.F. Harmuth**, "Transmission of Information by Orthogonal Time Functions", Springer Verlag, Berlin, 1969

[2] **H.F. Harmuth**, "On the Transmission of Information by Orthogonal Time Functions", *AIEE*, July 1960

[3] **H.F. Harmuth**, "Die Orthogonalteilung als Verallgemeinerung der Zeit- und Frequenzteilung", *AEÜ 18.*, pp. 43-50, 1964

[4] **D.Saha and T.G.Birdsall**, "Quadrature-Quadrature Phase Shift Keying", *IEEE Trans. Comms.* Vol. 37 No. 5 May 1989 pp437-448.

[5] **H.J.Landau and H.O.Pollak**, "Prolate Spheroidal Wave Functions...", *BSTJ* Vol. 41 July 1962 pp 1295-1336.

[6] **W.T.Webb, L.Hanzo and R.Steele**, "Bandwidth Efficient QAM Schemes For Rayleigh Fading Channels", *IEE Conf. Radio Receivers*, Cambridge July 1990 pp139-142.

[7] **N.G.Kingsbury**, "Transmit and Receiver Filters For QPSK Signals..", *IEE Proc. Vol 133 Pt. F* No. 4 July 1986 pp345-355.

[8] **K.Feher**, "Digital Communications - Satellite/Earth Station Engineering", Prentice Hall 1983.

[9] **R.Bultitude et al**, "A Comparison of Indoor Radio Propagation Characteristics at 910 MHz and 1.75 GHz", *IEEE J-SAC* Vol 7 No. 1 Jan 1989 pp20-30.

[10] **C-E.W.Sundberg, W.C.Wong and R.Steele**, "Logarithmic PCM weighted QAM over Gaussian and Rayleigh fading channels", *IEE Proc Pt. F* Vol 134 Oct 1987 pp557-570.

[11] **R.Steele, C-E.W.Sundberg and W.C.Wong**, "Transmission of log-PCM via QAM over Gaussian and Rayleigh fading channels", *ibid* pp539-556.

[12] **W.T.Webb, L.Hanzo and R.Steele**, "Bandwidth efficient transmission of QAM over Rayleigh fading channels", *IEE Proc. Pt. I.*Vol.138, No.3, June 1991, pp169-175.

[13] **J.C.I.Chuang**, "The effects of time-delay spread on QAM with non-linearly switched filters in a portable radio communications channel", *IEEE Trans Comms* Vol.38 No.1 Feb 1989 pp9-13.

Chapter 17

Spectral Efficiency of QAM

17.1 Introduction

Within fixed communications links where co-channel interference is often not significant, the increase in efficiency, or the increase in the number of, say, speech channels available when QAM is used in place of lower efficiency modulation is often readily found. A parameter is defined known as the channel efficiency which details the number of channels that can be provided within a given bandwidth. For two systems, one using 1 bit/symbol modulation, and the other 4 bits/symbol modulation, the channel efficiency will typically be increased four-fold. It is this increased efficiency which has promoted the widespread use of QAM in fixed link systems.

However, in mobile radio applications the situation is less clear. Here we define a different efficiency which we term spectrum efficiency. We define this as the number of channels that can be provided in a cellular system with frequency reuse. For cellular systems, the system capacity is directly related to spectrum efficiency, but bears little relation to the channel efficiency. This is because changing from 1 bit/symbol to 4 bits/symbol modulation will typically require an increased co-channel interference ratio. To obtain this increased ratio frequencies must be reused less often, so the cluster size (i.e. the number of orthogonal frequency sets available within the complete system) will increase assuming a constant overall bandwidth. Increasing the cluster size will reduce the amount of frequency available within each cell. This will reduce the number of channels available in each cell. Therefore, in order to have a clear picture of the true effect of a change of modulation scheme in mobile radio applications we must consider the spectrum efficiency.

According to Lee [1] the calculation of spectrum efficiency for cellular systems proceeds as follows. Firstly an idealised cell structure with six significant interferers is postulated as shown in Figure 17.1. Regardless of the cluster size there will always be six significant interferers. These may not all be equidistant but for simplicity it is assumed they are all at their average distance from the transmitter. This leads to a small inaccuracy which will not significantly affect the result. With this assumption the signal-to-interference ratio SIR is given by

$$SIR = \frac{S}{\sum_{k=1}^{6} I_k + n} \qquad (17.1)$$

where S is the signal power, I_k is the interference power from the k-th interfering cell, and n is the local noise. Based on a logarithmic path loss model, neglecting noise, and assuming that the signal level from all the interferers is approximately equal, Equation 17.1 may be re-written as

$$SIR = \frac{R^{-\gamma}}{6.D^{-\gamma}} \qquad (17.2)$$

where R is the radius of a cell, D the distance between interfering cells and γ the path loss law. For more details on propagation path loss models the interested reader is referred to Chapter 2. A diagrammatic representation of the interferers is shown in Figure 17.1 where the centre hexagon is the wanted cell and the significant interferers are labelled with the letter I. It then follows that

$$\frac{D}{R} = (6.SIR)^{1/\gamma}. \qquad (17.3)$$

For a hexagonal cell configuration [1],

$$\frac{D}{R} = \sqrt{3K} \qquad (17.4)$$

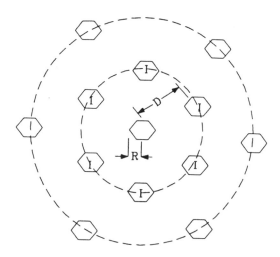

Figure 17.1: Idealised cell structure with interferers

where K is the number of cells in a frequency reuse pattern. Equating Equations 17.3 and 17.4 yields

$$K = \frac{1}{3}(6.SIR)^{2/\gamma}. \tag{17.5}$$

The radio capacity in terms of the number of channels available is defined by

$$m = \frac{B_t}{B_c.K} \tag{17.6}$$

where B_t is the total bandwidth available and B_c is the bandwidth required per channel. Substituting for K from Equation 17.5 in terms of SIR and assuming that $\gamma = 4$, gives

$$m = \frac{B_t}{B_c\sqrt{\frac{2}{3}SIR}} \tag{17.7}$$

which is known as the radio capacity equation for a hexagonal cellular structure with a cluster size of K.

17.2 Spectrum Efficiency in Conventional Cells

We have evaluated Equation 17.7 for a wide variety of modulation schemes using a computer simulation. This simulation considered frequency shift keying (FSK), phase shift keying (PSK), and fixed level and variable level QAM. The QAM simulations are for differential Star QAM introduced in Chapter 11, and the variable level QAM schemes are for variable rate star QAM introduced in Chapter 13. The 8 and 16 level star QAM constellations have two amplitude rings, whereas the 32 and 64 level constellations have four rings.

The simulation program used includes clock and carrier recovery, co- and adjacent channel interferers using a range of modulation schemes, Rayleigh fading at a variety of symbol rates, and a wide range of convolutional and block coding systems. Shadow fading is not included as it does not affect the results in any way. For the simulations, near optimal root raised cosine filtering at transmitter, receiver and co-channel transmitter was used. The interference was generated using a single interferer with the same modulation scheme and filtering as the transmitter. This was subject to a Rayleigh fading path between interferer and receiver, and arranged such that the average interference power was as selected in the simulation parameters. A carrier frequency of 1.8GHz, mobile speed of $15m/s \approx 30$mph and data rate of 25kBaud was assumed while the SNR was fixed at 40dB.

Using this tool the BER against SIR performance for a range of modulation schemes, each using a range of coding techniques was established. This lead to over sixty performance curves the most important of which are shown in Figures 17.2 to 17.3. In these figures BCH coders have been used where the numbers in brackets refer to the number of bits corrected per 63 bit block, and the coding rate is 0.9, 0.81, 0.71, and 0.62 for correction powers of 1 to 4 respectively. Curves for square QAM have been omitted due to its poor performance, although we note that proposed schemes using pilot symbol assisted modulation (PSAM) as discussed in Chapter 10 are expected to provide similar efficiency levels to that of star QAM, albeit at a higher complexity. The curves for 16FSK have also been omitted, again due to poor performance.

Using these curves, spectrum efficiency for a variety of BERs was established. In order to achieve this, nine BER values spanning the range 5×10^{-2} to 1×10^{-4} were selected. For each modulation scheme and each FEC coding scheme, the SIR at which these error rates were achieved, if it was possible to achieve them, was read off the performance curves drawn previously. The SIR and bandwidth required after FEC coding were then fed into Equation 17.7. The resulting number, m, is the number of channels available within an idealised cellular system, neglecting frequency-domain guard band space between adjacent channels. For any BER and any given modulation scheme there were five curves relating to the four error control codes used, and to no error control coding. Each of these lead to a different channel bandwidth requirement B_c and SIR, leading to a different number of channels supported, or radio capacity m. The highest value of m was selected. This meant that at different BERs, different error control codes are optimal in spectral efficiency terms for any one particular modulation scheme. Explicit specification of the error control code favoured for every condition would be unduly complicated and unnecessary as it can be readily inferred from the graphs supplied. In general, low power error control was best for high BERs and high power error control for low BERs.

The graphs showing the radio capacity in terms of the number of channels m supported by different modems at different BER values are given in Figure 17.4. In the figures "nPSK", where n is integer, refers to n-level PSK [2], similarly for FSK, and for QAM "n fixed" refers to n-level star QAM where the number of levels are fixed over the duration of the transmission, whereas the variable level scheme employed an average of 4 bits per symbol. From these graphs we can see that the performance of all the schemes is broadly similar. The 4PSK scheme is superior for all values of BER, closely followed by the variable rate scheme. There is a tendency for the schemes which use fewest modulation levels to give the best performance, so that 8PSK is superior to 16PSK and 16QAM. Schemes which use the same number of levels, such as 16PSK and 16QAM, had broadly similar performances.

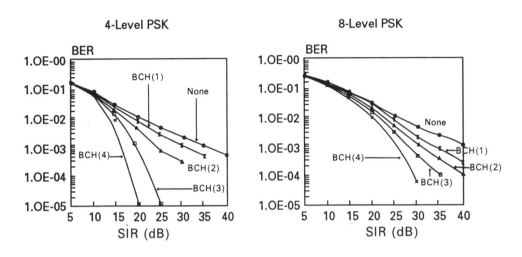

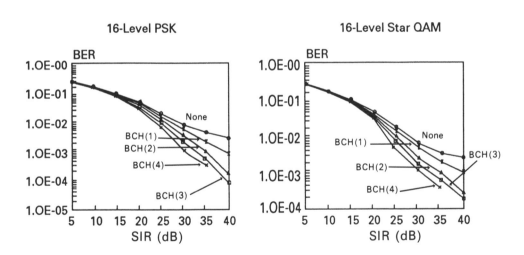

Figure 17.2: BER versus SIR performance of 4, 8, 16 PSK and 16 QAM at 30mph, 1.8GHz, 25kBd, using SNR=40dB and various BCH codes

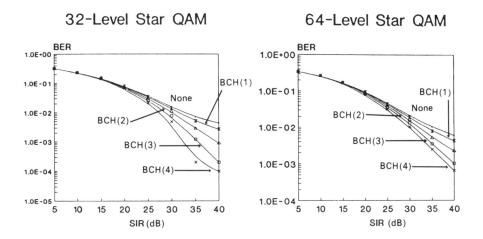

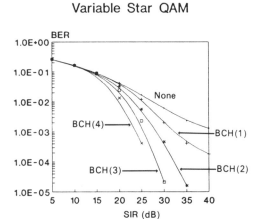

Figure 17.3: BER versus SIR performance of 32, 64 and variable rate star QAM at 30mph, 1.8GHz, 25kBd, using SNR=40dB and various BCH codes

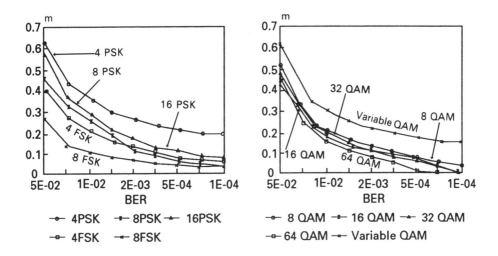

Figure 17.4: Spectrum efficiency versus BER performance of a range of modulation schemes at 30mph, 1.8GHz, 25kBd, using SNR=40dB

17.3 Spectrum Efficiency in Microcells

Whilst the above equations hold for idealised hexagonal cellular systems, they are not applicable to microcellular systems. This is because in microcells the clusters are different from those in conventional cells, and the interference is not so straightforward to calculate. This necessitates a change in Equation 17.7. It was with this in mind that an investigation was undertaken into spectrum efficiency in microcells. With this incentive a number of microcell clusters were constructed on an idealised grid pattern based on maps of New York City and the interference resulting from these clusters was established. The results were then applied to Lee's formula which allowed conclusions to be drawn as to the most appropriate modulation schemes for microcellular systems. This approach is now described in detail.

17.3.1   Microcellular Clusters

In a microcell, the interference from any given co-channel interferer varies throughout the microcell, due to the small size and rapid decrease in signal level as the mobile moves away from the BS. As a result of this, it is difficult to calculate SIRs for given clusters. Instead we resorted to a microcellular prediction tool developed at Multiple Access Communications (MAC), known as Microcellular Design System (MIDAS). This tool can predict both signal and interference levels for any microcellular cluster in both practical and idealised situations and has been proven by comparison with a large database of microcellular measurement data established at MAC.

An idealised grid map based on the layout of New York City, with 100m blocks and 20m wide streets was loaded into MIDAS and a range of predictions were performed at both 900MHz and 1.8GHz. In order to establish the microcell size, the cell boundary was set based approximately on the minimum received power of the CT-2 cordless telephone system. With a 10mW transmitter and 0dB gain antennas, the effective radiated power was 10dBm. Given a minimum signal level at which the data can be received of -95dBm and a fast-fading margin of 20dB, the minimum received signal level was -75dBm, relating to a path loss of 85dB. This process was visualised in Figure 2.13 of Chapter 2. With microcell BSs placed midway along blocks, which is a suitable set of locations to produce a cluster with regular frequency assignment, this path loss of 85dB gives a range of 180m at 1.8GHz, giving a microcell length of 360m. The path loss versus distance relationship was established using the MIDAS prediction system with its six break-point model rather than the less accurate $\gamma = 4$ fourth power law. This requires a microcell every third block as shown in Figure 17.5, which also illustrates the BS pattern for a four-cell cluster. In this figure, which is not drawn to scale, the square areas represent city blocks and the letters represent a BS location and its specific frequency assignment.

At 900MHz, the same path loss leads to a range of 300m giving a microcell length of 600m and a BS every fifth block as shown in Figure 17.6, which also shows the frequency assignment for a six-cell cluster, where the same representation as in Figure 17.5 applies.

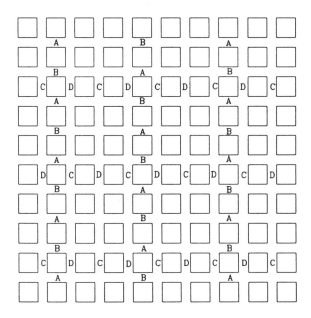

Figure 17.5: Microcellular BS pattern at 1.8GHz for a four-cell cluster using MIDAS propagation prediction

Using these BS patterns we considered the SIRs. This was simply achieved by placing the BSs appropriately within the MIDAS modelling package, and then selecting the SIR option. The package produces a visual display of the SIR on a $1m^2$ basis which is used to determine the worst case SIR. At 1.8GHz using four cells per clusters only the BSs along the same street cause significant interference at a level of 25 - 30dB close to the microcell edge. In contrast the use of six-cell clusters leads to there being no significant interference since with three frequency sets available for the horizontal streets, BSs can be spaced further apart on the same street and also staggered on neighbouring streets to cause less interference. With K=6 the microcell becomes SNR limited as opposed to SIR limited.

At 900MHz, the interference from BSs using the same frequency on parallel adjacent streets becomes more significant, due to the increase in reflection and diffraction around corners at this frequency. A similar method to that used to construct the cluster at 1.8GHz was used at 900MHz, but with the wider microcell spacing caused by

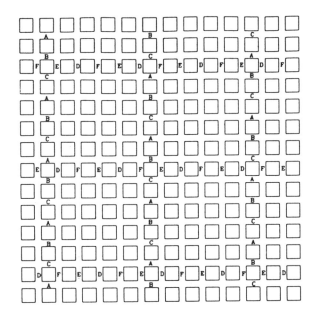

Figure 17.6: Microcellular BS pattern at 900MHz for a six cell cluster using MIDAS propagation prediction

increased propagation distances at the lower frequency. With K=4, areas where the SIR dropped to 20dB were experienced, this SIR was lower than that for 1.8GHz, due to the higher diffraction and reflection of energy around corners. With K=6, the system again became SNR limited.

17.3.2 System Design for Microcells

Communications systems are generally designed for worst case propagation. Consequently, despite the fact that microcells only experience significant interference in certain places, a communications system should nevertheless be designed to cope with this level of interference. It is possible that future designers will find ways of overcoming, or reducing the interference even in four cell clusters, by a combination of dynamic channel allocation, and switching the frequencies of mobiles experiencing significant interference to different frequencies within the same set. However, here we only consider a simple system with fixed allocation, and investigate its results. More intelligent systems will tend to reduce the cluster size.

17.3.3   Microcellular Radio Capacity

When deriving his equation for spectrum capacity, Lee used a formula for conventional cells linking SIR with the number of cells per cluster, K. We performed the above work in an effort to produce a similar equation for microcells, but because of the limited range of K that it is practical to use, we feel it inappropriate to produce a formula of this sort. Instead we substitute our results directly into Equation 17.6 for the values of K for which we have results.

Hence, for K=4 we use the simulation results pertaining to 20dB SIR, whereas for K=6, where transmission is SNR limited, we use the simulation results for a range of SNRs, particularly 20, 30 and 40dB. The BSs are maintained in the same position for each of the SNRs, and the operation of the mobiles with each SNR is examined.

Equation 17.6 is evaluated for both K=4 and K=6, and the cluster giving the highest number of channels is selected for each BER and each modulation scheme. In most cases a cluster size of four was selected. The microcellular SNR is of great importance in deciding upon the optimum modulation scheme and depends on transmitter power and receiver sensitivity for any given system. Here we give results for a range of SNRs, always using the most efficient cluster size for each SNR value to derive the number of available channels.

17.3.4   Modulation Schemes for Microcells

Given SNRs of 20, 30 and 40dB and assuming a SIR of 20dB for the four cell cluster and infinite for the six cell cluster, we can consider the most efficient modulation schemes to use within the microcellular environment. Graphs showing the BER against number of channels are given in Figure 17.7. These graphs have been derived in the same way as the graphs for the conventional cells, but with appropriate SIRs assumed. The same procedure was followed as with macrocells in that for each BER along the x-axis the SIR at which this was achieved was read off Figures 17.2 and 17.3. However, if this SIR was greater than that available within the microcell for a given cluster size the scheme was disallowed. If it was less, the scheme was

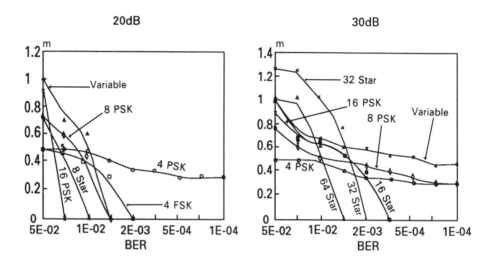

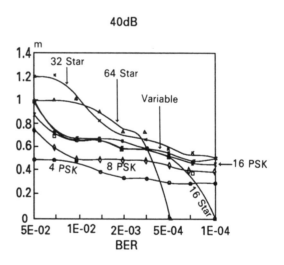

Figure 17.7: Spectrum efficiency versus BER performance in
microcells of a range of modulation schemes
at 30mph, 1.8GHz, 25kBd, using SNR=20dB,
30dB and 40dB

allowed at the cluster size under consideration. Therefore, achieving the BER with a SIR significantly lower than that available was disadvantageous compared to achieving it with a SIR closer to that available.

This procedure was followed for K=4 and K=6, and the cluster size giving the best result used at each point. The QAM schemes were star QAM, using two concentric circles with four and eight amplitude points per ring for the eight and sixteen level schemes, respectively. Curves with very poor performance have been omitted for clarity. In all cases a Rayleigh fading channel is assumed with transmission at 1.8GHz, mobile speed of 15m/s and data rate of 25kBaud. The results at 900MHz are similar because almost the same SIR and SNR values apply to both frequencies. Differential transmission and reception has been used along with near-optimal root raised cosine filtering, modified early-late clock recovery and with the interferer using the same modulation scheme as the transmitter. The same nomenclature has been used as in Figure 17.4.

For the 20dB SNR case, variable QAM is most effective for high BERs, with 4PSK giving the best performance for BERs below 1×10^{-2}. When the SNR is 30dB the variable level QAM is superior for all but the highest BERs. If only fixed level schemes are considered then 8PSK proves slightly better than 4PSK and 4FSK for low BERs. For the 40dB SNR case for high BERs the higher level modulation schemes, namely 32 and 64 level QAM prove best. At BERs below 2×10^{-4} the variable rate QAM schemes are in line with the 32 level QAM, with the 4 and 8 level schemes giving substantially worse performance due to their inability to make the best use of the SNR and SIR available. We note that if variable rate QAM giving an average of 5 bits/symbol had been employed we would have expected it to outperform 32 level QAM in all scenarios.

17.4 Summary

In this chapter the interference levels that might be expected in a range of conventional cellular and microcellular clusters have been considered. Simulation work has suggested that for conventional cell sizes the lower level modulation schemes such as 4PSK are best, with variable rate QAM schemes only incurring a slight penalty. For microcells with communication at both 900MHz and 1.8GHz, four or six cell clusters are advocated depending on the SNR expected. Based on the expected SNRs and interference levels we then surmised that variable rate QAM schemes are often superior to the other modulation schemes considered here. For low BERs and SNR=20 dB 4PSK provides the best performance, whereas for high BERs, particularly when the SNR is as high as 30 or 40 dB, then 32 and 64 level star QAM are most suitable.

Having considered the performance of the modulation scheme in isolation, in the next chapter we proceed to investigate QAM and other modulation schemes when used for the transmission of speech, and investigate means whereby the different bit error rates of different bits on the same QAM constellation can be linked advantageously with the properties of modern speech coders.

Bibliography

[1] **W.C.Y.Lee**, "Spectrum efficiency in cellular", *IEEE Trans on Vehicular Tech.*, Vol.38, No.2, May 1989, pp69-75.

[2] **B.Sklar**, "Digital communications", *Prentice Hall*, 1988.

Chapter 18

QAM-based Speech Systems and Bench-Mark Schemes

18.1 Introduction

In the previous chapter we portrayed a variety of 1-6 bits/symbol modems and studied their true spectral efficiency in macro- and microcellular environments with a range of frequency reuse patterns. Our only concern was in maximising the capacity of the cellular system when expressed in terms of speech channels supported in both SNR and SIR limited environments.

In this closing Chapter we propose a variety of QAM-based mobile radio speech communications systems including speech and FEC codecs, 1-4 bits/symbol modems, and a dynamic multiple access scheme in order to explore the range of trade-offs and to illustrate ways in which QAM schemes might be employed [1]–[4]. We consider systems both with and without error correction coding using the 32 kbps CCITT G721 adaptive differential pulse code modulation (AD-PCM) standard and the 13 kbps regular pulse excited (RPE) speech codecs used in the pan-European digital mobile radio system GSM. Simulation results are presented giving BER, bandwidth occupancy and an estimate of complexity for 4 bit/symbol 16-Star QAM modems, 2 bit/symbol $\frac{\pi}{4}$-shifted differential quadrature phase shift keying ($\frac{\pi}{4}$-DQPSK) modems and binary Gaussian minimum shift keying (GMSK) modems.

The Chapter is organised as follows. After a short system overview in the next section, in Sections 18.2 and 18.3 we briefly consider radio modems and speech codecs. Speech quality measures and discontinuous transmissions are discussed in Sections 18.4 and 18.5, while Section 18.6 is devoted to bit protection issues and channel codecs. Section 18.7 is dedicated to the description of a menu of candidate speech systems and Section 18.8 to a dynamic multiple access scheme known as packet reservation multiple access (PRMA).

18.2 Modem Schemes

The choice of modem is influenced by the constraints imposed by equipment complexity, power consumption, spectral efficiency, robustness against channel errors, cochannel and adjacent channel interference and the propagation phenomena, which depends on the cell size [5]. Most of these issues have been addressed in Chapter 17. Equally important are the associated issues of linear or non-linear amplification and filtering addressed in Chapter 4, the applicability of non-coherent differential detection (Chapter 11), soft-decision detection, equalisation (Chapters 7 and 14) and so forth. Here we briefly describe two schemes which we will use for comparison with our QAM system. These are Gaussian minimum shift keying (GMSK) modulation, which is used in the European second generation digital mobile radio systems and $\frac{\pi}{4}$–shifted differential quadrature phase shift keying (DQPSK) modulation favoured by the Americans in their IS-54 D-AMPS network as well as by the Japanese digital cellular system.

18.2.1 GMSK Modulation

Gaussian Minimum Shift Keying (GMSK) was introduced in Section 7.6 in the context of Viterbi Equalisation of partial response modems, where the phase transitions between adjacent phase states are given by the convolution of a Gaussian pulse shaping function with the symbol sequence [5]. If the length of the Gaussian pulse exceeds the symbol period, the response of the modulator to a symbol is spread over several symbol periods introducing controlled intersymbol interference (CISI). We have seen the effect of signalling pulse width extension in the context of the OMPX modem of Chapter 15, although there no partial-response type overlapping signalling was allowed. Permitting the modulation pulses to overlap has the advantage of reducing the bandwidth of the modulated signal but requires a more complex receiver. The length of the Gaussian response is controlled by the normalised bandwidth, $B_N = B_b T$, where B_b is the Gaussian lowpass filter bandwidth, and T is the symbol period. If the phase transitions are unfiltered, $B_N = \infty$ and we have a Minimum Shift Keying (MSK) modulator. As B_N is reduced, more and more CISI occurs, but the out-of-band spectral spillage is reduced correspondingly. The Pan-European system, GSM uses a GMSK modulator with $B_N = 0.3$ having an impulse response extending over approximately three signalling periods, which requires sophisticated equalisation to achieve good performance. The digital European cordless telecommunications (DECT) system's modulator uses $B_N = 0.5$, which eases clock recovery. The typical spectral occupancy in terms of bits per Hz of a GSM-like GMSK modem is 1.35.

As B_N is reduced, the spectrum becomes more compressed as the phase transitions follow a smoother curve, but more CISI is introduced, rendering bit-by-bit detection using a frequency discriminator more prone to channel impairments. Full-response continuous phase modulation (CPM) schemes where no CISI is introduced, such as MSK can be demodulated by a frequency discriminator, by simply measuring the change of phase over a symbol period. When the phase increases, its derivative, the frequency is positive and a logical '1' is detected, and vice versa, when the phase decreases. Maximum Likelihood Sequence Estimation (MLSE) using the Viterbi algorithm [5] is generally employed to remove both the CISI and the ISI introduced by the channel. Furthermore, with decreasing B_N the eye-pattern becomes more complicated and the reduced eye-opening makes clock and carrier recovery more difficult to achieve.

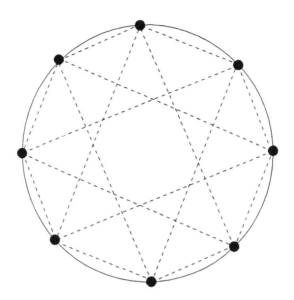

Figure 18.1: $\frac{\pi}{4}$-DQPSK phasor constellation

18.2.2 $\frac{\pi}{4}$-DQPSK Modulation

A particular form of differential quadrature phase shift keying, known as $\frac{\pi}{4}$-DQPSK, transmits 2 bits/symbol, allowing the bandwidth to be reduced compared to binary schemes at the cost of increased complexity and degraded SNR and signal-to-interference ratio (SIR) performance. Careful filtering and linear amplification of the modulated signal as described for QAM in Chapter 4 is required in order to maintain low spectral side-lobes and hence achieve good adjacent channel performance. Because there are 2 bits/symbol, the bitrate can be higher than with GMSK before it is necessary to use a channel equaliser.

In this linear modulation scheme the amplitude variations are reduced compared to conventional DQPSK due to the rotation of the constellation by $\frac{\pi}{4}$ every symbol period, ensuring that no phasor transition path passes through the zero amplitude point as demonstrated by the phasor constellation of Figure 18.1. The data stream is differentially encoded to allow low-complexity differential detection to be employed. Alternatively, MLSE Viterbi detection [5] can be implemented to achieve better performance at higher complexity.

In the scheme we simulated a 129th order Blackman-windowed root raised cosine finite impulse response (FIR) Nyquist transmit and receive filters with a roll-off factor of $\alpha = 0.35$ are employed and an equaliser is only required when operating in a wide-band environment. The $\frac{\pi}{4}$-DQPSK spectral occupancy is 1.62 bit/Hz.

This differentially encoded scheme is readily demodulated by a non-coherent differential detector which evaluates the phasor changes between adjacent sampling instants. Since coherent carrier recovery is not necessary, reduced complexity is achieved and carrier recovery false locking problems are eliminated. However, at low SNR and SIR values some performance penalty is incurred.

18.3   Speech Codecs

In recent years speech coders have experienced dramatic increases in complexity resulting in codecs with bit rates as low as 4.8 kbps [5][Chapter 3]. The choice of an appropriate speech codec is based on the requirements of speech quality, computational complexity, power consumption, bit rate, delay, and robustness against channel errors. The two speech codecs used in our experiments are the CCITT G 721. 32 kbps adaptive differential pulse code modulation (ADPCM) codec proposed for the digital European cordless telephone (DECT) system portrayed in Section 13.6, and the 13 kbps Regular Pulse Excited (RPE), Long Term Predictor (LTP) assisted codec used in the GSM system.

18.3.1   Adaptive Differential Pulse Code Modulation

The 32 kbit/s transmission rate ADPCM codec is specified in the CCITT G.721 Recommendation. The encoder/decoder pair is shown in Figure 18.2.

The A-law or μ-law companded PCM signal is first converted into linear PCM format. Since this is a predictive codec, each linear PCM-coded sample is estimated by an adaptive predictor on the basis of the locally reconstructed past samples. This estimate is subtracted from the PCM sample to be encoded in order to form the prediction error or difference signal. This reduced variance dif-

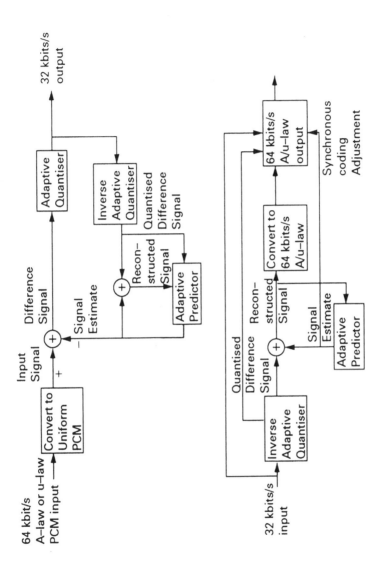

Figure 18.2: 32kbits/s CCITT G721 ADPCM Encoder/Decoder

ference signal can be quantised with approximately the same noise variance as the original linear PCM signal, using a 4-bit adaptive quantiser. Hence an 8-bit PCM sample is represented by a 4-bit AD-PCM sample, giving a transmission rate of 32 kbit/s at a sampling rate of 8 kHz. This ADPCM stream is transmitted to the decoder. Also it is locally decoded, using the inverse adaptive quantiser, to deliver the quantised difference signal, which is added to the previous signal estimate to yield the locally reconstructed signal. Based on the quantised difference signal and the locally reconstructed signal the adaptive predictor derives the subsequent signal estimate. This local decoder is identical to the ADPCM decoder of the receiver, and hence both decoders generate the same signal estimates. These are then added to the difference signal in order to generate the reconstructed signal.

The ADPCM decoder is constituted by the local decoder part of the encoder, and additionally it comprises the linear PCM to A-law or μ-law converter. The synchronous coding adjustment block shown in Figure 18.2 attempts to eliminate the cumulative tandem distortion occurring in subsequent synchronous PCM/ADPCM operations.

18.3.2 Analysis-by-synthesis speech coding

18.3.2.1 The RPE-LTP Speech Encoder

The schematic diagram of the RPE-LTP encoder is shown in Figure 18.3, where following Vary's approach four functional parts can be recognised [6], [7]:

1. Pre-processing

2. STP analysis filtering

3. LTP analysis filtering

4. RPE computation

1 Pre-processing: Initially the speech to be encoded is pre-emphasized in order to increase the numerical precision in computations by emphasizing the high-frequency, low-power part of the

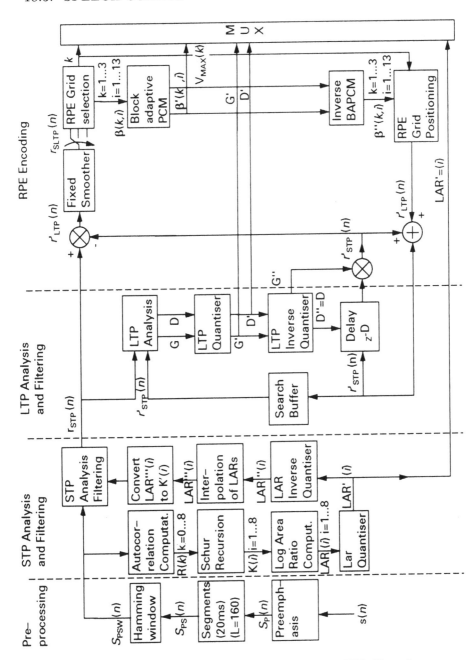

Figure 18.3: Blockdiagram of the RPE-LTP Encoder

speech spectrum using a single-pole filter with the transfer function of: $H(z) = 1 - c_1 z^{-1}$, where $c_1 \approx 0.9$ is an appropriate choice. The pre-emphasized speech $s_P(n)$ is segmented into blocks of 160 samples in a buffer, where they are windowed by a Hamming-window in order to mitigate the spectral domain Gibbs oscillation, caused by rectangular windowing of the speech signal outside the analysis frame. The Hamming-window has a tapering effect towards the edges of a block, while it has no influence in its middle ranges. Hence the windowed, pre-emphasized speech is given by: $s_{PSW}(n) = s_{PS}(n) \cdot c_2 \cdot (0.54 - 0.46 \cos 2\pi n/L)$, where $s_{PS}(n)$ represents the pre-emphasized, segmented speech, $s_{PSW}(n)$ is its windowed version and the constant $c_2 = 1.5863$ is determined from the condition that the windowed speech must have the same power as the input speech.

2 STP analysis filtering: For each segment of L=160 samples nine autocorrelation coefficients R(k) are computed from $s_{PSW}(n)$ by evaluating $R(k) = \sum_{n=0}^{L-1-k} s_{PSW}(k) s_{PSW}(n+k), k = 0 \ldots 8$. From the speech autocorrelation coefficients R(k) eight so-called reflection coefficients $K(i)$ are determined according to the Schur-recursion [8], which is a computationally efficient recursive method for inverting matrices. The reflection coefficients $K(i)$ are then converted to logarithmic area ratios defined as $LAR(i) = \log_{10}\left(\frac{1+K(i)}{1-K(i)}\right)$, because the logarithmically companded LARs have better quantisation properties than the coefficients $K(i)$. The various LAR(i) $i = 1 \ldots 8$ filter parameters have different dynamic ranges and differently shaped probability density functions (PDFs). This justifies the allocation of 6, 5, 4 and 3 bits to the first, second, third and fourth pairs of LARs, respectively.

The quantised LAR(i) coefficients LAR'(i) are locally decoded into the set LAR"(i) as well as transmitted to the speech decoder. In order to mitigate the abrupt changes in the nature of the speech spectral envelope around the STP analysis frame edges, the LAR parameters are linearly interpolated, and towards the edges of an analysis frame the interpolated LAR"'(i) parameters are used. Now the locally decoded reflection coefficients K'(i) are computed by converting LAR"'(i) back into K'(i), which are used to compute the STP residual $r_{STP}(n)$ in a so-called PARCOR structure. The PARCOR scheme directly uses the reflection coefficients K(i) to compute the STP residual $r_{STP}(n)$, and it constitutes the natural analogy to the acoustic tube model of the human speech production.

3 LTP analysis filtering: The LTP prediction error is minimised by that LTP delay D, which maximises the cross correlation between the current STP residual $r_{STP}(n)$ and its previously received and buffered history at delay D, i.e., $r_{STP}(n - D)$. To be more specific, the L=160 samples long STP residual $r_{STP}(n)$ is divided into four N=40 samples long subsegments, and for each of them one LTP is determined by computing the cross correlation between the presently processed subsegment and a continuously sliding N=40 samples long segment of the previously received 128 samples long STP residual segment $r_{STP}(n)$. The maximum of the correlation is found at a delay D, where the currently processed subsegment is the most similar to its previous history. This is most probably true at the pitch periodicity or at a multiple of the pitch periodicity. Hence the most redundancy can be extracted from the STP residual, if this highly correlated segment is subtracted from it, multiplied by a gain factor G, which is the normalised cross correlation found at delay D. Once the LTP filter parameters G and D have been found, they are quantised to give G' and D', where G is quantised only by two bits, while to quantise D' seven bits are sufficient.

The quantised LTP parameters (G',D') are locally decoded into the pair (G",D") in order to produce the locally decoded STP residual $r'_{STP}(n)$ for use in the forthcoming subsegments to provide the previous history of the STP residual for the search buffer, as shown in Figure 18.3. With the LTP parameters just computed the LTP residual $r_{LTP}(n)$ is calculated as the difference of the STP residual $r_{STP}(n)$ and its estimate $r''_{STP}(n)$, which has been computed by the help of the locally decoded LTP parameters (G",D) as shown below: $r_{LTP}(n) = r_{STP}(n) - r''_{STP}(n), r''_{STP}(n) = G''' r'_{STP}(n - D)$. Here $r'_{STP}(n - D)$ represents an already known segment of the past history of $r'_{STP}(n)$, stored in the search buffer. Finally, the content of the search buffer is updated by using the locally decoded LTP residual $r'_{LTP}(n)$ and the estimated STP residual $r''_{STP}(n)$ to form $r'_{STP}(n)$, as shown below: $r'_{STP}(n) = r'_{LTP}(n) + r''_{STP}(n)$.

4 RPE computation: The LTP residual $r_{LTP}(n)$ is weighted with the fixed smoother, which is essentially a gracefully decaying band limiting low-pass filter with a cut-off frequency of 4 kHz/3=1.33 kHz according to a decimation by three about to be deployed. The smoothed LTP residual $r_{SLTP}(n)$ is decomposed into three excitation candidates, constituted by 14, 13 and 13 samples. Then the energies E1, E2, E3 of the three decimated sequences are computed, and the candidate with the highest energy is chosen to be the best representation of the LTP residual. The excitation pulses are afterwards normalised to the highest amplitude $v_{max}(k)$ in the sequence of the 13 samples, and they are quantised by a three bit uniform quantiser, whereas the logarithm of the block maximum $v_{max}(k)$ is quantised with six bits. According to three possible initial grid positions k, two bits are needed to encode the initial offset of the grid for each subsegment. The pulse amplitudes $\beta(k, i)$, the grid positions k and the block maxima $v_{max}(k)$ are locally decoded to give the LTP residual $r'_{LTP}(n)$, where the 'missing pulses' in the sequence are filled with zeros.

18.3.2.2   The RPE-LTP Speech Decoder

The block diagram of Vary's RPE-LTP decoder [6], [7] is shown in Figure 18.4, which exhibits an inverse structure, constituted by the functional parts of:

1. RPE decoding

2. LTP synthesis filtering

3. STP synthesis filtering

4. Post-processing

1 RPE decoding: In the decoder the grid position k, the subsegment excitation maxima $v_{max}(k)$ and the excitation pulse amplitudes $\beta'(k, i)$ are inverse quantised, and the de-normalised pulse amplitudes are computed by multiplying the decoded amplitudes with their corresponding block maxima. The LTP residual model $r'_{LTP}(n)$ is recovered by appropriately positioning the pulse amplitudes $\beta(k, i)$ according to the initial offset k.

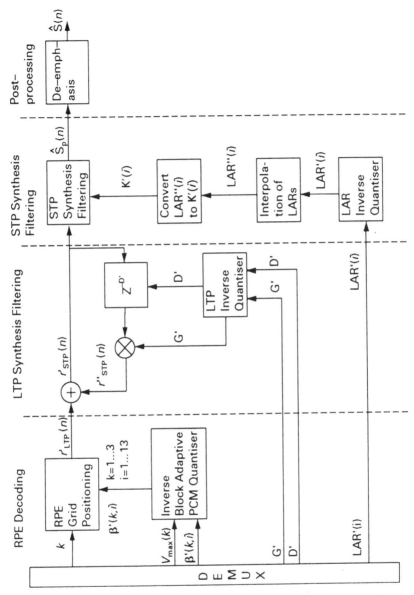

Figure 18.4: Blockdiagram of the RPE-LTP Decoder

2 LTP synthesis filtering: Firstly the LTP filter parameters (G',D') are inverse quantised in order to derive the LTP synthesis filter. Then the recovered LTP excitation model $r'_{LTP}(n)$ is invoked to excite this LTP synthesis filter (G',D') to recover a new subsegment of length N=40 of the estimated STP residual $r'_{STP}(n)$. To do so, the past history of the recovered STP residual $r'_{STP}(n)$ is used, appropriately delayed by D' samples and multiplied by G' to deliver the estimated STP residual $r''_{STP}(n)$, according to: $r''_{STP}(n) = G'.r'_{STP}(n-D')$, and then $r''_{STP}(n)$ is used to compute the most recent subsegment of the recovered STP residual, as given by: $r'_{STP}(n) = r''_{STP}(n) + r'_{LTP}(n)$.

3 STP synthesis filtering: To compute the synthesized speech $\hat{s}(n)$ the PARCOR synthesis is used, where similarly to the STP analysis filtering the reflection coefficients k(i) i=1...8 are required. The LAR'(i) parameters are decoded by using the LAR inverse quantiser to give LAR"(i), which are again linearly interpolated towards the analysis frame edges between parameters of the adjacent frames to prevent abrupt changes in the character of the speech spectral envelope. Finally, the interpolated parameter set is transformed back into reflection coefficients, where filter stability is guaranteed, if recovered reflection coefficients, which fell outside the unit circle are reflected back into it, by taking their reciprocal values. The inverse formula to convert LAR(i) back into k(i) is given by: $k(i) = \frac{10^{LAR(i)}-1}{10^{LAR(i)}+1}$.

4 Post-processing: The post-processing is constituted by the de-emphasis, using the inverse filter given below: $H(z) = 1 + c_1 z^{-1}$.

In our implementation of the RPE-LTP codec we used ten Line Spectral Frequencies (LSFs) [5], rather than eight LARs for the short-term predictor coefficients and encoded them using again a total of 36 bits. Due to the LSFs' ordering property channel errors can be detected and the appropriate ordering can be restored at the receiver. This improves the codec's robustness. A further variation in our codec was that we used four bits to quantise the long-term predictor's gain (LTPG) instead of the standardised two bits. The summarised RPE-LTP bit allocation scheme is tabulated in Table 18.1 for a period of 20 ms, which is equivalent to the encoding of L=160 samples.

Parameter to be encoded	No. of bits	Bitpos.
10 LSF coefficients	36	1-36
4 RPE Grid-positions	4 x 2 = 8	37,38, etc.
4 RPE Block maxima	4 x 6 = 24	39-44, etc.
4x13=52 Pulse amp.	52 x 3 = 156	45-83, etc.
4 LTP Gain (LTPG)	4 x 4 = 16	84-90, etc.
4 LTP Delay (LTPD)	4 x 7 = 28	91-94, etc.
Total no. of bits/20ms	268	
Transmission bitrate	13.4 kbit/s	

Table 18.1: Summary of the 13.4 kbits/s RPE-LTP bit-allocation scheme

18.4 Speech Quality Measures

In general the speech quality of communications systems is difficult to assess and quantify. The most reliable quality evaluation methods are subjective, such as the so-called mean opinion score (MOS), which uses a five-point scale between one and five. MOS-tests use evaluation of speech by untrained listeners, but their results depend on the test conditions. Specifically, the selection and ordering of the test material, the language, and listener expectations all influence their outcome. A variety of other subjective measures is discussed in references [9], [10], [11], but subjective measures are tedious to derive and difficult to quantify during system development.

Objective speech quality measures do not provide results that could be easily converted into MOS values, but they facilitate quick comparative measurements during research and development. Most objective speech quality measures quantify the distortion between the speech communications system's input and output either in time or in frequency domain. The conventional SNR can be defined as

$$SNR = \frac{\sigma_{in}^2}{\sigma_e^2} = \frac{\sum_n s_{in}^2(n)}{\sum_n [s_{out}(n) - s_{in}(n)]^2}, \qquad (18.1)$$

where $s_{in}(n)$ and $s_{out}(n)$ are the sequences of input and output speech samples, while σ_{in}^2 and σ_e^2 are the variances of the input speech and that of the error signal, respectively. A major drawback of the conventional SNR is its inability to give equal weighting to high- and low-energy speech segments, because its computation will be dominated by the higher-energy voiced speech segments. Therefore the reconstruction fidelity of voiced speech is given higher priority than that of low-energy unvoiced sounds, when computing the arithmetic mean of the SNR. Hence a system optimised for maximum SNR usually is suboptimum in terms of subjective speech quality.

Some of the problems of SNR computation can be overcome by using the segmental SNR (SEGSNR)

$$SEGSNR^{dB} = \frac{1}{M} \sum_{m=1}^{M} 10 \log_{10} \frac{\sum_{n=1}^{N} s_{in}^2(n)}{\sum_{n=1}^{N} [s_{out}(n) - s_{in}(n)]^2}, \quad (18.2)$$

where N is the number of speech samples within a segment of typically 15–25 ms, while M is the number of 15–25 ms segments, over which $SEGSNR^{dB}$ is evaluated. The advantage of using $SEGSNR^{dB}$ over conventional SNR is that it averages the SNR^{dB} values of 15–20 ms segments, giving a better weighting to low-energy unvoiced segments by effectively computing the geometric mean of the SNR values due to averaging in the logarithmic domain instead of the arithmetic mean. Hence the SEGSNR values correlate better with subjective speech quality measures, such as the MOS.

For linear predictive hybrid speech codecs, such as the 13 kbps RPE GSM codec, spectral domain measures typically have better correlation with perceptual assessments than time domain measures. The so-called cepstral distance measure physically represents the logarithmic spectral envelope distortion and is computed as [9, 10] :

$$CD = \sqrt{[C_0^{in} - C_0^{out}]^2 + 2 \sum_{j=1}^{3p} [C_j^{in} - C_j^{out}]^2}, \quad (18.3)$$

where C_j^{in} and C_j^{out}, $j = 0 \ldots 3p$ are the cepstral coefficients of the input and output speech, respectively, and p is the order of the short term predictor filter which is typically 8–10. These cepstral coefficients can be readily computed from the coefficients of the short-term predictor using the results of Reference [10].

18.5 Discontinuous Transmission

The idea of discontinuous transmission (DTX) has long been known in bandwidth and power limited satellite systems, where spectral efficiency is improved using Digital Speech Interpolation (DSI). In mobile radio communications however, the Pan-European system [5] (Chapter 8), GSM is the first digital system to use voice activity detection (VAD) and DTX to further reduce the MS's power consumption and increase spectral efficiency through reducing interference during silent periods. Assuming an average speech activity of 50% and a high number of interferers combined with frequency hopping to randomise the interference load, significant spectral efficiency gains can be achieved. The fundamental problem with DTX is differentiating between speech and noise, while keeping false noise triggering and speech spurt clipping as low as possible. In vehicle-mounted MSs the speech/noise recognition problem is aggravated by the vehicle noise. This problem can be resolved by deploying a combination of threshold comparisons [12, 13], and spectral domain techniques [14], [15]. Another important associated problem is the annoying effect of noiseless inactive segments, which is mitigated by introducing comfort noise in these segments at the receiver. This problem is also addressed in references [14], [15].

Another important application of VADs is found in packet reservation multiple access (PRMA) schemes. PRMA is a statistical multiplexing arrangement contrived to improve the efficiency of conventional TDMA systems which will be discussed later in Section 18.8.

18.6 Channel Coding and Bit-mapping

In mobile communications both convolutional and block codes having different strengths and weaknesses are deployed [5][Chapter 4].

In the higher complexity, more robust, lower bit rate speech transmission systems based on the RPE-LTP codec [16] we favour binary Bose-Chaudhuri-Hocquenghem (BCH) block codes. They combine low computational complexity with high error correcting power. They also have reliable error detection properties, which can be used in speech post-enhancement schemes [17], when the received speech is corrupted due to an FEC decoding failure.

For robustness against channel errors some speech bits must be better protected than others. In order to identify the effect of bit errors on speech quality we systematically corrupted each of the 268 RPE-LTP bits and performed a bit sensitivity analysis based on a combination of Segmental SNR (SEGSNR) and Cepstral Distance (CD) degradation [18], [16] as defined in Section 18.4. Specifically, the SEGSNR and CD degradations are shown in Figure 18.5, respectively, where the first 94 bits of a 268-bit frame are portrayed. These bits represent the 36 line spectral frequency(LSF) bits as well as the 58 excitation bits of the first subsegment. Impairments caused by the second, third and fourth subsegments for the bits in positions 95-268 in the frame are identical to those of the first one, i.e. to bits 37-94, whence they are not depicted here. The LSFs determine the spectral envelope, while the LTP parameters determine the fine spectral structure. However, the SEGSNR sensitivities seem to emphasise the low-frequency LSFs and the LTP parameters, while the CD suggests that almost all LSFs are equally important, but underestimates the role of the LTP parameters. This is intuitively likely as the CD excels in measuring the envelope distortion, but not in estimating waveform fidelity. This is why the excitation bits hardly inflict CD degradation, although their role is clearly recognised down to the least (LSB), medium, and most significant bit (MSB) in terms of SEGSNRs in Figure 18.5. Nonetheless, CD objective measures are regarded to have the highest correlation with subjective listening tests.

Our basic observation is that corruption of the bits at beginning and end of both of the SEGSNR and CD figures results in more serious degradations than that of the central bits. The reason for using degradations, rather than the absolute values of SEGSNR and CD is that their absolute values are speaker-dependent, while we are only interested in their degradations due to specific bit errors when compared to their values for unimpaired transmissions. In order to form a balanced view of objective bit-sensitivities and take proper account of subjective quality degradations we decided to amalgamate the SEGSNR and CD measures into a combined sensitivity figure

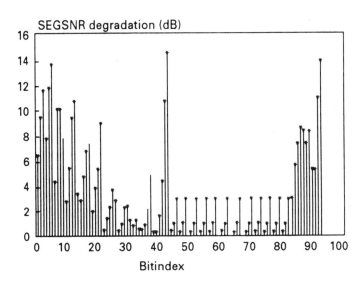

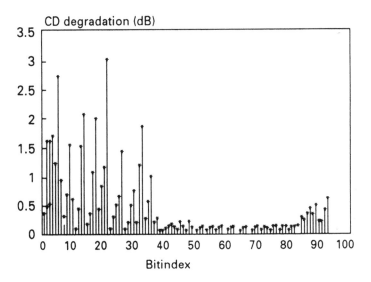

Figure 18.5: Bit-Sensitivities in SEGSNR and CD Degradation for the 13.4 kbps RPE Codec

S. Therefore the bits were assigned a sensitivity rank in terms of both CD and SEGSNR, where the most sensitive bit inflicting the highest SEGSNR and CD degradation was allocated the sensitivity figure 1 and the least sensitive the figure of 94. Then for each bit between 1 and 94 the SEGSNR and CD sensitivity indices deduced from Figure 18.5 and listed in Table 18.2 were added to form the dimensionless combined sensitivity figure S. Following this the bits were sorted in ascending order of S as tabulated in Table 18.2, where the constituent SEGSNR and CD sensitivities are also shown. Armed with the sensitivity figures S, an arbitrarily complex embedded FEC scheme can be implemented. For practical reasons we opted for two protection classes. Note that assigning any subsegment bit in the RPE frame with an index $95 > X > 36$ to a specific category implies the inclusion of the corresponding bits $(X + 58)$, $(X + 116)$ and $(X + 174)$ of the other subsegments in the same class.

After careful consideration we accommodated 116 bits in the high protection class and assigned a shortened binary BCH(62,29,6) code, while the remaining 152 less significant speech bits are protected by a less powerful shortened BCH(62,38,4) code. The codes are appropriately shortened to embrace the 116 and 152 class one and class two speech bits by four rectangularly interleaved BCH codewords in each category. Then in case of serious speech impairments the reliable error detection capability of the high protection BCH code is invoked to activate the correlative speech post-processing algorithm proposed by D.J. Goodman et al [19], portrayed in [17]. The bit rate of the RPE/BCH system is computed as follows. The 116 highly protected bits are coded into four consecutive BCH(62,29,6) codewords giving a total of 248 bits. Similarly, the 152 low-protection bits are encoded by four BCH(62,38,4) codewords yielding equally 248 bits. Then a total of 496 bits per 20 ms LPC frame are transmitted.

18.7   Speech Transmission Systems

In our simulations we used the GMSK, $\frac{\pi}{4}$-DQPSK and 16-Star QAM modems combined with both the unprotected low-complexity 32 kbps ADPCM codec (as in DECT and CT2) and the 13 kbps RPE-

No. in Frame	Index in Frame	SEGSNR Sensit.	CD Sensit.	S	No. in Frame	Index in Frame	SEGSNR Sensit.	CD Sensit.	S
1	6	3	2	5	71	82	67	69	136
2	14	8	3	11	72	41	54	83	137
3	22	13	1	14	73	45	78	59	137
4	3	5	9	14	74	55	59	84	143
5	5	4	10	14	75	48	81	63	144
6	9	9	6	15	76	63	84	62	146
7	18	11	4	15	77	91	55	93	148
8	13	10	7	17	78	78	76	73	149
9	94	2	19	21	79	70	57	94	151
10	8	14	17	31	80	54	77	75	152
11	2	12	21	33	81	49	63	89	152
12	93	6	27	33	82	61	70	86	156
13	10	18	16	34	83	27	94	66	160
14	17	22	13	35	84	57	82	79	161
15	21	25	12	37	85	39	92	72	164
16	90	17	22	39	86	69	87	82	169
17	26	33	8	41	87	72	91	78	169
18	88	16	25	41	88	81	88	81	169
19	4	19	23	42	89	28	80	90	170
20	44	1	43	44	90	40	85	85	170
21	87	15	31	46	91	60	79	92	171
22	1	23	28	51	92	51	83	88	171
23	89	21	30	51	93	75	89	87	176
24	12	26	26	52	94	66	86	91	177
25	43	7	47	54					
26	20	32	24	56					
27	85	24	33	57					
28	16	29	29	58					
29	86	20	38	58					
30	38	28	35	63					
31	7	31	32	63					
32	33	58	5	63					
33	30	51	15	66					
34	25	50	18	68					
35	92	27	42	69					
36	42	30	46	76					
37	84	34	44	78					
38	32	72	11	83					
39	36	69	14	83					
40	59	35	50	85					
41	71	38	51	89					
42	53	37	53	90					
43	15	48	45	93					
44	19	53	40	93					
45	37	52	41	93					
46	24	56	37	93					
47	35	74	20	94					
48	50	39	56	95					
49	56	41	54	95					
50	83	40	57	97					
51	47	45	52	97					
52	11	49	48	97					
53	62	44	55	99					
54	77	36	67	103					
55	29	71	39	110					
56	80	46	68	114					
57	68	43	74	117					
58	46	62	60	122					
59	74	42	80	122					
60	65	47	77	124					
61	23	75	49	124					
62	34	90	36	126					
63	64	65	61	126					
64	31	93	34	127					
65	76	73	58	131					
66	58	61	70	131					
67	73	66	65	131					
68	79	68	64	132					
69	67	64	71	135					
70	52	60	76	136					

Table 18.2: Bit-Sensitivities in SEGSNR and CD Degradation for the 13.4 kbps RPE Codec

LTP codec with its twin-class FEC. Each modem had the option of either a low or a high complexity demodulator. The high complexity demodulator for the GMSK modem was a maximum likelihood sequence estimator based on the Viterbi algorithm [5], while the low complexity one was a frequency discriminator. For the two multi-level modems either low complexity non-coherent differential detection or a maximum likelihood correlation receiver (MLH-CR) was invoked. Synchronous transmissions and perfect channel estimation were used in evaluating the relative performances of the systems listed in Table 18.3. Our results represent performance upper bounds, allowing relative performance comparisons under identical circumstances.

The system performances apply to microcellular conditions. The carrier frequency was 2GHz, the data rate 400 kBd, and the mobile speed 15m/s. At 400 kBd in microcells the fading is flat and usually Rician. The best and worst Rician channels are the Gaussian and Rayleigh fading channels, respectively, and we performed our simulations for these channels to obtain upper and lower bound performances. Our conditions of 2GHz, 400 kBd and 15m/s is arbitrary. They correspond to a fading pattern that can be obtained for a variety of different conditions, for example, at 900 MHz, 271 kBd and 23m/s. We compare the performances of the systems defined in Table 18.3 when operating according to our standard conditions.

Returning to Table 18.3, the first column shows the system classification letter, the next the modulation used, the third the demodulation scheme employed, the fourth the FEC scheme and the fifth the speech codec deployed. The sixth column gives the estimated relative order of the complexity of the schemes, where the most complex one having a complexity parameter of 12 is the 16-Star QAM, MLH-CR, BCH, RPE-LTP arrangement. All the BCH-coded RPE-LTP schemes have complexity parameters larger than six, while the unprotected ADPCM systems are characterised by values of one to six, depending on the complexity of the modem used. The speech Baud rate and the TDMA user bandwidth are given next. A signalling rate of 400 kBd was chosen for all our experiments, irrespective of the number of modulation levels, to provide a fair comparison for all the systems, under identical propagation conditions. The 400 kBd systems have a total bandwidth of $400/1.35 = 296$ kHz, $2 \cdot 400/1.62 = 494$ kHz and $4 \cdot 400/2.4 = 667$ kHz, respectively. When computing the user bandwidth requirements we will take account of the different bandwidth constraints of GMSK, $\frac{\pi}{4}$-DQPSK and 16-QAM, assuming an identical Baud rate.

In order to establish the speech performance of systems A-L we evaluated the SEGSNR versus channel SNR, and CD versus channel SNR characteristics of these schemes. These experiments yielded 24 curves for AWGN, and 24 curves for Rayleigh fading channels, constituting the best and worst case channels, respectively. Then for the twelve different systems and two different channels we derived the minimum required channel SNR value for near-unimpaired speech quality in terms of both CD and SEGSNR. These values are listed in columns 13 and 14 of Table 18.3.

18.8 Packet Reservation Multiple Access

Packet reservation multiple access (PRMA) is a statistical multiplexing method for conveying speech signals via time division multiple access (TDMA) systems. A full treatment of PRMA was given in references [20], [21] by Goodman et al, while various PRMA-assisted CT systems were proposed in [1, 13, 22]. The operation of PRMA is based on the voice activity detector (VAD) being able to reliably detect inactive speech segments. In our systems a VAD similar to that of the GSM system was used, which is described in Chapter 8 of Reference [5]. Inactive users' TDMA time slots are allocated to other users, who become active. The users who are just becoming active have to contend for the available time slots with a certain permission probability, which is an important PRMA parameter. Previously colliding users contend for the next available time-slot with a less than unity permission probability in order to prevent them from consistently colliding in their further attempts to attain reservation. If more than one user is contending for a free slot, neither of them will be granted it. If, however, only one user requires the time slot, he can reserve it for future use until he becomes inactive. Under

System	Modulator	Detector	FEC	Speech Codec	Complexity Order	Baud Rate (KBd)	TDMA User Bandw. (kHz)	No of TDMA Users/Carrier	No of PRMA Users/Carrier	No of PRMA Users/slot	No of PRMA Bandw. (kHz)	Min SNR (dB) AWGN	Min SNR (dB) Rayleigh
A	GMSK	Viterbi	No	ADPCM	2	32	23.7	11	18	1.64	14.5	7	∞
B	GMSK	Freq. Discr.	No	ADPCM	1	32	23.7	11	18	1.64	14.5	21	31
C	$\frac{\pi}{4}$ DQPSK	MLH-CR	No	ADPCM	4	16	19.8	22	42	1.91	10.4	10	28
D	$\frac{\pi}{4}$ DQPSK	Differential	No	ADPCM	3	16	19.8	22	42	1.91	10.4	10	28
E	16-StQAM	MLH-CR	No	ADPCM	6	8	13.3	44	87	1.98	6.7	20	∞
F	16-StQAM	Differential	No	ADPCM	5	8	13.3	44	87	1.98	6.7	21	31
G	GMSK	Viterbi	BCH	RPE-LTP	8	24.8	18.4	12	22	1.83	10.1	1	15
H	GMSK	Viterbi	BCH	RPE-LTP	7	24.8	18.4	12	22	1.83	10.1	8	18
I	$\frac{\pi}{4}$ DQPSK	MLH-CR	BCH	RPE-LTP	10	12.4	15.3	24	46	1.92	8	5	20
J	$\frac{\pi}{4}$ DQPSK	Differential	BCH	RPE-LTP	9	12.4	15.3	24	46	1.92	8	6	18
K	16-StQAM	MLH-CR	BCH	RPE-LTP	12	6.2	10.3	48	96	2.18	4.7	13	25
L	16-StQAM	Differential	BCH	RPE-LTP	11	6.2	10.3	48	96	2.18	4.7	16	24

GMSK: Gaussian Minimum Shift Keying
$\frac{\pi}{4}$ DQPSK: Differential Phase Shift Keying
16-StQAM: 16-level Quadrarure Amplitude Modulation
MLH-CR: Maximum Likelihood Correlation Receiver
BCH: Bose Chaudhuri Hocquenghem FEC coding
ADPCM: Adaptive Differential Pulse Code Modulation
RPE-LTP: Regular Pulse Excited speech codec with Long Term Prediction
TDMA: Time Division Multiple Access
PRMA: Packet Reservation Multiple Access

Table 18.3: System parameters [1], ©IEEE, 1994, Williams, Hanzo et al

PRMA parameter	
Channel rate	400 kBd
Source rate	variable (Table 18.3, col. 7)
Frame duration	20 ms
No. of slots (users/carrier)	variable (Table 18.3, col. 9)
Slot duration	variable (20 ms/No. of slots)
Header length	64 bits
Maximum speech delay	32 ms
Permission probability	variable

Table 18.4: Summary of PRMA parameters

heavily loaded network conditions, when many users are contending for a reservation, a speech packet might have to contend for a number of consecutive slots. When the contention delay exceeds 32 ms, the speech packet of 20 ms duration must be dropped. The probability of packet dropping must be kept below 1%, a value inflicting minimal degradation in perceivable speech quality.

Further important PRMA parameters are listed in Table 18.4. The transmitted Baud rate was fixed to 400 kBd, while the source rate was variable, depending on the system used. The source Baud rates for systems A-L are listed in column 7 of Table 18.3. The PRMA frame duration was 20 ms and the number of PRMA slots was identical to the number of TDMA slots per frame or TDMA users per carrier.

The number of TDMA and PRMA slots per frame is computed from the frame duration as follows. During a PRMA frame of 20 ms the 32 kbps ADPCM speech encoder generates 640 bits of speech information. A header length of 64 bits was assumed to serve signalling and control purposes and so the 704 bits/20 ms = 35.2 kbps source information rate allowed us to support the integer of 400/35.2, namely 11 time slots, i.e., 11 TDMA users per 400 kBd bearer in case of unprotected binary transmissions, such as in systems A and B. When using the 2 and 4 bit/Hz $\frac{\pi}{4}$-DQPSK and 16-Star QAM modems, the packet length was decreased by factors of 2 and 4, respectively, causing the number of slots per frame to increase by similar factors. Thus the use of multilevel modulation increases the number of PRMA slots.

For the FEC-protected scenarios using the 13.4 kbits/s RPE-LTP codec a $2 \times 29 = 58$ bits long header was used. Each 29 bits block in the header was BCH(62,29,6) coded to give an FEC-coded header of 124 bits. Recall from Section 18.6 that the 268 RPE-LTP bits were FEC coded to 496 bits and hence after adding the signalling header the 20 ms PRMA frame was constituted by $496 + 124 = 620$ bits, yielding a bitrate of 31 kbps. The number of PRMA slots supported in case of the 1, 2 and 4 bits/symbol scenarios was 12, 24 and 48, respectively, as seen in column 9 of Table 18.3.

18.8.1 PRMA performance

PRMA efficiency was evaluated in terms of packet dropping probability (P_{drop}) versus number of users for systems A-L, using the number of slots listed in column 9 of Table 18.3. Our results are shown in Figure 18.6 for both the unprotected and FEC-coded scenarios represented by systems A-F and G-L, respectively.

The number of users supported by the schemes providing 11, 22 and 44 time slots at a 1% packet dropping probability is seen to be 18, 42 and 87, respectively. Their values are listed in column 10 of Table 18.3. Then the relative number of PRMA users per time slot is computed as 18/11=1.64, 37/20=1.85 and 67/35=1.91 users/slot, respectively. As seen from columns 9 and 10 of Table 18.3, the corresponding figures for the 1, 2, and 4 bits/symbol modem, 32 kbps speech codec combinations are 18/11=1.64, 42/22=1.91 and 87/44=1.98, respectively, emphasizing the higher efficiency of the systems with multi-level modems. This fact is further accentuated by their less steep dropping probability curves, yielding a more benign overloading characteristic and higher grade of service.

As seen from Figure 18.6, similar tendencies are valid for our FEC-protected RPE-LTP schemes as well. The number of users supported in case of the 1, 2, and 4 bit/symbol systems G-L is 22, 46 and 96, respectively. The associated PRMA efficiencies are expressed using columns 9 and 10 of Table 18.3 as 22/12=1.83, 46/24=1.92 and 2.18 users/slot, respectively. The relative number of PRMA users/slot

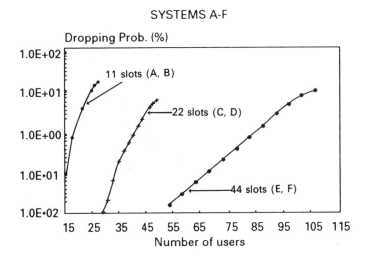

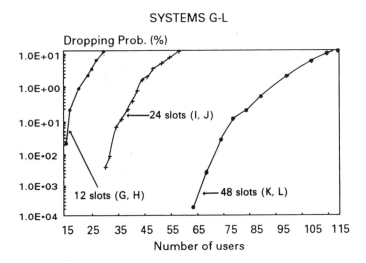

Figure 18.6: Packet dropping versus number of users performance of systems A-L with and without channel coding

values are listed in column 11 of Table 18.3. The normalised PRMA user bandwidth figures listed in column 12 of Table 18.3 can be derived by dividing the TDMA user bandwidth values in column 8 by the relative number of PRMA users/slot given in column 11 of Table 18.3. The normalised PRMA bandwidth figures vary between the extreme values of 14.5 and 4.7, emphasizing again the superiority of the multi-level schemes.

We note, however, that these gains are reduced in SIR-limited scenarios as we have seen in Chapter 17, due to the less dense frequency reuse of multilevel modems. Nevertheless, multilevel modulation schemes result in higher PRMA gains than their lower level counterparts.

18.9   Summary

In this Chapter we compared the performance of a QAM system against binary and quartenary modulation schemes, showing the advantages which can be gained in certain applications, in this case that of PRMA. This highlights the complex range of choices which face a mobile radio system designer and shows that the modulation scheme chosen can have far-reaching consequences as regards to system performance. A variety of further QAM-based speech, wideband audio and image communication schemes can be found in References [1, 2, 13], [16]–[18], [22]–[35].

Bibliography

[1] J.E.B.Williams, L.Hanzo, R.Steele and J.C.S.Cheung, "A comparative study of microcellular speech transmission schemes", *to appear in IEEE Trans. on Veh. Tech.*, 1994

[2] R.Steele, J.E.B.Williams and L.Hanzo, "Speech performance of adaptive transceivers for PCN", *IEE Colloquium on Advanced channel coding and modulation*, London, 16th Nov. 1992.

[3] J.E.B.Williams, "Simulation of digital modulation and demodulation", *Ph.D. mini-thesis*, University of Southampton 1992.

[4] R.Steele and J.E.B.Williams, "Third generation PCN and the intelligent multimode portable", *IEE Electronics & Comm. Jnl.*, Vol.5, No.3, June 1993, pp147-156.

[5] R. Steele, "Mobile Radio Communications", Pentech Press, London, 1992.

[6] P. Vary and R.J. Sluyter, "MATS-D speech codec: regular-pulse excitation LPC". *Proc. of the Second Nordic Seminar on Digital Land Mobile Radio Communication (DMRII), Stockholm, Sweden*, pp. 257-261, October, 1986.

[7] P. Vary and R. Hoffmann, "Sprachcodec für das europäische Funkfernsprechnetz". *Frequenz 42 (1988) 2/3*, pp. 85-93, 1988.

[8] J. Schur, "Über Potenzreihen, die im Innern des Einheitskreises beschränkt sind". *Journal für die reine und angewandte Mathematik, Bd 147*, pp. 205-232, 1917.

[9] **N. Kitawaki, M. Honda and K. Itoh**, "Speech-Quality Assessment Methods for Speech-coding Systems", *IEEE Communications Magazine*, vol. 22, no. 10, pp. 26-33, Oct. 1984

[10] **A.H. Gray and J.D. Markel**, "Distance Measures for Speech Processing", *IEEE Tr. on Acoutics, Speech and Signal Processing*, vol. ASSP-24, no. 5, pp. 380-391, Oct. 1976

[11] **N. Kitawaki, H. Nagabuchi and K. Itoh**, "Objective Quality Evaluation for Low-Bit-Rate Speech Coding Systems", *IEEE Tr. JSAC*, vol. 6, no. 2, pp. 242-249, Febr. 1988

[12] **E. Bacs and L. Hanzo**, "A simple real-time adaptive speech detector for SCPC systems". *Proc of ICC'85, Chicago*, pp. 1208-1212, May, 1985.

[13] **J.C.S.Cheung, L.Hanzo, W.Webb and R.Steele**, "A packet reservation multiple access assissted cordless telecommunication scheme", *to appear in IEEE Trans on Veh. Tech.*, 1994

[14] **D.K. Freeman, G. Cosier, C.B. Southcott and I. Boyd.** "The voice activity detector for the pan-European digital cellular mobile telephone service". *Proc. of ICASSP'89, Glasgow*, pp. 369-372, 23-26. May, 1989.

[15] **S. Hansen**, "Voice activity detection (VAD) and the operation of discontinuous transmission (DTX) in the GSM system". *Proc. of Digital Cellular Radio Conference, Hagen, FRG*, pp. 2b/1-2b/14, October 12-14, 1988.

[16] **L. Hanzo, W. Webb, R.A. Salami and R. Steele**, "On speech transmission schemes for microcellular mobile PCNs", *European Transactions on Communications*, Sept./Oct. 1993, vol. 4, no. 5, pp. 495-510

[17] **L.Hanzo, R.Steele and P.M.Fortune**, "A Subband Coding, BCH Coding and 16-QAM System for Mobile Radio Communication", *IEEE Trans. on VT*, Nov 1990, Vol 39., No 4, pp 327-340.

[18] **W. Webb, L. Hanzo, R.A. Salami and R. Steele**, "Does 16-QAM Provide an Alternative to a Half-Rate GSM Speech Codec?",

Proc. IEEE Vehicular Technology Conference, St. Louis, U.S.A., 19-22 May 1991, pp. 511-516.

[19] **O.J. Wasem, D.J. Goodman et al**, "The Effect of Waveform Substitution on the Quality of PCM Packet Communications", *IEEE Tr. ASSP*, vol. 36, no. 3, pp. 342-348, March 1988

[20] **S. Nanda, D.J.Goodman and U. Timor**, "Performance of PRMA: A Packet Voice Protocol for Cellular Systems", *IEEE Trans. on VT*, Vol 40, No 3, Aug., 1991, pp 584-598

[21] **D.J.Goodman**, "Cellular Packet Communications", *IEEE Trans Comms*, Vol. 38, No. 8, pp. 1272-1280, August 1990.

[22] **L.Hanzo, J.C.S.Cheung, R.Steele and W.T.Webb**, "Performance of PRMA schemes via fading channels", *Proc. IEEE VTC'93*, USA, May 1993, pp913-916.

[23] **L. Hanzo, R. Steele and P.M. Fortune**, "A Subband Coding, BCH Coding and 16-QAM System for Mobile Radio Speech Communications", *IEEE Vehicular Technology*, vol. 39, no. 4, pp. 327-339, 1990

[24] **L. Hanzo, R. Salami, R. Steele and P.M. Fortune**, "Transmission of Digitally Encoded Speech at 1.2 KBd for PCN", *IEE Proc.Pt.I*, vol. 139, no. 4, pp. 437-447, Aug. 1992

[25] **K.H.J.Wong, L.Hanzo and R.Steele**, "A Subband Codec with Embedded Reed-Solomon Coding for Mobile Radio Speech Communication", *Proc. of IEEE, Singapore, ICCS'88*, pp. 709-713, 1988

[26] **X.Lin, L.Hanzo, R.Steele and W.T.Webb**, "A subband multipulse digital audio broadcasting scheme for mobile receivers", *IEEE Trans. on Broadcasting*, Dec. 1993, vol. 39, no. 4, pp. 373-382

[27] **R.Stedman, H.Gharavi, L.Hanzo and R.Steele**, "Transmission of subband coded images via mobile channels", *IEEE Trans. on Circuits and systems for video tech.*, Vol.3, No.1, Feb 1993, pp15-26.

[28] **X. Lin, L. Hanzo, R. Steele and W.T. Webb**, "A Subband-Multipulse digital audio broadcasting scheme for mobile receivers", *IEEE Tr. on Broadcasting*, Dec. 1993, Vol. 39, No. 4, pp 373-482

[29] **L. Hanzo, J.C.S. Cheung, R. Steele and W.T. Webb**, "A packet reservation multiple access assisted cordless telecommunication scheme", to appear in *IEEE Tr. on Veh. Techn.*, 1994

[30] **L. Hanzo, W. Webb, R. Steele, R.A. Salami**, "On QAM speech transmission schemes for microcellular mobile PCNs", *European Transactions on Telecommunication*, Vol. 4, No. 5, Sept.-Oct. 1993, pp 495-510

[31] **L. Hanzo, et al**, "A low-rate multi-level transceiver for personal communication", submitted to *IEEE Tr. on Veh. Techn.*, 1994

[32] **L. Hanzo, et al**, "A mobile speech, video and data transceiver scheme, *Proc. of VTC'94, Stockholm*, 7-10 June, 1994

[33] **L. Hanzo, et al**, "A mobile HI-FI digital audio broadcasting scheme, *ibid*

[34] **J. Woodard, L. Hanzo**, "A dual-rate algebraic CELP-based speech transceiver", *ibid*

[35] **J. Streit, L. Hanzo**, "A fractal video communicator *ibid*

Glossary

8-DPSK	8-Phase Differential Phase Shift Keying
ACF	autocorrelation function
ADC	analogue to digital conversion
ADM	adaptive delta modulation (speech codec)
ADPCM	adaptive differential pulse code modulation (speech codec)
AGC	automatic gain control
AM-PM	amplitude modulation and phase modulation
AWGN	additive white Gaussian noise
BAPCM	block adaptive pulse code modulation (in speech coding)
BB	baseband
BCH	Bose-Chaudhuri-Hocquenghem (error correction code)
BCM	block coded modulation
BER	bit error rate
BPF	bandpass filter
BPSK	binary phase shift keying
BS	base station

C	channel capacity
CCITT	International Telegraph and Telephone Consultative Committee
CD	cepstral distance (speech quality measure)
CISI	controlled inter-symbol interference (in partial response modulation)
CPM	continuous phase modulation
CT-2	an European cordless telephone system
CT	cordless telecommunications
DAB	digital audio broadcasting
DECT	digital European cordless telephone
DFP	Davidson-Fletcher-Powell (optimisation technique)
DFT	discrete Fourier transform
DTX	discontinuous transmission (using VAD)
EL	early-late (clock recovery)
EQ	equaliser
FD	frequency detector
FDD	frequency division duplex
FDM	frequency division multiplexing
FEC	forward error correction coding
FFT	fast Fourier transform
FIR	finite impulse response (filter)
FSK	frequency shift keying
GF	Galois field (in RS and BCH FEC coding)

GMSK	Gaussian minimum shift keying (partial response modulation)
GSM	Pan-European mobile radio system
ICI	inter-channel interference
IEEE	Institute of Electrical and Electronics Engineers
IF	intermediate frequency
IFFT	inverse fast Fourier transform
IMD	intermodulation distortion
ISI	inter-symbol interference
kBd	kilo Baud (signaling rate in modulation)
kbps	kbits/s (transmission bit rate)
LAR	logarithmic area ratio (describing spectral envelope in speech coding)
LMS	least mean squared (equalisers)
LOS	line of sight (radio wave propagation)
LPF	low pass filter
LS	least squared (equalisers)
LSB	least significant bit
LSF	least squares fitting
LTP	long term predictor
MDI	multi-dimensional interference (in OMPX modems)
MLH-CR	maximum likelihood correlation receiver
MLSE	maximum likelihood sequence estimator
mmse	minimum mean squared error
MOS	mean opinion score (speech quality measure)

MS	mobile station
MSK	minimum shift keying (modulation)
NLA	non-linear amplification
NLF	non-linear filtering
OMPX	orthogonal multiplexing (modulation method)
OOB	out of band (intermodulation products due to NLA)
OQAM	offset quadrature amplitude modulation (to reduce amplitude fluctuation)
OQPSK	offset quadrature phase shift keying
OSWE	one symbol window equaliser
PAM	pulse amplitude modulation
PARCOR	partial correlation coefficients (in speech coding)
PCM	pulse code modulation
PCN	personal communications network
PD	phase detector
PDF	probability density function
PFD	combined phase and frequency detector (in clock recovery)
PLL	phase locked loop
PLMR	public land mobile radio system
PR	pseudo-random
PRMA	packet reservation multiple access
PS	portable station
PSAM	Pilot symbol assisted modulation
PSD	power spectral density

PSK	phase shift keying
PSTN	public switched telephone network
QAM	quadrature amplitude modulation
Q^2**AM**	quadrature-quadrature amplitude modulation
QMF	quadrature mirror filtering
QPSK	quaternary phase shift keying
RC	raised cosine (filtering)
RF	radio frequency
RLS	recursive least squares (equalisers)
RPE-LTP	regular pulse excited - long term predictive (speech coding)
RPE	regular pulse excited
RS	Reed-Solomon (error correction code)
RSSI	received signal strength indicator
SEGSNR	segmental signal-to-noise ratio (speech quality measure)
SIR	signal to interference ratio
SNR	signal-to-noise ratio
STP	short term predictor
TC	trellis-coded
TCM	trellis-coded modulation
TDD	time division duplex
TDMA	time division multiple access
TTIB	transparent tone in band
TWT	travelling wave tube

UHF	ultra high frequency
VA	Viterbi algorithm
VAD	voice activity detection
VCO	voltage controlled oscillator
VE	Viterbi equaliser
VT	vehicular technology (IEEE Journal)
VTC	vehicular technology conference (IEEE)
WN	white noise

Index